Statistics in Psychology and Educa

SECOND EDI

S.K. MANGAL

Formerly Principal, Professor and Head
Department of Postgraduate Studies and Research
C.R. College of Education
Rohtak, Haryana

PHI Learning Private Limited

Delhi-110092

2021

₹ 325.00

STATISTICS IN PSYCHOLOGY AND EDUCATION, Second Edition
by S.K. Mangal

ISBN-978-81-203-2088-8

Twenty-sixth Printing ... ... November, 2020

Published by Asoke K. Ghosh, PHI Learning Private Limited, Rimjhim House, 111, Patparganj Industrial Estate, Delhi-110092 and Printed by Mudrak, D-61, Sector 63, Noida, U.P.-201301.

Contents

Preface

The fundamental principles and techniques of statistics provide a firm foundation to all those who are pursuing courses in education, psychology and sociology, both at the undergraduate and postgraduate levels. Its application and importance is further widened and enhanced when they venture into specializing in their areas of research.

This second edition is a sequel to the first edition which was enthusiastically received by the students and well appreciated by the academics. As a number of years have elapsed after the first edition was published, it was felt necessary to bring out a new and updated edition to take into account the present syllabi of education in various universities and institutes of education and emphasize new areas of research.

This enlarged and improved edition incorporates several changes:

- The entire text has been thoroughly checked, corrected, and necessary modifications made wherever required.
- Chapter 7 has been renamed as "Linear Correlation" dealing only with the concept and computation of linear correlation, using rank difference and product moment method. Topics related to regression have been shifted to the newly added Chapter 14 entitled as "Regression and Prediction".
- Six new chapters have been added to the text, thereby enabling us to discuss more advanced statistical concepts and techniques such as the following:
  - Biserial correlation, point biserial correlation, tetrachoric correlation, phi coefficient, partial and multiple correlation.
  - Transfer of raw scores into standard scores, *T*, *C* and Stanine scores.
  - Non-parametric tests like the McNemar test, Sign test, Wilcoxon test, Median test, U-test, Runs test, and KS test.
  - Analysis of covariance.

Thus, attempts have been made to make the text more

comprehensive and elaborate, keeping in view the knowledge and skills required in understanding various statistical concepts and techniques included in the syllabi of M.A. (Education), M.Ed., M.A. (Psychology and Sociology) and M.Phil of Indian universities. Research students will also find this text quite useful.

I fervently hope that the new, substantially revised edition will prove quite beneficial to all the readers. Any constructive suggestions for further improvement will be highly appreciated.

S.K. MANGAL

Preface to the First Edition

This book offers an introductory course in statistics and will be useful for the students of education, psychology and sociology. It may also be used as a handbook by researchers.

The subject matter of this text has been divided into twelve chapters. The first eight chapters deal with descriptive statistics, and the next four chapters with an introduction to statistical inference.

This book differs from other books on the subject in a number of ways:

1. The various topics dealt with have been arranged sequentially and into correlated units so as to make the book useful for ready reference.
2. The contents have been presented in a simple, interesting and fairly non-mathematical manner for the benefit of those who have not studied mathematics beyond the elementary level and for the beginners.
3. Attempts have been made to minimize the complexities of statistical procedures and methods.
4. Numerous solved examples and assignment problems have been provided for practice and to illustrate applications of statistical concepts and methods used in research and field work.
5. Each chapter has been summarized briefly for convenience.

I am greatly indebted to the many authors and researchers whose works have provided an invaluable help in bringing out this book. Besides, I would like to thank my colleagues and students who have been a source of inspiration.

I sincerely hope that the book will prove beneficial to all for whom it has been written. They should feel free to write to me with their views for the improvement of the book.

S.K. MANGAL

1

Statistics—Meaning and Use

MEANING OF STATISTICS

The word, "Statistics", in general connotes the following:

1. Statistics refers to numerical facts. The state as well as Central Statistical departments and various other agencies are engaged in collecting valuable statistics (numerical facts) concerning birth and death, school attendance, employment market, industrial and agricultural outputs, and various other aspects.
2. Statistics also signifies the method or methods of dealing with numerical facts. In this sense, it is considered as a science of collecting, summarizing, analyzing and interpreting numerical facts.
3. Further, statistics refers to the summarized figures of numerical facts such as percentages, averages, means, medians, modes, and standard deviations. Each of these figures separately is referred to as *statistics*.

Tate (1955) has beautifully summarized the different meanings of statistics in the following witty comment:

> It's all perfectly clear; you compute statistics (mean, median, mode, etc.) from statistics (numerical facts) by statistics (statistical methods).

This comment sums up the different meanings that can be attached to the word 'statistics'. However, in the general sense, statistics as a subject or branch of knowledge is defined as one of the subjects of study that helps us in the scientific collection, presentation, analysis and interpretation of numerical facts.

NEED AND IMPORTANCE OF STATISTICS IN EDUCATION AND PSYCHOLOGY

Statistics renders valuable services in:

1. the collection of evidences or facts (numerical or otherwise);

2. the classification, organization and summarization of numerical facts; and
3. in drawing general conclusions and inferences or making predictions on the basis of particulars, facts and evidences.

On account of the above mentioned services, statistics is now regarded as an indispensable instrument in the fields of education and psychology, especially where any sort of measurement or evaluation is involved. Its need in these fields can be summarized now.

Evaluation and Measurement

In the fields of education and psychology various tests and measures for carrying out the task of evaluation and measurement are to be constructed and standardized. These may include intelligence tests, achievement tests, interest inventories, attitude scales, aptitude tests, social distance scales, personality inventories, and similar other measures of educational, social or psychological interests. The knowledge of statistical methods helps not only in carrying out the construction and standardization of these tests and measures but also in using them properly by presenting, comparing, analyzing and interpreting the results of these tests and measures.

Day-to-Day Tasks

Statistics and its methods help the people belonging to the fields of education and psychology in carrying out their day-to-day tasks and activities. For example, a teacher may utilize it for:

1. knowing individual differences of his students;
2. rendering guidance to the students;
3. comparing the suitablity of one method or technique with another;
4. comparing the results of one system of evaluation with another;
5. comparing the function and working of one institution with another;
6. making prediction regarding the future progress of the students;
7. making selection, classification and promotion of the students; and
8. maintaining various types of records.

Similarly, a psychologist or sociologist may also ask for the help of statistics in carrying out various psychological experiments, collecting important information through a sociological survey, interpreting the result of his experiments, surveying and carrying out the task of guidance and reporting, etc. In this way, for the desired success in carrying out activities related to their professions, teachers, educationists, psychologists and sociologists all need the help of statistics.

Research

Research and innovations are essential in any walk of life or field of knowledge for enrichment, progress and development. Education and psychology are no exception to this fact. A lot of research work is carried out in these disciplines and statistical methods help the researchers in carrying out these researches successfully. Guilford (1973) has summarized the advantages of statistical thinking and operations in research. According to him, they:

1. permit the most exact kind of description;
2. force us to be definite and exact in our procedures and in our thinking;
3. enable us to summarize our results in a meaningful and convenient form;
4. enable us to draw general conclusions;
5. enable us to predict; and
6. enable us to analyze some of the causal factors underlying complex and otherwise bewildering events.

Understanding and Using the Products of Research

Statistics and its methods help the practitioners—students, teachers, educationists, psychologists, guidance personnel, social workers and sociologists regardless of their fields—to keep abreast of the latest developments and research. They are helped in reading and understanding the reports of applied and theoretical research, including various statistical terms. The interpretation and proper use of the results of these researches also become possible with proper knowledge of statistics.

From the above account, it can be easily concluded that statistics carries wide application for the persons working in the fields of education, psychology and sociology not only in discharging their roles and duties effectively but also enriching and contributing significantly to their respective fields by bringing useful research and innovation for the welfare of the society and humanity at large.

PREREQUISITES FOR STUDYING STATISTICS

Statistics rests heavily on the use of numbers and formulae, requiring the fundamentals of mathematical computations and reasoning. Many students who have had little opportunity to study mathematics or have developed a bitter and unpleasant taste for it may feel that statistics is complicated and obscure. But if they proceed systematically in the learning of this subject, it may be overcome. One need not be a genius or a scholar in mathematics for learning the statistical methods presented in this fundamental work of statistics. If one has some arithmetical skill and has studied mathematics even upto 7th or 8th class, he or she may study all the essential statistical procedures. However, for beginners let us try to outline the essentials required for initiating the learning in statistics under five major heads discussed below:

Essential Mathematical Fundamentals

A student of statistics must try to build the necessary mathematical base by learning and practising the knowledge and skills about the following concepts:

1. Four fundamental rules—addition, subtraction, multiplication and division.
2. Addition, subtraction, multiplication and division of fractions (including decimal fractions).
3. Use of zero in addition, subtraction, multiplication and division.
4. Positive and negative numbers and their addition, subtraction, multiplication and division.
5. Computation of squares and square roots.
6. Proportions and percentages.
7. Removal of parentheses and simplifying the complex terms.

Types of Variables Employed in Statistical Measurement

In statistical measurement, the individuals may be found to differ in sex, age, intelligence, height, weight, attitude towards women education and many other ways. Such qualities or properties exhibiting differences are called variables. In the words of Garrett (1971):

> The term 'variables' refers to attributes or qualities which exhibit differences in magnitude and which vary along some dimensions.

In general, variables are classified as continuous and discontinuous or discrete variables.

Continuous variables form a continuous series. A series is said to be continuous when it is capable of any degree of sub-division and in practice shows no real gaps. Therefore, a variable is said to be continuous when it passes from one value to the next by indefinitely small changes. Height, weight, length, temperature and so on are examples of such variables. In this way, the criterion for identification of a continuous variable lies in the answer to the question: Is it possible to measure it in the smallest degree of measurement? For example, in measuring height we can get measurement in metres capable of being broken down into centimetres, millimetres, etc. with a greater degree of precision. Here, scores and measurements concerning height, exhibit no real gaps. Within the given range, any 'score'—integral or fractional—may exist and have meaning. The same is true for weight and other measures of physical as well as mental traits, i.e. scores on an intelligence or achievement test. Such measurement data can be represented as points on a line as given in Figure 1.1.

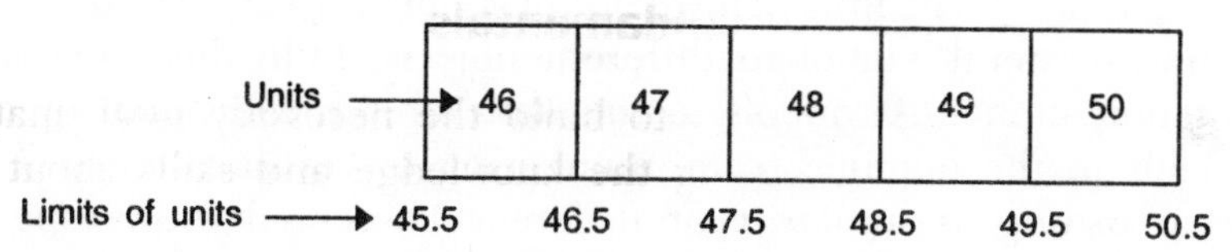

Figure 1.1 Representation, on a line, of continuous data showing upper and lower limits.

It clearly shows that a score of 46 in a continuous series means a value ranging from its lower limit 45.5 to the upper limit 46.5. It is therefore clearly understood by the students of statistics, while dealing with continuous data or scores, that a score is never a point on the scale but just occupies an interval from a .5 unit below to a .5 unit above its face value. For calculating the lower limit of a given score, we must subtract .5 from the given numerical value of that score and for upper limit, add .5.

Discontinuous or discrete variables, on the other hand, fall into discontinuous or discrete series. A series is said to be discontinuous or discrete when it exhibits real gaps. Consequently a variable is said to be discontinuous or discrete when there are real gaps between one value and the next. The data regarding such variables can only be expressed in whole units (numbers). Some examples are the number of eggs laid by a hen, the number of children in a family, the number of books in a library, number of words spelled correctly, the number of cycles passing a crossing during a certain period of time and so on.

With the above description of continuous and discontinuous variables or series, the students may now clearly visualize that most of the variables dealt with in education, psychology and sociology are continuous or may be normally treated as continuous rather than discontinuous or discrete.

Scales of Measurement

Various scales are employed in the field of measurement. Stevens (1946) has recognized four types of scales—nominal, ordinal, interval and ratio.

Nominal scale. Each vehicle—bicycle, scooter, car and so on—is alloted a classification symbol by the State Transport Authorities. Every student is assigned a roll number in his class. A player is identified as a player of a particular team by the type of dress he wears and also by the number on the back of his sports shirt. In this way, we see that different numbers, identifying the different objects or individuals. These numbers or symbols constitute a nominal scale. It is a primitive type of measurement in which we adopt a general rule: Do not assign the same numeral/symbol to different objects, individuals or classes or different numerals/symbols to the same object, individual or class.

Thus in the nominal scale, numbering or classification is always made according to similarity or difference observed with respect to some characteristic or property. For example, if we take eye colour as a variable, then we will be able to:

1. classify the individuals in categories like blue-eyed, brown-eyed, green-eyed or black-eyed, and
2. further identify them as individuals by assigning them numbers symbols within each category.

By all means, operations in a nominal scale only permit the making of statements on the basis of equality or difference. Here, numerals and symbols are assigned to represent classes or individuals, but such statements are merely the mark of identification (levels) and the only purpose they serve is to classify or identify objects or individuals. This is why the numbers worn by the players only classify them as a member of a team or identify one player of the team from another but tell us nothing about the quality of the player.

Ordinal scale. Ordinal scales are somewhat more sophisticated than nominal scales. Whereas nominal scale numbers serve as labels to identify the individuals or objects belonging to a group or a class, in ordinal scales, numbers reflect their rank order or merit position within their own group or class with respect to some quality, property or performance. An ordinary example of such a scale is ordering or ranking the students of a class as I, II, III (or 1, 2, 3), and so on, based on the marks obtained by them on an achievement test. Here, large scores reflect more of the quality or characteristic on the basis of which the individuals are ordered in higher rank or position.

The defect in such scales lies in the fact that the units along the scale are unequal in size. The difference in the achievement scores between the first and the second merit position holder is not necessarily equal to the difference between the second and the third. In this way, these scales tell us the order or serial position of an individual within a group, in relation to a particular trait or attribute but they do not provide an exact measurement on account of inequality in distance between the points on the scale. However, we often come across ordinal scales and measures in education, psychology and sociology irrespective of their statistical limitation. Statistics like median, percentiles, and rank order correlation coefficient can be easily computed through such data.

Interval scale. This type of scale does not merely identify or classify individuals in relation to some attribute or quality by a number (on the basis of sameness or difference) or rank (in order of their merit position) but advances much ahead by pointing out the relative qualitative as well as quantitative differences. The major strength of interval scales lies in the fact that they have equal units of measurement. However, they do not possess a true zero. Examples of this scale are the Fahrenheit and Centigrade thermometers, and scores on intelligence tests.

In the above thermometers we have equal units of measurement along the scale but zero on these thermometers does not indicate a total absence of heat. In the interval scales, the zero point for convenience sake, is more often arbitrarily defined. This is why it is not proper to say that 40° (on Monday) is twice the temperature of 20° (on Tuesday). Similarly nothing can be said about the interpretation of scores related to an achievement and intelligence test. We cannot conclude that an individual has zero intelligence, on the basis of the standard scores on an intelligence test.

In psychology, education and sociology we usually come across measurement data heavily dependent upon interval scales. That is why we resort to approximation and estimates rather than true measurement and exact computation as found in physical sciences.

Ratio scale. It constitutes the final and highest type of scale in terms of measurement. Here measures are not only expressed in equal units but are also taken from a true zero. The zero on such scales essentially means an absence of quality or attribute being assessed. Examples of such scales are measures of length, width, weight, capacity, loudness and the line. In the measurement of all these attributes, all the concerned measuring scales start from a true zero. These scales easily permit statements regarding the comparative ratio in relation to some quality or property existing among the different individuals or objects. Consequently, one object may be safely declared twice as long or four times as heavy than the other. In physical sciences, we usually come across such types of measures and measurement scales but in education, psychology and sociology the possibility of such measures is quite uncommon.

Type of Approximation or Exactness Required in Statistics

Measurement concerning statistics in education, psychology and sociology cannot be so absolute and exact as in the physical sciences. Therefore, statistical computation is most often based on approximation instead of the sophisticated mathematical precision. For this purpose the following general rules may be observed:

1. Carrying out computation to too many decimal places is not so much needed. As a general rule, the computed answer may have only one digit more than in the raw data. For example, if the data contains test scores of two digits then ordinarily we should not have more than three digits in the mean and with this, the other statistics can be calculated from the data.
2. Rounding off numbers to the nearest whole number or to the nearest decimal place is often carried out in the statistical computation, depending upon the number of decimal places required in a given solution. For this purpose, the following rules may be employed:
   (a) If the last digit is less than 5, it is dropped.
   (b) If the last digit is more than 5, the preceding digit is raised to the next higher digit.
   (c) If the last digit ends in 5 and the digit preceding the 5 is an even number, the 5 is dropped, but if the digit preceding the 5 is an odd number, this digit is raised to the next higher one.

The following illustrations may help in understanding the rules:

(i) 0.754 = 0.75 and 0.673 = 0.67

(ii) 0.756 = 0.76 and 0.677 = 0.68

(iii) 0.755 = 0.76 and 0.675 = 0.68

(iv) 0.725 = 0.72 and 0.665 = 0.66

Various Statistical Symbols

It is also necessary to know in advance about the symbolic language to be employed in statistics. In the present text we are going to make use of some of the statistical symbols given in Table 1.1.

Table 1.1

Statistical term	*Symbol used*
Raw score on some measure/mid-points of the class interval in a frequency distribution	X
Deviation score (indicating how much a score deviates from the mean of the group)	$X - M$ or x
Sum of the scores in a given series of variable X	ΣX (Σ is known as capital sigma)
Class interval in a frequency distribution	i
Frequency (the number of cases with a specific score or in a particular class interval)	f
Cumulative frequencies	cf
Total frequencies (the total number of cases in the group)	Σf or N
Mean, median and mode	M, M_d and M_o
First quartile, second quartile, third quartile, etc.	Q_1, Q_2, Q_3, etc.
First, second, third—percentiles	P_1, P_2, P_3, etc.
First, second, third—deciles	D_1, D_2, D_3, etc.
Standard deviation	σ
Quartile deviation	Q
Product moment correlation coefficient	r
Spearman's rank order correlation coefficient	ρ
Chi square	χ^2
Degree of freedom	df
Observed and expected frequencies	f_o and f_e
Variance ratio	F
Standard error	SE
Null hypothesis	H_o
Alternate hypothesis	H_A
Biserial correlation	γ_{bis}
Point biserial correlation	$\gamma_{p,\,\text{bis}}$
Tetrachoric correlation	γ_t
Phi-coefficient	ϕ
Multiple correlation	R

SUMMARY

The word "statistics" may refer to numerical facts, methodology of dealing with numerical facts or summarized figures of numerical facts. However, as a subject, statistics refers to that branch of knowledge which helps in the scientific collection, presentation, analysis and interpretation of numerical facts.

In the fields of education, psychology and sociology, statistics helps in:

1. the task of evaluation and measurement;
2. in carrying out day to day professional activities;
3. keeping various types of records and furnishing statistics;
4. in carrying out research; and
5. in understanding and using the products of research.

The subject statistics for being employed in the above purposes, requires a minimum basic knowledge of some fundamentals of mathematical computation and statistical language from its users. Therefore, a beginner in this subject must have knowledge about:

1. mathematical fundamentals like four fundamental rules, square and square roots and so on;
2. the continuous and discrete variables employed in statistical measurement;
3. the various scales of measurement like nominal, ordinal, interval and ratio scales;
4. the nature of exactness or approximation required in statistical measurement; and
5. the various statistical symbols.

EXERCISES

1. What do you mean by the term statistics? Enumerate its needs and importance in the fields of education and psychology.

2. What do you mean by continuous and discrete variables? Illustrate with examples.

3. Classify the following variables into continuous and discrete series:

(a) Height (b) weight (c) distance travelled by train (d) scores on an achievement test (e) number of electric poles in a colony (f) number of individuals sitting in a bus (g) intelligence test scores.

4. Point out the range (lower limit to upper limit) of the following scores belonging to a continuous series:

   14, 22, 46, 72 and 85.

5. Write in detail about the various scales of measurement. What type of scales are frequently used for collecting data in education, psychology and sociology and why?

6. What type of scale—nominal, ordinal, interval or ratio scale—may be used in measuring each of the following variables:

   (a) Sex (b) eye colour (c) temperature (d) height (e) weight (f) rating of performance in a task (g) scores on an achievement test (h) scores on an intelligence test (i) calendar time (j) length.

7. Round off the following numbers to two decimal places:

   (a) 52.726 (b) 0.315 (c) 0.845 (d) 2.374 (e) 8.675 (f) 23.72558.

2

Organization of Data

THE MEANING OF THE TERM 'DATA'

The word "data" is plural, the singular being *datum*. Dictionary meaning of the word datum is 'fact' and, therefore, in plural, the word data signifies more than one fact. In a wider sense, the term data denotes evidence or facts describing a group or a situation. In other words, it may refer to any details regarding numerical records or reports. However, in a practical sense, the statistical term is generally used for numerical facts such as measures of height, weight and scores on achievement and intelligence tests.

METHODS OF ORGANIZING DATA

Tests, experiments and survey studies in education and psychology provide us valuable data, mostly in the shape of numerical scores. These data in their original form, have little meaning for the investigator or reader. For understanding the meaning and deriving useful conclusion, the data have to be organized or arranged in some systematic way. The organization and arrangement of original data or computed statistics in a proper way for deriving useful interpretation is termed organization of data. In general, this task can be carried out in the following ways:

1. Organization in the form of statistical tables
2. Organization in the form of Rank order
3. Organization in the form of Frequency Distribution (distribution into suitable groups).

Let us discuss these one by one.

Statistical Tables

In this form of arrangement, the data are tabulated or arranged into rows and columns of different headings. Such tables can list original raw scores as well as the percentages, means, standard deviations and so on. This organization of data into statistical tables may be understood through the following examples.

Example 2.1: *Literacy survey of the village Bohar made by the students of B.Ed., C.R. College of Education, Rohtak for age group 15–35.*

Literacy status	*Upper caste Hindu*			*Backward classes*			*Scheduled caste/Tribe*		
	Male	Female	Total	Male	Female	Total	Male	Female	Total
Literate	2650	550	3200	1208	312	1520	453	52	505
Illiterate	2702	3498	6200	1625	1515	3140	404	606	1010
Total	5352	4048	9400	2833	1827	4660	857	658	1515

Source: Record of N.S.S. Activities, C.R. College of Education, Rohtak, 2000–2001.

Example 2.2: *Pass percentage of the High Schools of Rohtak City in the High School Public Examination.*

	Name of school	*Pass percentage*	*Girls' pass percentage*	*Boys' pass percentage*
High Schools of Rohtak City	*A*			
	B			
	C			
	D			
	E			
	.			
	.			
	.			
	N			

Source: Result record collected by the District Education Officer's Office, Rohtak.
Note: In place of actual figures, we have produced only a format for the desired statistical table.

General rules for constructing tables. For the construction of tables in general, the following rules prove quite useful:

1. Title of the table should be simple, concise and unambiguous. As a rule, it should appear on the top of the table.
2. The table should be suitably divided into columns and rows according to the nature of data and purpose. These columns and rows should be arranged in a logical order to facilitate comparisons.
3. The heading of each column or row should be as brief as possible. Two or more columns or rows with similar headings may be grouped under a common heading to avoid repetition and we may have sub-headings or captions.

4. Sub-totals for each separate classification and a general total for all combined classes are to be given. These totals should be given at the bottom or at the right of the concerned items (members).
5. The units (e.g. weight in kg, height in centimeters, percentage, etc.) in which the data are given must invariably be mentioned, preferably, in the headings of columns or rows.
6. Necessary footnotes for providing essential explanation of the points to ambiguous interpretation of the tabulated data must be given at the bottom of the table.
7. The source/sources from where the data have been received should be given at the end of the table. In case the primary source is not traceable, then the secondary source may be mentioned.
8. In tabulating long columns of figures, space should be left after every five or ten rows.
9. If the numbers tabulated have more than three significant figures, the digits should be grouped in threes. For example, we should write 5732981 as 5 732 981.
10. For all purposes and by all means, the table should be as simple as possible so that it may be studied by the readers with minimum possible strain and it should provide a clear picture and interpretation of the statistical data in the quickest possible time.

Rank Order

The original raw scores can be successfully arranged in an ascending or a descending series exhibiting an order with respect to the rank or merit position of the individual. For this purpose, we usually adopt a descending series, arranging the highest score on the top and the lowest at the bottom.

Example 2.3: Fifty students of the B.Ed. class obtained the following scores (roll numberwise) on an achievement test. Tabulate this data in the form of a rank order:

62, 21, 26, 32, 56, 36, 37, 39, 53, 40, 54, 42, 44, 61, 68, 28, 33, 56, 57, 37, 52, 39, 40, 54, 42, 43, 63, 30, 34, 58, 35, 38, 50, 38, 52, 41, 51, 44, 41, 42, 43, 45, 46, 45, 47, 48, 49, 45, 46, 48.

The rank order tabulation of this data will be as follows:

S. No.	*Scores*	*S. No.*	*Scores*	*S. No.*	*Scores*	*S. No.*	*Scores*
1	68	14	51	27	43	40	37
2	63	15	50	28	43	41	37
3	62	16	49	29	43	42	36
4	61	17	48	30	42	43	35
5	58	18	48	31	42	44	34
6	57	19	47	32	41	45	33
7	56	20	46	33	41	46	32
8	56	21	46	34	40	47	30
9	54	22	45	35	40	48	28
10	54	23	45	36	39	49	26
11	53	24	45	37	39	50	21
12	52	25	44	38	38		
13	52	26	44	39	38		

Frequency Distribution

Organization of data in the form of rank order as depicted in Example 2.3, enables us to arrange the available test scores of 50 students in a systematic way according to the relative scores, rank or merit position. But this type of arrangement does not help us to summarize a series of raw scores. It only helps us in their re-arrangement. It does not also tell us the frequency of a particular score. By frequency of a score, we mean the number of times the score is repeated in the given series. In education, psychology and sociology, many times the data contains a large number of scores and a long series. It needs to be adequately summarized for its proper handling, organization, presentation and interpretation. Organization of the data into frequency distribution provides a proper solution.

In this form of organization and arrangement of data, we group the numerical data into some arbitrarily chosen classes or groups. For this purpose usually, the scores are distributed into groups of scores (classes) and each score is alloted a place in the respective group or class. It is also seen how many times a particular score or group of scores occurs in the given data. This is known as the frequency of a score or group of scores. In this way, frequency distribution may be considered as a method of presenting a collection of groups of scores to show the frequency in each group of scores or class.

How to Construct a Frequency Distribution Table

The task of organizing data into a frequency distribution is a technical one. It is carried out through systematic steps. Let us illustrate the process by taking the data of 50 B.Ed. students in an achievement test, given in Example 2.3.

Finding the range. First of all, the range of the series to be grouped is found out. It is done by subtracting the lowest score from the highest. In the present problem the range of the distribution is 68 – 21, i.e. 47.

Determining the class interval or grouping interval. After finding out the range, the number and size of the classes or groups to be used in grouping the data are decided.

There exist two different rules for this purpose:

(i) *First rule*: To get an idea of the size of the classes, i.e. class interval, the range is divided by the number of classes desired. Class interval is usually denoted by the symbol '*i*' and is always a whole number. Thus the formula for deciding the class interval is:

$$i = \frac{\text{Range}}{\text{No. of classes desired}}$$

Now the question arises as in how many classes or groups should one distribute a given data. As a general rule, Tate (1955) writes,

> If the series contains fewer than about 50 items, more than about 10 classes are not justified. If the series contains from about 50 to 100 items, 10 to 15 classes tend to be appropriate; if more than 100 items, 15 or more classes tend to be appropriate. Ordinarily, not fewer than 10 classes or more than 20 are used.

If by dividing the range by the number of classes we do not get a whole number, the nearest approximate number is taken as the class interval.

(ii) *Second rule*: According to the second rule, class interval '*i*' is decided first and then the number of classes is determined. For this purpose usually, the class intervals of 2, 3, 5 or 10 units in length are used.

Both of the above mentioned rules are practised. In my opinion, it is better to use a combined procedure made out of both the rules. Actually the range, the number of classes and the class interval—all should be taken into consideration while planning for a frequency distribution and we must aim at selecting a proper class interval (i) that can yield appropriate categories (number of classes) as mentioned above by Tate.

In this way, the proper class interval (i) in this example is 5.

(Here, range = 47. Scores are 50 in number and thus about 10 classes are sufficient. Therefore, $i = 47/10 = 4.7$, i.e. the nearest whole number = 5.)

Writing the contents of the frequency distribution. After deciding the size and number of the class interval and locating the highest and lowest scores of the given data, we proceed to write the contents of the frequency distribution. For this purpose, three columns are drawn and work is carried out as under:

(i) *Writing the classes of the distribution.* In the first column, we write down all the classes of the distribution. For this purpose first of all, the lowest class is settled and afterwards other subsequent classes are written down. In the present problem, 20–24 can be taken as the lowest class and then we have higher classes 25–29, 30–34, etc. up to 65–69.

(ii) *Tallying the scores into proper classes.* In this step, the scores given in the data are taken one by one and tallied in their proper classes as shown in the 2nd column of Table 2.1. These tally marks against each class are then counted. These counted numbers are called the frequencies of that class. They are written in the third column as given in Table 2.1.

Table 2.1 Construction of a Frequency Distribution Table

Classes of scores	*Tallies*	*Frequencies*
65–69	|	1
60–64	|||	3
55–59	||||	4
50–54	~~||||~~ ||	7
45–49	~~||||~~ ||||	9
40–44	~~||||~~ ~~||||~~ |	11
35–39	~~||||~~ |||	8
30–34	||||	4
25–29	||	2
20–24	|	1
	Total frequencies (N) =	50

(iii) *Checking the tallies.* The total of the 3rd column should be equal to the number of individuals whose scores have been tabulated. In the above tabulation, the total of frequencies, i.e. 50 agrees with the total number of students given in the problem.

Grouping Error

While grouping the raw scores into a frequency distribution, we assume that the mid-point of the class interval is the score obtained by each of the individuals represented by that interval. If we take the frequency distribution given in Table 2.1, we may observe that four scores tabulated in the class interval 55–59 had the original values 56, 56, 57 and 58 respectively. In grouping, we assume that these measures have the values of the mid-point of their respective class or group, i.e. 57. They are represented by a single score 57. In making such an assumption, there is a possibility of an error known as the grouping error. The grouping error is likely to be caused by grouping the scores into a frequency distribution assuming that the measures have the values of the mid-point of their respective classes. The extent to which assumption is not satisfied is the extent to which errors of grouping are present. There is no way to eliminate errors of grouping. They are bound to occur and represent a unique characteristic of continuous series. In a continuous series, the grouping error varies with the size of the class interval, i.e. class interval $\propto$ grouping error. Therefore, its effect may be lessened by adopting a proper choice of the grouping scheme.

Cumulative Frequency and Cumulative Percentage Frequency Distributions

A frequency distribution table tells us the way in which frequencies are distributed over the various class intervals but it does not tell us the total number of cases or the percentage of cases lying below or above a class interval. This task is performed with the help of cumulative frequency and cumulative percentage frequency tables. The cumulative frequency and cumulative percentage frequency distribution may be obtained directly from a frequency distribution, as may be evident from Table 2.2.

Table 2.2 Computation of Cumulative Frequencies and Cumulative Percentage Frequencies

Class interval	*Frequency*	*Cumulative frequency*	*Cumulative percentage frequency*
65–69	1	50	100.00
60–64	3	49	98.00
55–59	4	46	92.00
50–54	7	42	84.00
45–49	9	35	70.00
40–44	11	26	52.00
35–39	8	15	30.00
30–34	4	7	14.00
25–29	2	3	6.00
20–24	1	1	2.00

Cumulative frequencies are thus obtained by adding successively, starting from the bottom, the individual frequencies. In the given table, when we start from the bottom the first cumulative frequency is to be written as 1 against the lowest class interval, i.e. 20–24. Then we get 3 as another cumulative frequency by adding 1 and 2, then 7 by adding 1, 2 and 4. Similarly, by adding 1, 2, 4 and 8, we get 15 as a cumulative frequency to be written against the interval 35–39. As the actual upper limit of this class interval is 39.5, it may be safely claimed that there are 15 students in the class of 50 students whose achievement scores lie below 39.5.

For converting cumulative frequencies into cumulative percentage frequencies, the particular cumulative frequency is multiplied by 100/*N*, where *N* is the total number of frequencies (total number of students whose achievement scores have been included in the present example). These frequencies tell us the percentage of cases lying below a given score or class limit. For example, the cumulative frequency of 15 can be converted into cumulative percentage frequency by multiplying by 100/*N*, i.e. 100/50 × 2. Thus, we obtain 30 as the cumulative percentage frequency against the class interval 35–39. This cumulative percentage frequency may help us conclude that there are 30% of students in the class of fifty, whose achievement scores lie below the score 39.5. Similarly, the cumulative percentage frequency of 70 may tell us that there are 70% of students whose scores lie below the upper limit of the class interval 45–49, i.e. 49.5.

The cumulative frequencies and cumulative percentage frequencies also help us to tell the relative position, rank or merit of an individual with respect to the members of a group. For example, in the present distribution, if a student secures 54 marks, then it can be immediately concluded from the cumulative frequency distribution that he is better than 42 students in his class of 50 students or in the form of percentage he is better than 84 percent students of his class.

In this way, the cumulative frequency and cumulative percentage frequency distribution tables render valuable help in proper organization, presentation and interpretation of the collected data. These tables also prove quite helpful in the construction of cumulative frequency curves and cumulative percentage frequency curves as well as in the computation of the statistics like median, quartiles, percentiles, quartile deviation and percentile rank.

SUMMARY

The term 'data' refers to numerical facts such as measures of height, weight and scores on intelligence and achievement tests and the like.

Statistical data may be organized in three different ways—statistical tables, rank order and frequency distribution tables.

In statistical tables, the data are tabulated or arranged in to rows and columns of different headings. In these the classes of data are shown according to the nature of data and purpose of the study. Proper headings are given for the contents of these columns and rows. Similarly, care is taken in writing proper footnotes, units of measure, sub-totals and grand totals and source from where the data have been received.

For arranging data in the form of a rank order we usually arrange it in the descending series by taking highest score on the top and lowest in the bottom.

In organizing data through frequency distribution table, we group it into some arbitrarily chosen classes or groups and try to show the frequency in each group of scores or class.

For the construction of a frequency distribution table, we first find out the range (highest – lowest score) and then determine the number of classes and class intervals by the formula

$$i = \frac{\text{Range}}{\text{No. of classes}}$$

Class intervals of 2, 3, 5 and 10 units are generally preferred. For less than 50 items, 10 classes, and between 50 and 100 items, 10 to 15 classes and more than 100 items, 15 to 20 classes are preferred to be chosen. The aim is to select a proper class interval (i) that can yield appropriate categories.

After deciding the class interval and number of classes, and locating the highest and the lowest scores of the given data, the contents of the frequency distribution are written in three columns. In the first column, we write down all the classes of the distribution, in the second column, tallies of individual scores in their proper classes are marked and in the third column the total of the tallies converted into numerical figures is written down. In the end, the total of the 3rd column is checked against the total number of individuals or scores.

Organization of data into a frequency distribution may involve grouping error. This is because of the assumption that the measures have the values of the mid-points of their respective classes. The extent to which this assumption is not satisfied is the extent to which errors of grouping are present. Grouping errors are bound to occur. However, their effect may be minimized by adopting a proper choice of the grouping scheme.

Cumulative frequencies are obtained by adding successively, starting from the bottom of the given frequency distribution table, the individual frequencies. For converting cumulative frequencies into cumulative percentage frequencies, the respective cumulative frequency is multiplied by 100/N where N is the total number of frequencies. Cumulative frequencies and cumulative percentage frequencies tell us the number of individuals and the percentage of the number of individuals respectively lying below a given score or a class limit. In this way, they may be used to tell the relative position or rank of an individual with respect to the members of his group and to compute statistics like median, quartiles, percentiles and percentile rank.

EXERCISES

1. What do you understand by the term 'data' as used in statistics? Why is it essential to organize data?
2. What do you understand by the term 'organization' of data? Discuss in brief the various methods employed for the organization of data.
3. Give the format for organizing the following data into some appropriate statistical tables:
   (a) Literacy figures of different districts of Haryana according to religion and sex.
   (b) The middle standard results of the board in the different districts of Haryana in terms of rural/urban and Govt./non-Govt. schools.
4. What is frequency distribution? How can you organize data in the form of a frequency distribution? Illustrate with the help of an example.
5. In each of the following distributions, indicate
   (a) the size of the class interval,
   (b) the mid-point of the intervals shown, and
   (c) the actual class limits of the intervals.

(i)	(ii)	(iii)
5–8	16–18	30–39
9–12	19–21	40–49
13–16	22–24	50–59
17–20	25–27	60–69
21–24	28–30	70–79

6. Tabulate the following 25 scores into a frequency distribution using an appropriate interval:

   72 75 77 67 72 81 68 65 86 73 67 82 76
   76 70 83 71 63 72 72 61 67 84 69 64

7. The following table represents raw scores on a teaching aptitude test:

30	35	36	58	54	53	50	52	39	49
33	36	34	57	55	38	39	51	48	46
37	54	52	53	39	47	44	41	43	40
52	53	38	51	39	46	45	40	42	41

Make a frequency distribution with a class interval of 3.

8. What do you understand by the terms cumulative frequency distribution and cumulative percentage frequency distribution? Illustrate with the help of some hypothetical data.

9. The following scores were obtained by a group of 40 students on an achievement test:

32	78	27	65	88	83	63	52
86	70	42	66	56	44	63	59
73	52	43	69	59	46	71	65
42	55	39	70	57	49	78	70
34	61	62	77	81	72	79	69

Prepare a frequency distribution table and extend it to a cumulative frequency distribution and cumulative percentage frequency distribution tables for the above data by using a class interval of 5.

3 Graphical Representation of Data

In Chapter 2, we have discussed the organization of data in the form of statistical and frequency distribution tables. Such organization and arrangement of the obtained raw scores on some tests, experiments and surveys helps in the proper understanding and interpretation of the collected data. Thus, valuable ideas can be derived about the progress and development in respective fields. Graphical representation of data also serves the same purpose in more effective ways. Here, the data collected through a practical experiment, test, study or survey is represented or illustrated with the help of some graphic aids, e.g. pictures and graphs.

MEANING OF GRAPHICAL REPRESENTATION OF DATA

A graphic representation is the geometrical image of a set of data. It is a mathematical picture. It enables us to think about a statistical problem in visual terms. A picture is said to be more effective than words for describing a particular thing or phenomenon. Consequently, the graphic representation of data proves quite an effective and an economic device for the presentation, understanding and interpretation of the collected statistical data.

ADVANTAGES OF GRAPHICAL REPRESENTATION OF DATA

The advantages of graphic representation may be summarized as below:

1. The data can be presented in a more attractive and an appealing form.
2. It provides a more lasting effect on the brain. It is possible to have an immediate and a meaningful grasp of large amounts of data through such presentation.

3. Comparative analysis and interpretation may be effectively and easily made.
4. Various valuable statistics like median, mode, quartiles, may be easily computed. Through such representation, we also get an indication of correlation between two variables.
5. Such representation may help in the proper estimation, evaluation and interpretation of the characteristics of items and individuals.
6. The real value of graphical representation lies in its economy and effectiveness. It carries a lot of communication power.
7. Graphical representation helps in forecasting, as it indicates the trend of the data in the past.

MODES OF GRAPHICAL REPRESENTATION OF DATA

We know that the data in the form of raw scores is known as ungrouped data and when it is organized into a frequency distribution, then it is referred to as grouped data. Separate methods are used to represent these two types of data—ungrouped and grouped. Let us discuss them under separate heads.

Graphical Representation of Ungrouped Data

For the ungrouped data (data not grouped into a frequency distribution) we usually make use of the following graphical representation:

1. Bar graph or bar diagrams
2. Circle graph or Pie diagrams
3. Pictograms
4. Line graphs

Bar graph or bar diagram. In bar graphs or diagrams the data is represented by bars. Generally these diagrams or pictures are drawn on graph paper. Therefore these bar diagrams are also referred to as bar graphs.

These diagrams or graphs are usually available in two forms, vertical and horizontal. In the construction of both these forms, the lengths of the bars are in proportion to the amount of variables or traits (height, intelligence, number of individuals, cost, and so on) possessed. The width of bars is not governed by any set rules. It is an arbitrary factor. Regarding the space between two bars, it is conventional to have a space about one half of the width of a bar.

The data capable of representation through bar diagrams may be in the form of raw scores, total scores or frequencies, computed statistics and summarized figures like percentages and averages.

Let us now try to illustrate the task of drawing the bar graph.

Example 3.1: The following data was collected about the strength of students of Govt. Boys' Higher Secondary School in different years.

Years	*No. of students*
1996–1997	1200
1997–1998	1040
1998–1999	960
1999–2000	1000
2000–2001	1400

Represent the above data through a bar graph.

Solution. Bar graph of the date given in a Example 3.1

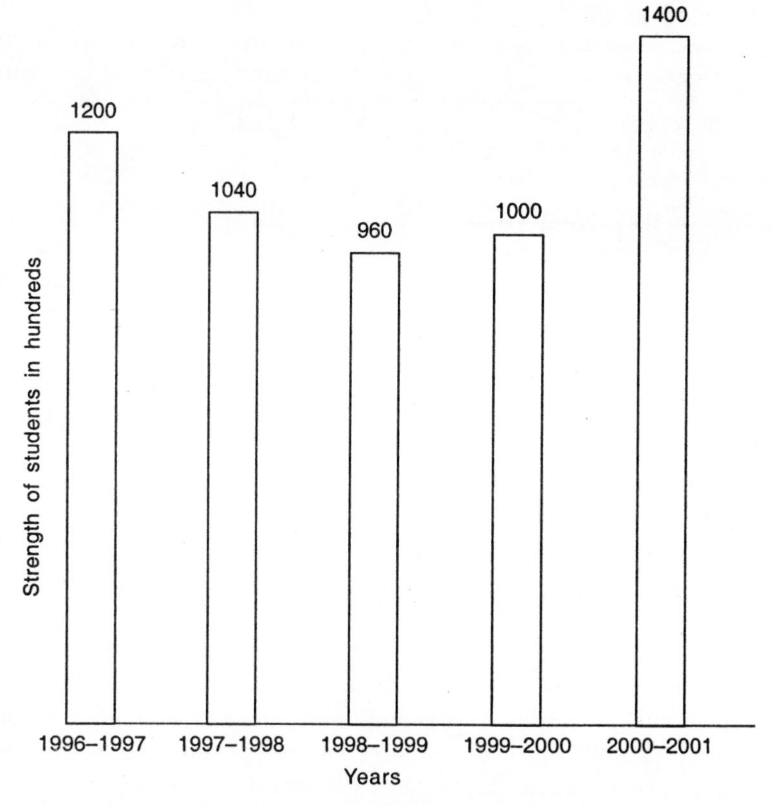

Figure 3.1 Bar graph—Vertical—Strength of students in different years at the Govt. Boys' Higher Secondary School, City A. (*Source:* Official record of school)

The task of drawing the bar graph may be further illustrated as in the following example:

Example 3.2: 120 class X students of a school were asked to opt for different work experiences. The details of these options are given in Table 3.1:

Table 3.1

Area of work experience	*No. of students*	*Per cent*
Photography	6	5
Clay modelling	30	25
Kitchen gardening	48	40
Doll-making	12	10
Book-binding	24	20

Represent the above data through a bar graph.

Solution. The bar graph of the data given in Example 3.2 can be depicted as in Figure 3.2.

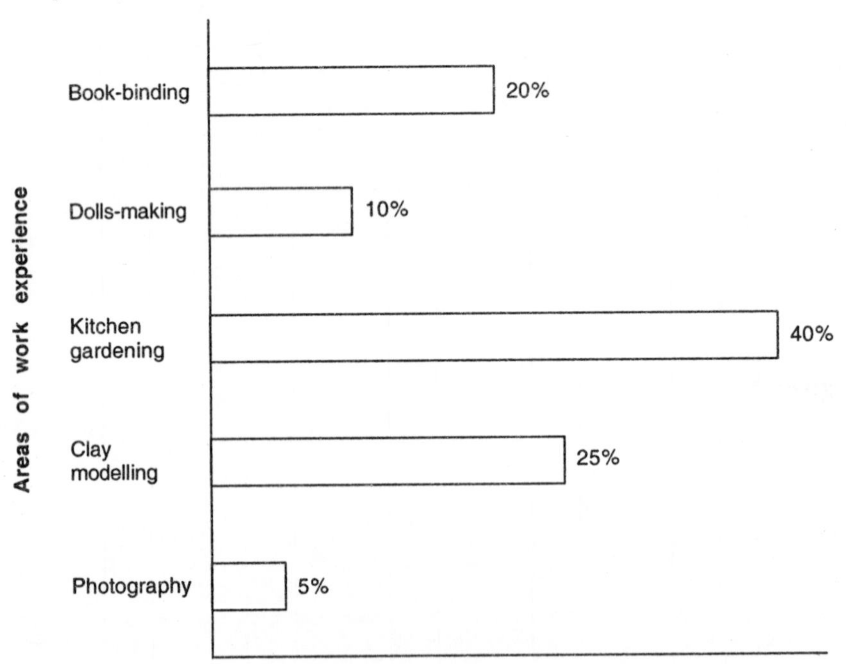

Figure 3.2 Bar graph—Horizontal—Percentage of students of class X opting for different work experience. (*Source:* Record of work experience activities of the school)

Circle graph or pie diagram. In this form of graphical representation, the data is represented through the sections or portions of a circle. The name pie diagram is given to a circle diagram because in determining the circumference of a circle we have to take into consideration a quantity known as 'pie' (written as π).

Method of construction. The surface area of a circle is known to cover 2π or 360°. The data to be represented through a circle diagram may therefore be presented through 360°, parts or sections of a circle. The total frequencies or value is equated to 360° and then the angles corresponding to component parts are calculated (or the component parts are expressed as percentages of the total and then multiplied by 360/100 or 3.6). After determining these angles, the required sectors in the circle are drawn.

For illustration let us take the data given in Example 3.2 (see Table 3.2) concerning bar diagram.

Table 3.2

Area of work experience	*No. of students*	*Angle of the circle*
Photography	6	$\frac{6}{120} \times 360 = 18°$
Clay modelling	30	$\frac{30}{120} \times 360 = 90°$
Kitchen gardening	48	$\frac{48}{120} \times 360 = 144°$
Doll-making	12	$\frac{12}{120} \times 360 = 36°$
Book-binding	24	$\frac{24}{120} \times 360 = 72°$
Total	120	360°

The numerical data may be converted into angles of a circle, as given in Figure 3.3):

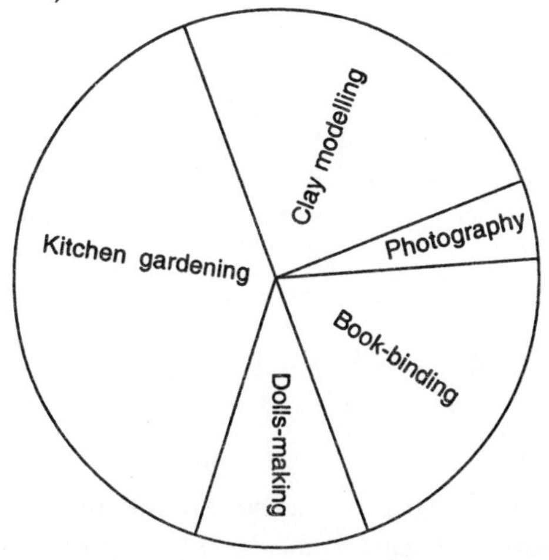

Figure 3.3 Representation of data through the Pie diagram—areas of work experience opted for by students of class X.

Pictogram. Numerical data of statistics may be represented by means of a *pictogram*. Such representation may be illustrated with the help of Figure 3.4.

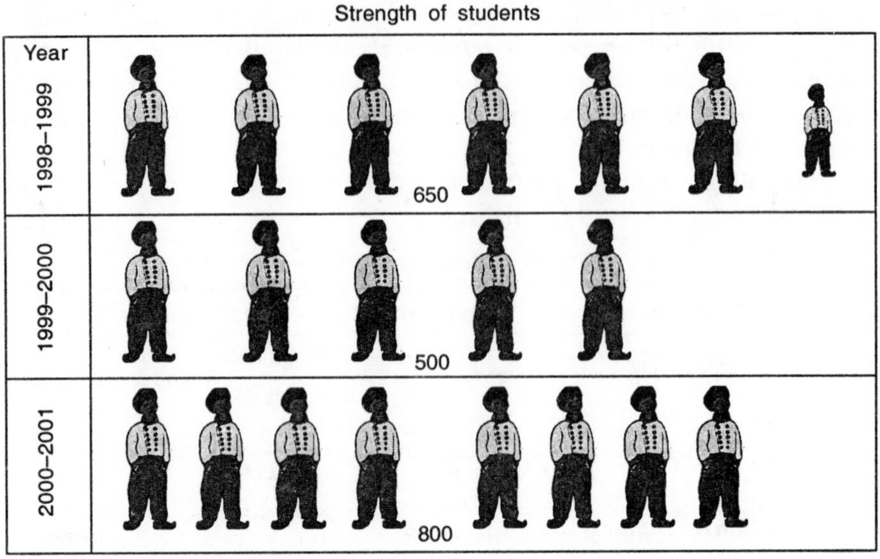

Strength of students

Year

1998–1999 650

1999–2000 500

2000–2001 800

Figure 3.4 Pictogram—Strength of students in different years at the Govt. Boys' High School, City B.
(*Source:* Official record of the school)
Note: Each student represents a strength of 100.

Line graph. Line graphs are simple mathematical graphs that are drawn on the graph paper by plotting the data concerning one variable on the horizontal x-axis and other variable of data on the vertical y-axis. With the help of such graphs the effect of one variable upon another variable during an experimental or a normative study, may be clearly demonstrated. The construction of these graphs can be understood through the following example:

Example 3.3: A nonsense syllables association test was administered on a student of class X to demonstrate the effect of practice on learning. The data so obtained may be studied from the following table:

Trial No.	1	2	3	4	5	6	7	8	9	10	11	12
Score	4	5	8	8	10	13	12	12	14	16	16	16

Draw a line graph for the representation and interpretation of the above data.

The line graph for the data given in example 3.3 can be drawn as per presentation in Figure 3.5

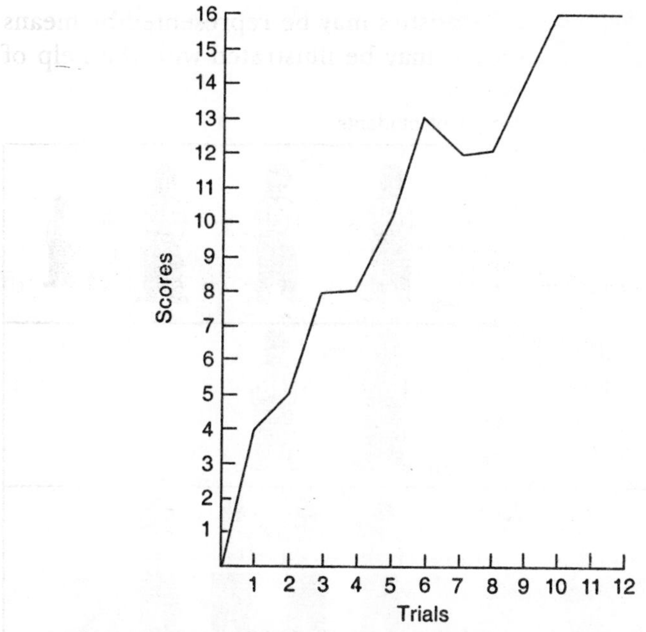

Figure 3.5 Line graph—the effect of practice on learning.

Graphical Representation of Grouped Data (Frequency Distribution)

There are four methods of representing a frequency distribution graphically:

1. The histogram
2. The frequency polygon
3. The cumulative frequency graph
4. The cumulative frequency percentage curve or ogive

Let us discuss these methods one by one.

Histogram. A histogram or column diagram is essentially a bar graph of a frequency distribution. The following points are to be kept in mind while constructing the histogram for a frequency distribution. (For illustration purposes, we can use the frequency distribution given in Table 2.1.)

1. The scores in the form of actual class limits as 19.5–24.5, 24.5–29.5 and so on are taken as examples in the construction of a histogram rather than the written class limits as 20–24, 25–30 and so on.
2. It is customary to take two extra intervals (classes) one below and the other above the given grouped intervals or classes (with zero frequency). In the case of frequency distribution

given in Table 2.1, we can take 14.5–19.5 and 69.5–74.5 as the two required class intervals.

3. Now we take the actual lower limits of all the class intervals (including the extra intervals) and try to plot them on the *x*-axis. The lower limit of the lowest interval (one of the extra intervals) is taken at the intersecting point of *x*-axis and *y*-axis.
4. Frequencies of distribution are plotted on the *y*-axis.
5. Each class or interval with its specific frequency is represented by a separate rectangle. The base of each rectangle is the width of the class interval (*i*) and the height is the respective frequency of that class or interval.
6. It is not essential to project the sides of the rectangles down to the base line.
7. Care should be taken to select the appropriate units of representation along the *x*-axis and the y-axis. Both the *x*-axis and the *y*-axis should not be too short or too long. A good general rule for this purpose as suggested by Garrett (1971) is:

   To select *x* and *y* units which will make the height of the figure approximately 75% of its width.

The above procedure may be properly understood through Figure 3.6 which shows the histogram of the frequency distribution given in Table 2.1.

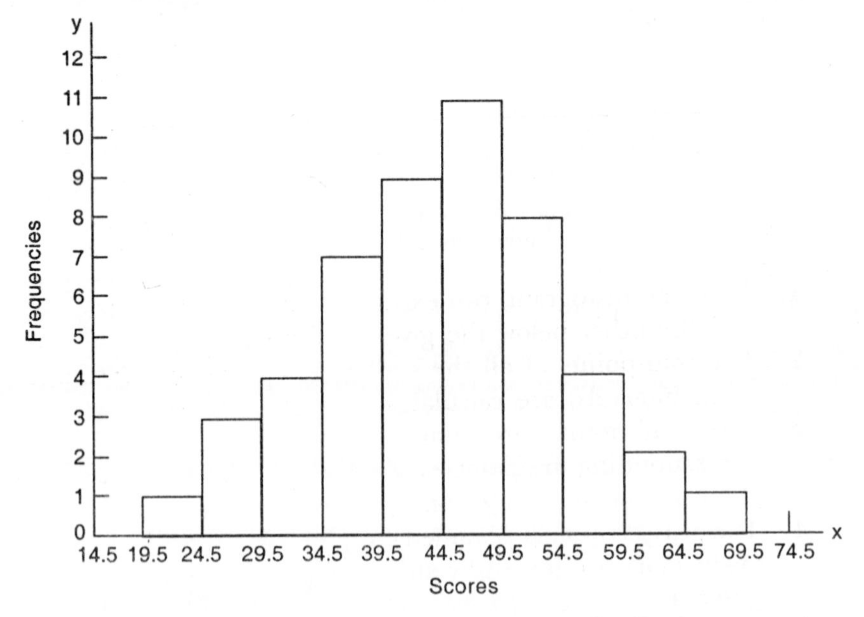

Figure 3.6 Histogram of frequency distribution.

Frequency polygon. A frequency polygon (Figure 3.7) is essentially a line graph for the graphical representation of the frequency distribution. We can get a frequency polygon from a histogram, if the midpoints of the upper bases of the rectangles are connected by straight lines. But it is not essential to plot a histogram first to draw a frequency polygon. We can construct it directly from a given frequency distribution. The following points are helpful in constructing a frequency polygon:

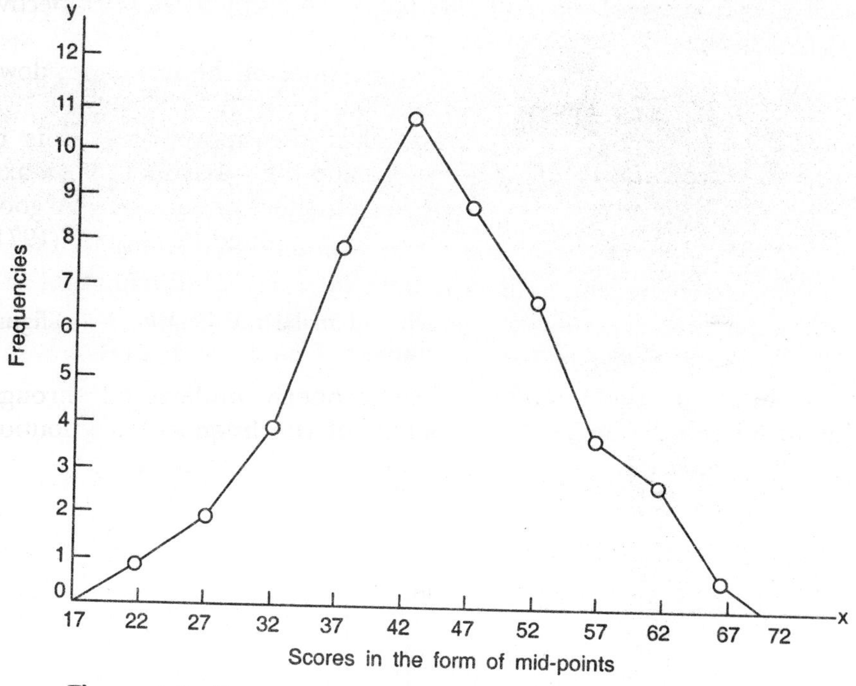

Figure 3.7 Frequency polygon of the frequency distribution given in Table 2.1.

1. As in the histogram, two extra intervals or classes, one above and the other below the given intervals are taken.
2. The mid-points of all the classes or intervals (including two extra intervals) are calculated.
3. The mid-points are marked along the *x*-axis and the corresponding frequencies are plotted along the *y*-axis by choosing suitable scales on both axes.
4. The various points obtained by plotting the mid-points and frequencies are joined by straight lines to give the frequency polygon.
5. For approximate height of the figure and selection of *x* and *y* units, the rule emphasized earlier in the case of histogram should be followed.

Difference between a frequency polygon and a frequency curve. A polygon is a many-sided figure. It is essentially a closed curve while a frequency curve is not a closed curve. In a frequency curve we do not take two extra intervals or classes. But in a frequency polygon, we take these two extra classes in order to close the figure.

Comparison between the histogram and the frequency polygon. Although both histogram and frequency polygon are used for the graphic representation of frequency distribution and are alike in many respects, they possess points of difference. Some of these differences are cited below:

1. Where histogram is essentially the bar graph of the given frequency distribution, the frequency polygon is a line graph of this distribution.
2. In frequency polygon, we assume the frequencies to be concentrated at the mid-points of the class intervals. It points out merely the graphical relationship between mid-points and frequencies and thus is unable to show the distribution of frequencies within each class interval. But the histogram gives a very clear as well as accurate picture of the relative proportions of frequency from interval to interval. A mere glimpse of the figure answers such questions as:
   (a) Which group of class intervals has the largest or smallest frequency?
   (b) Which pair of groups or class intervals has the same frequency?
   (c) Which group has its frequency double that of another?
3. In comparing two or more distributions by plotting two or more graphs on the same axis, frequency polygon is more useful and practicable than the histogram.
4. In comparison to the histogram, frequency polygon gives a much better conception of the contours of the distribution. With a part of the polygon curve, it is easy to know the trend of the distribution but a histogram is unable to tell such a thing.

The cumulative frequency graph. The data organized in the form of a cumulative frequency distribution (discussed in Chapter 2) may be graphically represented through the cumulative frequency graph (Figure 3.8). It is essentially a line graph drawn on graph paper by plotting actual upper limits of the class intervals on the x-axis and the respective cumulative frequencies of these class intervals on the y-axis. Let us consider the data given in the cumulative frequency distribution in Table 2.2 to explain the process of construction of a cumulative frequency graph. Main points may be summarized in the following manner:

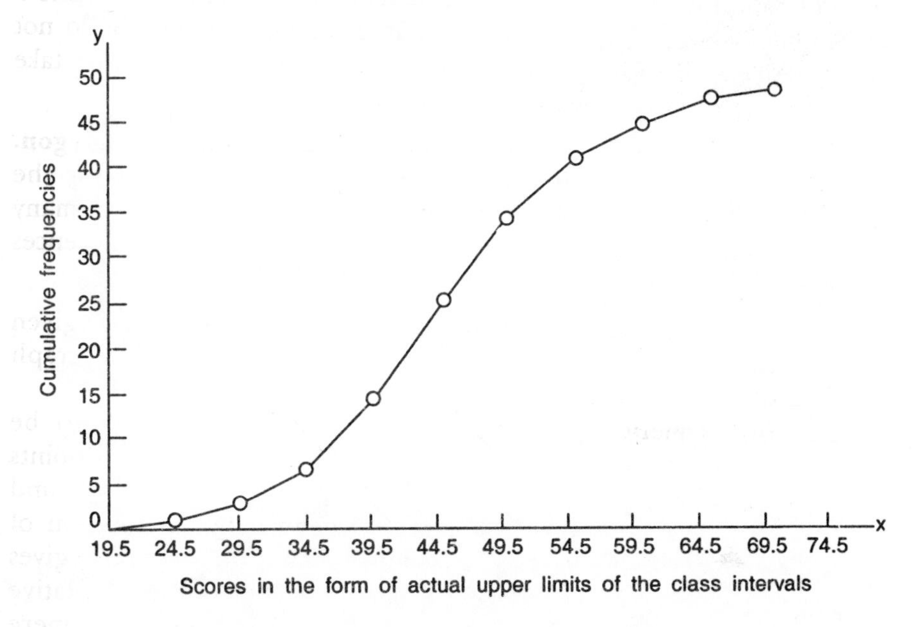

Figure 3.8 Cumulative frequency curve of the frequency distribution given in Table 2.1.

1. First of all, we will calculate the actual upper limits of the class intervals as 24.5, 29.5, 34.5, 39.5, 44.5, 49.5, 54.5, 59.5, 64.5, 69.5 and 74.5.
2. Then we will use the cumulative frequencies given next to the class intervals. In the case of a simple frequency distribution table like 2.1, the cumulative frequencies are first determined and written at the proper place against the respective class intervals.
3. Now, for plotting the actual upper limits of the class intervals on the *x*-axis and respective cumulative frequencies on the *y*-axis of the graph paper, we must select a suitable scale with reference to the range of data to be plotted and the size of graph paper to be used.
4. All the plotted points representing upper limits of the class interval with their respective cumulative frequencies will then be joined through a successive chain of straight lines resulting in a line graph.
5. To plot the origin of the curve on the *x*-axis, it is customary to take one extra class interval with zero cumulative frequency and thus calculate the actual upper limit of this class interval. In the present case the upper limit will be 19.5. It will be the starting point of the curve.

The cumulative percentage frequency curve or ogive. The cumulative percentage frequency curve or ogive (Figure 3.9) is the graphical representation of a cumulative percentage frequency distribution such as given in Table 2.2. It is essentially a line graph drawn on a piece of graph paper by plotting actual upper limits of the class intervals on the *x*-axis and their respective cumulative percentage frequencies on the *y*-axis. Ogive differs from the cumulative frequency graph in the sense that here we plot cumulative percentage frequencies on the *y*-axis in place of cumulative frequencies.

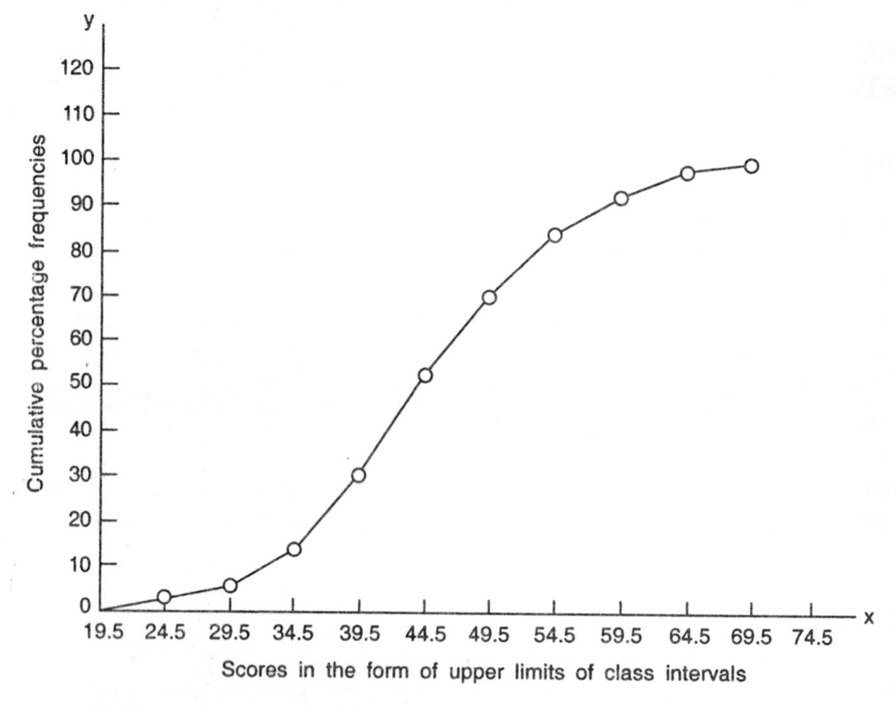

Figure 3.9 Cumulative percentage frequency curve or ogive.

The task of construction of this curve may be understood through the graphical representation in Figure 3.9 based on the data given in Table 2.2.

Use of the cumulative percentage frequency curve or ogive. Cumulative percentage frequency curve (ogive) helps in the following tasks:

1. The statistics like median, quartiles, quartile deviations, deciles, percentiles and percentile ranks may be determined quickly and fairly accurately.
2. Percentile norms (a type of norm representing the typical performance of some designated group or groups) may be easily and accurately determined.

3. We can have an overall comparison of two or more groups or frequency distributions by plotting the ogives concerning these distributions on the same coordinate axes. A frequency curve may also be used for such comparison. The difference lies in the fact that a frequency curve is used in the case when the total frequencies (N) in the distributions are the same; but when the total frequencies are different, we have to draw the frequency percentage curve or ogive.

SMOOTHING OF FREQUENCY CURVES—POLYGON AND OGIVE

Why Smooth?

Many times frequency curves obtained from some frequency distributions are so irregular and disproportionate that it becomes quite difficult to get some useful interpretation from them. It usually happens in the situation when (a) the total number of frequencies (N) is small, and (b) the frequency distribution is somewhat irregular.

These irregularities in frequency distribution might have been minimized if the data collected were numerous. In other words, there is a need for a fairly large sample to reduce the effect of sampling fluctuations upon frequencies in the classes. Addition of cases or increase in the sample size always results in eliminating sample irregularities. But if we cannot increase the size of the sample (where N is small), the kinks and irregularities in the frequency curves may only be removed by the process of smoothing the curve.

Thus, to iron out chance irregularities and also to get a better notion of how the curve might look if the data were more numerous (what we might expect to get from larger groups or additional sampling), the curve may be smoothed.

How to Smooth

One of the methods of smoothing a frequency distribution or curve is the method of "moving" or "running" averages. The formula for this is as under:

$$\text{Smoothed frequency of a class interval} = \frac{1}{3}\left[\begin{array}{l}\text{Frequency of the given class}\\ \text{interval + Frequencies of the}\\ \text{two adjacent class intervals}\end{array}\right]$$

Let us illustrate the computation of smoothed frequencies as given in Table 3.3.

Explanation

It is clear from Table 3.3 that in the process of smoothing a frequency polygon, we average actual frequencies, while in the case of an ogive, the cumulative percentage frequencies are averaged. For illustration, in the case of a frequency polygon, the smooth frequency related to the class interval 55–59 is (4 + 3 + 7)/3 = 4.66 or 4.7 (approx.), while in the case of ogive, the smooth cumulative percentage frequency related to this class interval is (92 + 98 + 84)/3 = 91.33 or 91.3 (approx.).

Table 3.3 Data for the Computation of Smoothed Frequencies for Polygon and Ogive

	For polygon		*For ogive*		
Class intervals	Frequencies (f)	Smoothed frequencies	Cumulative frequencies (cf)	Cumulative percentage frequencies	Smoothed frequencies
65–69	1	1.3	50	100	99.3
60–64	3	2.7	49	98	96.7
55–59	4	4.7	46	92	91.3
50–54	7	6.7	42	84	82.0
45–49	9	9.0	35	70	68.7
40–44	11	9.3	26	52	50.7
35–39	8	7.7	15	30	32.0
30–34	4	4.7	7	14	16.7
25–29	2	2.3	3	6	7.3
20–24	1	1.0	1	2	2.7

A slightly different procedure is to be adopted for calculating smooth frequencies for the class intervals at the extremes of the distributions. For example, the smooth frequency in the case of polygon for class intervals 20–24 and 65–69 will be calculated as respectively.

$$\frac{1+2+0}{3} = 1, \quad \frac{1+0+3}{3} = 1.33 \text{ or } 1.3 \text{ (approx.)}$$

In the case of the ogive the smoothed cumulative percentage frequencies for these intervals are

$$\frac{100+100+98}{3} = \frac{298}{3} = 99.3, \qquad \frac{2+0+6}{3} = \frac{8}{3} = 2.7$$

respectively. The smoothed frequency curves in the case of polygon and ogive, for the data given in Table 3.3, can be draw in just as given in Figures 3.10 and 3.11, respectively:

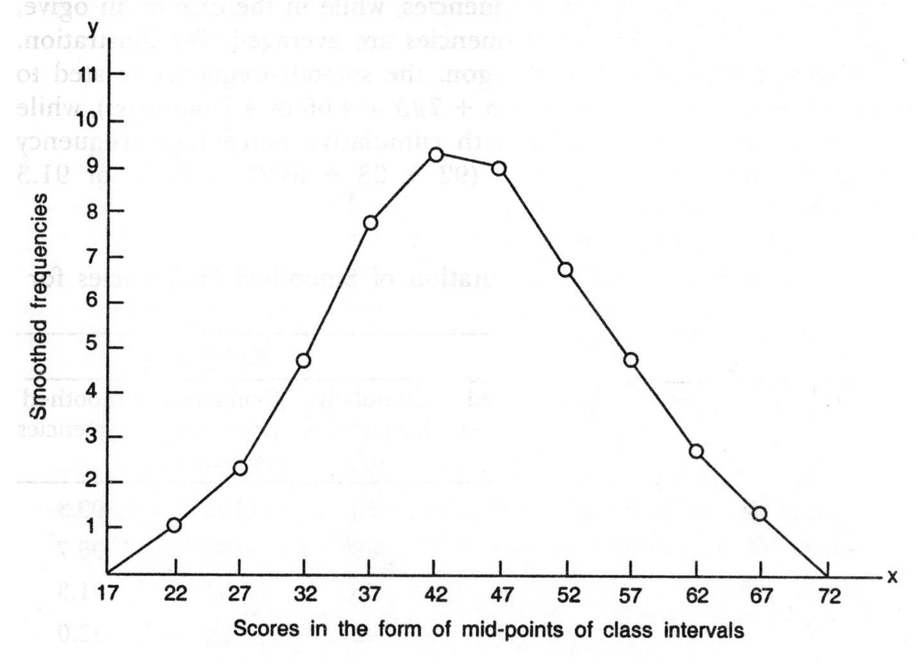

Figure 3.10 Smoothed frequency polygon.

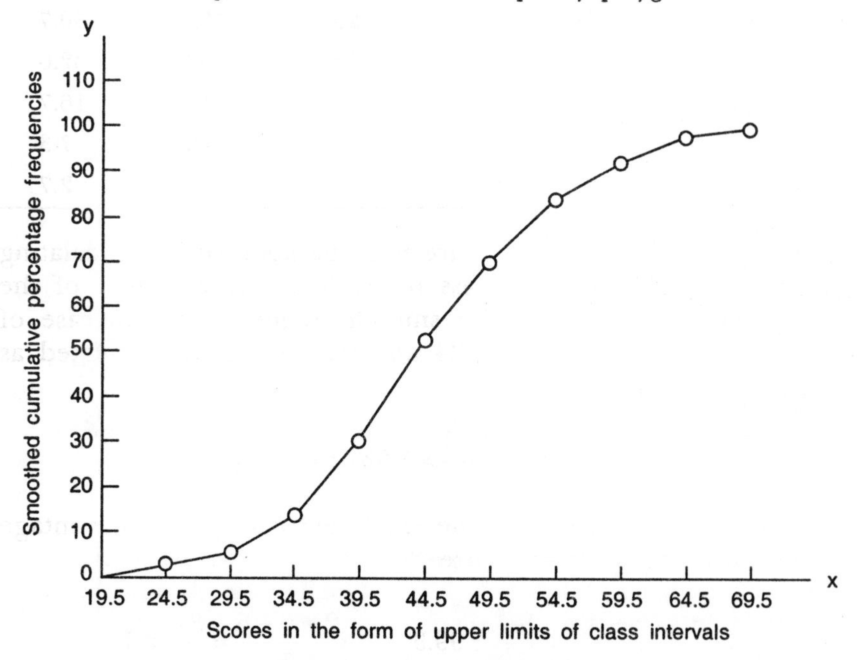

Figure 3.11 Smoothed ogive.

SUMMARY

The statistical data may be presented in a more attractive form appealing to the eye with the help of some graphic aids, i.e. pictures and graphs. Such presentation carries a lot of communication power. A mere glimpse of these pictures and graphs may enable the viewer to have an immediate and meaningful grasp of the large amount of data.

Ungrouped data may be represented through a bar graph, circle graph (pie diagram), pictograph and line graph.

Bar graphs represent the data on the graph paper in the form of vertical or horizontal bars.

In a *pie diagram,* data is represented by a circle of 360° divided into parts, each representing the amount of data converted into angles. The total frequency value is equated to 360 degrees and then the angles corresponding to component parts are calculated.

In *pictograms,* the data is represented by means of picture figures appropriately designed in proportion to the numerical data.

Line graphs represent the data concerning one variable on the horizontal and other variable on the vertical axis of the graph paper.

Grouped data (frequency distribution) may be represented graphically by histogram, frequency polygon, cumulative frequency graph and cumulative frequency percentage curve or ogive.

A *histogram* is essentially a bar graph of a frequency distribution. The actual class limits plotted on the x-axis represent the width of various bars (rectangles) and respective frequencies of these class intervals represent the height of these bars.

A *frequency polygon* is essentially a line graph for the graphical representation of frequency distribution. To construct a frequency polygon, the mid-points of all classes (including two extra intervals) are plotted on the x-axis and the corresponding frequencies are plotted along the y-axis by choosing suitable scales for both axes. Frequency polygon is much better than histogram in the task of comparing two or more distributions and revealing the contour and forecasting the trend of the distribution. Histogram is more helpful in giving a very clear as well as an accurate picture of the relative proportions of frequency from interval to interval.

The *cumulative frequency graph* represents the cumulative frequency distribution by plotting actual upper limits of the class intervals on the x-axis and the respective cumulative frequencies of these class intervals on the y-axis.

The *cumulative percentage frequency curve or ogive* represents the cumulative percentage frequency distribution by plotting upper limits of the class intervals on the x-axis and the respective cumulative percentage frequencies of these class intervals on the y-axis. An ogive proves quite useful in the computation of median, quartiles, deciles percentiles, percentile ranks and percentile norms as well as for the overall comparison of two or more groups or frequency distributions.

In the case of some frequency distributions, their frequency curves show many kinks and irregularities which may be safely removed by the process of smoothing. The formula of the moving average, i.e. smoothed frequency of a class interval = 1/3 (Frequency of the given class interval + Frequencies of the two adjacent class intervals) is used to compute the smoothed frequencies for the corresponding class intervals. In drawing smoothed curves (polygon or ogive), we plot these calculated smoothed frequencies on the *y*-axis in place of the given frequencies (in case of polygon) and cumulative percentage frequencies (in case of ogive). The task of understanding and interpretation of data becomes simple, accurate and practicable with the help of such smoothing of the frequency curves.

EXERCISES

1. What do you understand by the term 'graphical representation of data'? Enumerate its advantages.
2. What are the various modes utilized for the graphical representation of ungrouped data? Discuss in brief.
3. What are bar graphs or diagrams? How are they constructed? Illustrate with some hypothetical examples.
4. What are circle graphs or pie diagrams? Illustrate their construction through an example.
5. What are pictograms? How can statistical data be represented through such diagrams? Illustrate with an example.
6. What are line graphs? Discuss their utility in the presentation of statistical data. Illustrate their construction with the help of some hypothetical data.
7. Point out the various methods utilized for the graphic representation of grouped data (frequency distribution). Discuss them in brief.
8. What is a histogram? How does it differ from a frequency polygon and frequency curve?
9. What do you understand by the term cumulative frequency? Discuss the process of construction of a cumulative frequency curve.
10. What is a cumulative percentage frequency curve or ogive? Illustrate, how it is constructed. Enumerate its different uses.
11. What do you understand by the term smoothing of a curve?

Why is it essential to smooth a frequency curve, polygon or ogive? Discuss the process of smoothing a polygon and on ogive with the help of suitable examples.

12. Show by suitable bar diagrams the absolute as well as relative changes in the student population of colleges *A* and *B* in the different faculties from 1999 to 2001.

	College A		*College B*	
Faculties	1999	2001	1999	2001
Arts	300	350	100	200
Science	120	500	150	250
Commerce	200	650	130	150
Law	100	300	100	120

13. Draw a pie diagram to represent the following data detailing the monthly expenses of an institution:

Salary of the staff	60,000.00
Electricity, water and telephone bills	15,000.00
Office stationery	10,000.00
Miscellaneous expenses	15,000.00
Total	**1,00,000.00**

14. Plot histograms, frequency polygons, cumulative frequency curves and ogives separately on the different axes for the following distributions:

(*a*)		(*b*)		(*c*)	
Scores	*f*	*Scores*	*f*	*Scores*	*f*
75–79	1	60–69	1	37–39	2
70–74	3	70–79	2	34–36	4
65–69	5	80–89	3	31–33	6
60–64	8	90–99	4	28–30	10
55–59	11	100–109	7	25–27	12
50–54	18	110–119	12	22–24	7
45–49	10	120–129	8	19–21	7
40–44	8	130–139	5	16–18	3
35–39	6	140–149	3	13–15	2
30–34	3	150–159	3	10–12	1
25–29	1	160–169	2		
20–24	1				
	$N = 75$		$N = 50$		$N = 54$

15. Smooth the curves of the frequency polygon and ogive constructed from the data given for the three distributions in Problem 14.

4 Measures of Central Tendency

MEANING OF THE MEASURES OF CENTRAL TENDENCY

If we take the achievement scores of the students of a class and arrange them in a frequency distribution, we may sometimes find that there are very few students who either score very high or very low. The marks of most of the students lie somewhere between the highest and the lowest scores of the whole class. This tendency of a group about distribution is named as central tendency and the typical score lying between the extremes and shared by most of the students is referred to as a measure of central tendency. In this way a measure of central tendency as Tate (1955) defines is:

> a sort of average or typical value of the items in the series and its function is to summarize the series in terms of this average value.

The most common measures of central tendency are:

1. Arithmetic mean or mean
2. Median
3. Mode

Each of them, in its own way, can be called a representative of the characteristics of the whole group and thus the performance of the group as a whole can be described by the single value which each of these measures gives. The values of mean, median or mode also help us in comparing two or more groups or frequency distributions in terms of typical or characteristic performance.

Arithmetic Mean (*M*)

This is the simplest but most useful measure of central tendency. It is nothing but the 'average' which we compute in our high school arithmetic and, therefore, can be easily defined as the sum of all the values of the items in a series divided by the number of items. It is represented by the symbol *M*.

Calculation of mean in the case of ungrouped data. Let X_1, X_2, X_3, X_4, X_5, X_6, X_7, X_8, X_9 and X_{10} be the scores obtained by 10 students on an achievement test. Then the arithmetic mean or mean score of the group of these ten students can be calculated as:

$$M = \frac{X_1 + X_2 + X_3 + X_4 + X_5 + \ldots + X_{10}}{10}$$

The formula for calculating the mean of an ungrouped data is

$$M = \frac{\Sigma X}{N}$$

where ΣX stands for the sum of scores or values of the items and N for the total number of items in a series or group.

Calculation of mean in the case of grouped data (Data in the form of frequency distribution)

General method. In a frequency distribution where all the frequencies are greater than one, the mean is calculated by the formula:

$$M = \frac{\Sigma fX}{N}$$

where X represents the mid-point of the class interval, f its respective frequency, and N the total of all frequencies.

We can illustrate the use of this formula by taking the frequency distribution given in Table 2.1 of Chapter 2 as follows:

Example 4.1

Scores	*f*	*Mid-point (X)*	*fX*
65–69	1	67	67
60–64	3	62	186
55–59	4	57	228
50–54	7	52	364
45–49	9	47	423
40–44	11	42	462
35–39	8	37	296
30–34	4	32	128
25–29	2	27	54
20–24	1	22	22
	$N = 50$		$\Sigma fX = 2230$

$$M = \frac{\Sigma fX}{N} = \frac{2230}{50} = 44.6$$

Short-cut method of computing the mean of grouped data. Mean for the grouped data can be computed easily with the help of the following formula:

$$M = A + \frac{\Sigma fx'}{N} \times i$$

where

A = Assumed mean
i = Class interval
f = Respective frequency of the mid-values of the class intervals
N = Total frequency
$x' = \dfrac{X - A}{i}$ (The quotient obtained after division of the difference between the mid-value of the class and assumed mean by i, the class interval.)

The use of this formula can be easily understood through the following illustration:

Example 4.2: Assumed mean (A) = 42.

Scores	f	X *(Mid-point)*	$x' = (X - A)/i$	fx'
65–69	1	67	5	5
60–64	3	62	4	12
55–59	4	57	3	12
50–54	7	52	2	14
45–49	9	47	1	9
40–44	11	42	0	0
35–39	8	37	–1	–8
30–34	4	32	–2	–8
25–29	2	27	–3	–6
20–24	1	22	–4	–4
	N = 50			$\Sigma fx'$ = 26

Computation

$$M = A + \frac{\Sigma fx'}{N} \times i = 42 + \frac{26}{50} \times 5$$

$$= 42 + \frac{26}{10} = 42 + 2.6 = 44.6$$

Median (M_d)

If the items of a series are arranged in ascending or descending order of magnitude, the measure or value of the central item in the series is is termed as *median*. We may thus say that the median of a distribution is the point on the score scale below which half (or 50%) of the scores fall. Thus, median is the score or the value of that central item which divides the series into two equal parts. It should therefore be understood that the central item itself is not the median. It is only the measure or value of the central item that is known as the median. For example, if we arrange in ascending or descending order the marks of 5 students, then the marks obtained by the 3rd student from either side will be termed as the median of the scores of the group of students under consideration.

Computation of median for ungrouped data. The following two situations could arise:

1. *When N (No. of items in a series) is odd.* In this case where N, is odd (not divisible by 2), the median can be computed by the formula M_d = the measure or value of the $(N+1)/2$-th item.

Example 4.3: Let the scores obtained by 7 students on an achievement test be 17, 47, 15, 35, 25, 39, 44. Then, first of all, for calculating median, we have to arrange the scores in ascending or descending order: 15, 17, 25, 35, 39, 44, 47. Here N (= 7) is odd, and herefore, the score of the $(N + 1)/2$-th item or 4th student, i.e. 35 will be the median of the given scores.

2. *When N (No. of items in a series) is even.* In the case where N is even (divisible by 2), the median is determined by the following formula:

$$M_d = \frac{\text{the value of } (N/2)\text{th item} + \text{the value of } [(N/2)+1]\text{th item}}{2}$$

Example 4.4: Let there be a group of 8 students whose scores in a test are, 17, 47, 15, 35, 25, 39, 50, 44. For calculating mean of these scores we proceed as follows:

Arrangement of scores in ascending series: 15, 17, 25, 35, 39, 44, 47, 50

The score of the $(N/2)$th, i.e. 4th student = 35
The score of the $[(N/2) + 1]$th, i.e. 5th student = 39
Then,

$$\text{Median} = \frac{35+39}{2} = 37$$

Computation of median for grouped data (in the form of frequency distribution). If the data is available in the form of a frequency distribution like below, then calculation of median first requires the location of median class.

Example 4.5

Scores	*f*
65–69	1
60–64	3
55–59	4
50–54	7
45–49	9
40–44	11
35–39	8
30–34	4
25–29	2
20–24	1
	N = 50

Actually, as defined earlier, median is the measure or score of the central item. Therefore, it is needed to locate the central item. It may be done through the formulae given earlier in the case of ungrouped data for the odd and even values of N (total frequencies). Here, in th present distribution, N (= 50) is even. Therefore, median will fall somewhere between the scores of 25th and 26th items in the given distribution. In the given frequency distribution table, if we add frequencies either from above or below we may see that the class interval designated as 40–44 is to be labelled as the class where the score representing median will fall.

After estimating the median class, the median of the distribution may be interpolated with the help of following formula:

$$M_d = L + \left[\frac{(N/2) - F}{f}\right] \times i$$

where

L = Exact lower limit of the median class
F = Total of all frequencies before in the median class
f = Frequency of the median class
i = Class interval
N = Total of all the frequencies

By applying the above formula, we can compute the median of the given distribution in the following way:

$$M_d = 39.5 + \frac{(50/2) - 15}{11} \times 5 = 39.5 + \frac{10}{11} \times 5$$

$$= 39.5 + \frac{50}{11} = 39.5 + 4.55 = 44.05$$

Example 4.6: Some Special Situations in the Computation of Median

(a)		(b)		(c)	
Scores	*f*	*Scores*	*f*	*Scores*	*f*
55–59	5	45–49	2	20–21	2
50–54	3	40–44	5	18–19	1
45–49	8	35–39	6	16–17	0
40–44	18	30–34	0	14–15	0
35–39	15	25–29	8	12–13	2
30–34	10	20–24	3	10–11	0
25–29	7	15–19	2	8–9	0
20--24	2			6–7	2
				4–5	1
				2–3	1
				0–1	1
	$N = 68$		$N = 26$		$N = 10$

Let us analyse the medians of the above distributions.

1. We know by definition that median is the point on the score scale below and above which 50% cases lie. Thus the score representing median should be a common score falling in the classes 35–39 and 40–44. This score is nothing but the upper limit of class 35–39 which is also the lower limit of the class 40–44. Therefore, in this case the median is 39.5.
2. In the second distribution, if we try to add the frequencies from below, we see that upto class interval 25–29, 13 cases lie and by adding frequencies from above, we also find that upto the class interval 35–39, 13 cases lie. In this way, the class interval 30–34 divides the distribution into two equal parts below and above which 50% cases lie. It leads us to conclude that median should be the mid-point of the class interval 30–34 and, therefore, 32 is the median of this distribution.
3. In the third case, if we add the frequencies from below, we find that 5 cases lie upto the class interval 6–7. By adding the frequencies from above, we also find that, upto class 12–13, 5 cases lie. The median should then fall mid-way between the two classes 8–9 and 10–11. It should be the common score represented by both these classes. This score is nothing but the upper limit of the class 8–9 and lower limit of the class 10–11 and, therefore, it should be 9.5.

Mode (M_o)

Mode is defined as the size of a variable (say a score) which occurs most frequently. It is the point on the score scale that corresponds to the maximum frequency of the distribution. In any series, it is the value of the item which is most characteristic or common and is usually repeated the maximum number of times.

Computation of mode for ungrouped data. Mode can be easily be computed merely by looking at the data. All that one has to do is to find out the score which is repeated maximum number of times.

Example 4.7: Suppose we have to find out the value of the mode from the following scores of students:

25, 29, 24, 25, 27, 25, 28, 25, 29

Here the score 25 is repeated maximum number of times and thus, value of the mode in this case is 25.

Computation of mode for grouped data. When data is available in the form of frequency distribution, the mode is computed from the following formula:

$$\text{Mode } (M_o) = 3M_d - 2M$$

where M_d is the median and M is the mean of the given distribution. The mean as well as the median of the distribution are first computed and then, with the help of the above formula, mode is computed. For illustration, we can take the distribution given in Table 2.1.

Example 4.8: The mean and median of this distribution have already been computed as 44.6 and 44.05 respectively.

Therefore,

$$M = 44.6, \quad M_d = 44.05$$
$$M_o = 3 \times 44.05 - 2 \times 44.6$$
$$= 132.15 - 89.2 = 42.95$$

Another method for grouped data. Mode can be computed directly from the frequency distribution table without calculating mean and median. For this purpose, we can use the following formula:

$$M_o = L + \frac{f_1}{f_1 + f_{-1}} \times i$$

where

L = Lower limit of the model class (the class in which mode may be supposed to lie)

i = Class interval

f_1 = Frequency of the class adjacent to the modal class for which lower limit is greater than that for the modal class

f_{-1} = Frequency of the class adjacent to the modal class for which the lower limit is less than that for the modal class

Let us illustrate the use of the above formula by taking frequency distribution given in Table 2.1.

Example 4.9:

Scores	*f*
65–69	1
60–64	3
55–59	4
50–54	7
45–49	9
40–44	11
35–39	8
30–34	4
25–29	2
20–24	1
	N = 50

$$M_o = L + \frac{f_1}{f_1 + f_{-1}} \times i$$

The crude mode in this distribution may be supposed to lie within the class interval 40–44. Hence,

L = 39.5

f_1 = 9

f_{-1} = 8

Therefore,

$$M_o = 39.5 + \frac{9}{9+8} \times 5 = 39.5 + \frac{45}{17} = 39.5 + 2.65 = 42.15$$

For computing mode in the case of grouped data (frequency distribution), we can use any of these two methods. The first method is more useful in the case when we need the computation of mean and median. Otherwise, the use of the second method is convenient. However, it may also be observed that the mode values computed from these two methods are not identical. The value from the first method is always a little higher than the value obtained through the use of second (direct) method.

Computation of Median and Mode from the Curves of Frequency Distribution

Median. It can be computed directly from the following frequency curves with the help of simple observations and measurements:

From frequency graph. The value on the x-axis at the foot of the ordinate which bisects the area between the frequency graph and the x-axis is the median.

For cumulative frequency graph. A horizontal line is to be drawn from the middle point of the ordinate which represents the total frequency. The foot of the perpendicular from the point of intersection of this line and cumulative frequency graph gives the value of the median.

From cumulative frequency percentage curve or ogive. Here, for obtaining the median, a line parallel to the x-axis is drawn from the highest cumulative frequency shown on the y-axis. Now, from the point where this line cuts the curve, a perpendicular to the x-axis is drawn. The score located on the x-axis through this perpendicular gives the measure of the median.

Mode. It can be computed easily from the following frequency curves:

From frequency graph. For this purpose, a smoothed frequency graph is to be constructed from the given data. The abscissa of the highest point on this curve is taken to be the mode.

From histogram. For this purpose, the highest rectangle of the diagram is selected and at the top, the mid-point is marked. From this point, a perpendicular is drawn on the x-axis to indicate the measure of mode.

From cumulative frequency graph. In this curve, the abscissa of the point where the curve is steepest indicates the measure of the mode.

When to Use the Mean, Median and Mode

Computation of any of the three—mean, median and mode—provides a measure of central tendency. Which of these should be computed in a particular situation is a question that can be raised quite often. This can be answered in light of the characteristics and nature of all these measures.

When to use the mean

1. Mean is the most reliable and accurate measure of the central tendency of a distribution in comparison to median and mode. It has the greatest stability as there are less fluctuations

in the means of the samples drawn from the same population. Therefore, when a reliable and accurate measure of central tendency is needed, we compute the mean for the given data.

2. Mean can be given an algebraic treatment and is better suited to further arithmetical computation. Hence, it can be easily employed for the computation of various statistics like standard deviation, coefficient of correlation, etc. Therefore, when we need to compute more statistics like these, mean is computed for the given data.
3. In computation of the mean, we give equal weightage to every item in the series. Therefore, it is affected by the value of each item in that series. Sometimes there are extreme items which seriously affect the position of the mean. Thus, it is not proper to compute mean for the series that has extreme items and each score carries equal weight in determining the central tendency.

When to use the median

1. The median is the exact mid-point of a series, below and above which 50% of the cases lie. Therefore, when the exact mid-point of the distribution is desired, median is to be computed.
2. The median is not affected by the extreme scores in the series. Therefore, when a series contains extreme scores, the median is perhaps the most representative central measure.
3. In the case of an open end distribution (incomplete distribution "80 and above" or "20 and below"), it is impossible to calculate the mean, and hence the median is the most reliable measure that can be computed.
4. Mean cannot be calculated graphically. But in the case of median, we can compute it graphically. Therefore, when we have suitable graphs like frequency curve, polygon, ogive, and so on, we should try to compute median.
5. Median is specifically useful for the data of the items which cannot be precisely measured in quantities as for e.g. health, culture, honesty, intelligence and so on.

When to use the mode

1. In many cases, the crude mode can be computed by just having a look at the data. It gives the quickest, although approximate measure of central tendency. Therefore, in the cases where a quick and approximate measure of central tendency is all that is desired, we compute mode.

2. Mode is that value of the item which occurs most frequently or is repeated maximum number of times in a given series. Therefore, when we need to know the most often recurring score or value of the item in a series, we compute mode. On account of this characteristic, mode has unique importance in the large scale manufacturing of consumer goods. In finding the sizes of shoes and readymade garments which fit most men or women, the manufacturers make use of the average indicated by mode.
3. Mode can be computed from the histogram and other frequency curves. Therefore, when we already have a graphical representation of the distribution in the form of such figures, it is appropriate to compute mode instead of mean.

SUMMARY

The statistics, mean, median and mode, are known to be the most common measures of central tendency. A measure of central tendency is a sort of average or a typical value of the item in the series or some characteristics of the members of a group. Each of these measures of the central tendency provides a single value to represent the characteristics of the whole group in its own way.

Mean represents the 'average' for an ungrouped data, the sum of the scores divided by the total number of scores gives the value of the mean. The mean, in the case of a grouped data is best computed with the help of a short-cut method using the following formula:

$$M = A + \frac{\Sigma fx'}{N} \times i,$$

where A is the assumed mean,

$$x' = \frac{X - A}{i},$$

X is the mid-point of the class interval, i the class interval, and N the total frequencies of the distribution. Median is the score or value of that central item which divides the series into two equal parts. Hence when N is odd $(N + 1)/2$-th measure, and when N is even, the average of $(N/2)$-th and $[(N/2) + 1]$-th item's measure provides the value of the median. In the case of grouped data, it is computed by the formula

$$M_d = L + \frac{(N/2) - F}{f} \times i,$$

where L represents the lower limit of the median class, F, the total of all frequencies before the median class, and f, the frequency of the median class. The median can also be computed directly from curves like the frequency graph, cumulative frequency graph and ogive.

Mode is defined as the size of the variable which occurs most frequently. Crude mode can be computed by just having a look at the data. In the case of grouped data, it may be computed with the help of the formula, $M_o = 3M_d - 2M$. It can also be computed directly from the histogram and other frequency curves as also with the help of the following formula without first calculating mean and median:

$$M_o = L + \frac{f_1}{f_1 + f_{-1}} \times i$$

where f_1 and f_{-1} are the frequencies of the classes adjacent to the modal class for which lower limits are greater or less than those for the modal class.

Preference for the use of mean, median or mode can be understood from the following tabular matter:

Mean	*Median*	*Mode*
If we have	If we have	If we have
(i) to get a reliable and accurate measure of central tendency,	(i) to get an exact mid-point of the distribution,	(i) to get a quick and approximate measure of central tendency,
(ii) to compute further statistics like standard deviation, coefficient of correlation,	(ii) a series containing extreme scores,	(ii) to know the most often recurring score or value of the item in a series,
(iii) been given a series having no extreme items.	(iii) a distribution with the open end,	(iii) appropriate graphical representation of the data.
	(iv) appropriate graphical representation of data.	

EXERCISES

1. What do you understand by the term, 'measures of central tendency'? Point out the most common measures of central tendency.

2. What is an arithmetic mean? How can it be computed in the case of ungrouped as well as grouped data? Illustrate with the help of hypothetical data.
3. Define median. How can it be computed in the case of ungrouped as well as grouped data? Illustrate with examples.
4. What do you understand by the term mode of a data? Point out the methods of its computation in the case of grouped as well as ungrouped data. Explain the computation process through examples.
5. Define mean, median and mode. Discuss when each one of them should be computed and why.
6. In the situations described below, what measures of central tendency would you like to compute?
   (a) The average achievement of a group.
   (b) The most popular fashion of the day.
   (c) Determining the mid-point of the scores of a group in an entrance examination.
7. Find the mean IQ for the eight students whose individual IQ scores are:

   80, 100, 105, 90, 112, 115, 110, 120.
8. Compute median for the following data:
   (a) 8, 3, 10, 5, 2, 11, 14, 12.
   (b) 72, 74, 77, 53, 58, 63, 66, 82, 89, 69, 71.
9. Find the crude mode:
   (a) 15, 14, 8, 14, 14, 11, 9, 9, 11.
   (b) 3, 3, 4, 4, 4, 5, 7, 7, 9, 12.
10. Compute mean and median from the achievement scores of 25 students as given in the following (taking 2 as class interval):

    72, 75, 77, 67, 72, 81, 78, 65, 86, 83, 67, 82, 76, 76, 59, 70, 83, 71, 62, 72, 72, 61, 67, 68, 64.
11. Find the mean, median and mode for the following sets of scores:
    (a) 24, 18, 19, 12, 23, 20, 21, 22.
    (b) 20, 14, 12, 14, 19, 14, 18, 14.
    (c) 24, 18, 19, 20, 22, 25, 23, 12.
    (d) 9, 14, 8, 13, 10, 10, 11, 12, 10.
12. Compute the mean, median and mode for the following frequency distributions:

(*a*)		(*b*)		(*c*)		(*d*)	
Scores	*f*	*Scores*	*f*	*Scores*	*f*	*Scores*	*f*
70–71	2	120–122	2	45–49	2	135–144	1
68–69	2	117–119	2	40–44	3	124–134	2
66–67	3	114–116	2	35–39	2	115–124	8
64–65	4	111–113	4	30–34	17	105–114	22
62–63	6	108–110	5	25–29	30	95–104	33
60–61	7	105–107	9	20–24	25	85–94	22
58–59	5	102–104	6	15–19	15	75–84	9
56–57	1	99–101	3	10–14	3	65–74	2
54–55	2	96–98	4	5–9	2	55–64	1
52–53	3	93–95	2	0–4	1		
50–51	1	90–92	1				
	$N = 36$		$N = 40$		$N = 100$		$N = 100$

13. Compute the mean, median and mode for the following frequency distributions:

(*a*)		(*b*)		(*c*)		(*d*)	
Scores	*f*	*Scores*	*f*	*Scores*	*f*	*Scores*	*f*
100–104	1	57–59	1	58–60	1	90–94	1
95–99	2	54–56	1	55–57	1	85–89	4
90–94	1	51–53	5	52–54	1	80–84	2
85–89	6	48–50	9	49–51	2	75–79	8
80–84	7	45–47	5	46–48	2	70–74	9
75–79	3	42–44	8	43–45	3	65–69	14
70–74	2	39–41	10	40–42	3	60–64	6
65–69	1	36–38	6	37–39	7	55–59	6
60–64	2	33–35	4	34–36	8	50–54	4
55–59	4	30–32	7	31–33	7	45–49	3
50–54	0	27–29	0	28–30	5	40–44	3
45–49	1	24–26	1	25–27	4		
				22–24	3		
				19–21	3		
				16–18	2		
	$N = 30$		$N = 57$		$N = 52$		$N = 60$

5 Percentiles and Percentile Rank

In the fields of education, psychology and sociology, the scales of measurement used are not so absolute and exact as in physical sciences. They do not possess a true zero. Therefore, a score of 60 attained by a child on an achievement test will never mean twice as much as the score of 30 by another student on that test. In physical sciences, when we say that the length of the rod is 2.5 metres, we are certain about what we are saying. This measurement can be conveniently understood and properly interpreted as there is a possibility of absolute zero (the starting point of the measurement) in this scale of measurement. Here, it can be safely said that a rod of 5 metres length will be exactly double the rod of 2.5 metres length.

By the above discussion, we can conclude that in the cases of measurements in the field of education, psychology and sociology, we cannot derive any useful meaning directly from the raw data of such measurement. A score of 60 on an achievement test has no significance unless it is interpreted in terms of the performance of a reference group. In a class of 50 students, if one has attained a score of 60 on a certain test, then in order to gather same idea about his performance we must have clear-cut information regarding his position in the class, as follows:

Has the student got the highest score in his class? How many students of his class have got more than his score? How many students have secured less than him? All such questions concerned with the relative position or performance of an individual in relation to a reference group may be answered through the concept of percentiles and percentile rank.

MEANING OF THE TERM PERCENTILE

Percentile (also named centile by some writers) is nothing but a sort of measure used to indicate the relative position of a single item or an individual with reference to the group to which the item or individual belongs. In other words, it is used to tell the relative position of a given score among other scores. Some of such other measures are median, quartiles and deciles. The concept of percentile may be well understood with the help of the concept of median. Median is defined as a *point on the score scale below or above which 50% cases lie.* Hence we see that the median cuts the scores of the series into two equal parts. It is a score below or above which 50% cases lie, i.e. 50% of the individuals in a group score less or more than what has been described as a median score.

Proceeding on the same lines, the series of obtained scores or frequency distribution may be divided into more than two equal parts. We may have quartiles, deciles and percentiles (centiles) by dividing it into 4, 10 or 100 parts.

In this way, the measures like quartiles, deciles, percentiles all indicate some fixed points like median on the score scale below which a definite proportion of cases lie. In the case of percentiles, the scores series is divided into 100 equal parts, and each point is referred to as *centile* or *percentile.* Hence the number of percentiles for a given score series or frequency distribution may range from 1 to 100 (i.e. 1st percentile to 100th percentile).

DEFINITION

A percentile may be defined as *a point on the score scale below which a given percent of the cases lie.* Defined in this way, the 1st percentile (written as P_1) will mean "a score point in the given series or distribution below which one percent cases lie and above which 99% cases lie". Going further, the 15th percentile (P_{15}) will indicate that score point below which 15% of the cases lie. Similarly, the 70th percentile (P_{70}) will reveal a score point in a given series or distribution below which the scores of 70% and above which 30% members of the group fall.

DEFINING QUARTILES AND DECILES

Quartiles for a given score series or a distribution may be 4 in number. They are named 1st, 2nd, 3rd and 4th quartiles. Deciles are similarly ten in number and are described as 1st to 10th decile. These quartiles and deciles may be defined, on the same lines as the median and percentiles, in the following ways:

A quartile is the point on the score scale below which a given quarter of the cases lie.

A decile is the point on the score scale below which a given decile of the cases lie.

COMPUTATION OF PERCENTILES, QUARTILES AND DECILES

The formulae for the computation of quartiles, deciles and percentiles closely resemble the formula for the computation of the median, i.e.

$$M_d = L + \frac{N/2 - F}{f} \times i$$

as may be seen below:

1st quartile $$Q_1 = L + \frac{N/4 - F}{f} \times i$$

2nd quartile $$Q_2 = L + \frac{N/2 - F}{f} \times i$$

3rd quartile $$Q_3 = L + \frac{3N/4 - F}{f} \times i$$

1st decile $$D_1 = L + \frac{N/10 - F}{f} \times i$$

5th decile $$D_5 = L + \frac{5N/10 - F}{f} \times i = L + \frac{N/2 - F}{f} \times i$$

1st percentile $$P_1 = L + \frac{N/100 - F}{f} \times i$$

10th percentile $$P_{10} = L + \frac{10N/100 - F}{f} \times i = L + \frac{N/10 - F}{f} \times i$$

25th percentile $$P_{25} = L + \frac{25N/100 - F}{f} \times i = L + \frac{N/4 - F}{f} \times i$$

50th percentile $$P_{50} = L + \frac{50N/100 - F}{f} \times i = L + \frac{N/2 - F}{f} \times i$$

75th percentile $$P_{75} = L + \frac{75N/100 - F}{f} \times i = L + \frac{3N/4 - F}{f} \times i$$

The relationships existing among the median, quartiles, deciles and percentiles may be easily concluded from the above formulae, as follows:

(i) $P_{10} = D_1$ (iii) $P_{25} = Q_1$

(ii) $P_{75} = Q_3$ (iv) $P_{50} = D_5 = Q_2 = M_d$

It may also be generalized that the formula for the computation of percentile may be written as

$$\text{Percentile, } P = L + \frac{pN/100 - F}{f} \times i$$

where

L = Lower limit of the percentile class (the class in which the given percentile may be supposed to lie)
N = Total of all the frequencies
F = Total of the frequencies before the percentile class
f = Frequency of the percentile class
i = Size of the class interval
p = No. of the percentile which has to be computed

Let us illustrate the computation of various quartiles, deciles and percentiles by taking the following frequency distribution:

Example 5.1

1st Quartile (Q_1):

Scores	f
70–79	3
60–69	2
50–59	2
40–49	3
30–39	5
20–29	4
10–19	3
0–9	2
	$N = 24$

$$Q_1 = L + \frac{N/4 - F}{f} \times i$$

Here,

$$N/4 = \frac{24}{4} = 6$$

Adding frequencies from below, we see that up to the upper limit of the class 10–19, 5 cases lie. Hence, 20–29 is the class where the 1st quartile falls. Therefore,

$$Q_1 = 19.5 + \frac{6-5}{4} \times 10 = 19.5 + 2.5 = 22$$

3rd Quartile (Q_3):

$$Q_3 = L + \frac{3N/4 - F}{f} \times i$$

Here,

$$3N/4 = \frac{24 \times 3}{4} = 18$$

Adding frequencies from below, we see that upto the upper limit of the class 40–49 we have 17 frequencies. Therefore, the third quartile of the series falls in the interval 50–59. Hence

$$Q_3 = 49.5 + \frac{18-17}{2} \times 10 = 54.5$$

1st Decile (D_1):

$$D_1 = L + \frac{N/10 - F}{f} \times i$$

where

$$N/10 = 24/10 = 2.4$$

and D_1 lies in the interval 10–19, Therefore

$$D_1 = 9.5 + \frac{2.4-2}{3} \times 10$$

$$= 9.5 + \frac{4}{3} = 9.5 + 1.33$$

$$= 10.83$$

25th Percentile (P_{25}):

$$P_{25} = L + \frac{25N/100 - F}{f} \times i$$

$$= 19.5 + \frac{(25 \times 24)/100 - 5}{4} \times 10$$

$$= 19.5 + 2.5 = 22$$

60th Percentile (P_{60}):

$$P_{60} = L + \frac{\frac{60N}{100} - F}{f} \times i$$

Here,

$$\text{60th percentile of 24} = \frac{60 \times 24}{100} = \frac{72}{5} = 14.4$$

Adding the frequencies from below we see that upto the upper limit of the class 30–39, 14 cases lie. Therefore, 60th percentile of the distribution should fall in the interval 40–49. Hence,

$$P_{60} = 39.5 + \frac{14.4 - 14}{3} \times 10$$

$$= 39.5 + 4/3 = 39.5 + 1.33$$

$$= 40.83$$

PERCENTILE RANK

There is a class of 50 students. A student Ramesh of this class attains a score of 60 on an achievement test. There are 40 other students whose scores fall below the score 60. In other words, 40 out of 50 (40/50 × 100 = 80%) students lie below the score of 60. Therefore, 60 will be termed as the 80th percentile of the given data regarding achievement scores.

Proceeding further, it can be seen that Ramesh enjoys a relatively better position in his class in terms of the achievement score. The exact position that he enjoys in relation to the other students of his class may be ascertained by the fact that the scores of 40 out of the total 50 or 80% of the students fall below his score. He is better than 80% of the students of his class.

This conclusion can be translated into statistical language by saying that the achievement score of 60, attained by Ramesh has a percentile rank of 80.

Definition

The term percentile rank may be defined as *the number representing the percentage of the total number of cases lying below the given score.*

Computation of Percentile Rank

Computation of a particular percentile say p, gives us a point on the scale of measurement, i.e. score below which p percent of the cases lie.

Now in case, if we are provided with a specific score on the scale of measurement and required to find out the percentage of the cases lying below that score, we are supposed to compute the percentile rank of that specific score.

The task of computation of percentile rank thus requires computation of the rank or the position of an individual on a scale of 100 decided on the basis of his score. It may be carried out in some of the following ways:

From ungrouped data. In the case of ungrouped data, the data is first arranged in an order (descending order, preferably) and each score is provided a rank or a relative position in order of merit. Then, the following formula is employed for the computation of the percentile rank from this ordered data:

$$\text{Percentile rank } PR = 100 - \frac{100R - 50}{N}$$

where

N = Total number of individuals in the group

R = Rank position of the score of an individual whose percentile rank is to be determined.

Let us illustrate the use of this formula with the help of examples.

Example 5.2: In an achievement test, 20 students of a class have scored as below:

12, 20, 25, 15, 8, 32, 28, 35, 22, 44,
36, 17, 29, 13, 9, 37, 40, 21, 10, 42.

Find out the percentile rank of the score 17.

Solution. The scores are to be arranged in the descending form of ordered data as follows:

Scores	*Rank order*	*Scores*	*Rank order*
44	1	22	11
42	2	21	12
40	3	20	13
37	4	17	14
36	5	15	15
35	6	13	16
32	7	12	17
29	8	10	18
28	9	9	19
25	10	8	20

Here, rank R of the desired score 17 is 14 and N is given as 20. Putting these figures into the formula, we get

$$PR = 100 - \frac{100 \times 14 - 50}{20} = 100 - \frac{1350}{20}$$

$$= 100 - 67.5 = 32.5 \text{ or } 32$$

[**Ans.** The percentile rank of the score 17 is 32.]

Example 5.3: In an entrance examination, a candidate ranks 35 out of 150 candidates; find out his percentile rank.

Solution. The percentile rank is given by the formula

$$PR = 100 - \frac{100R - 50}{N}$$

In this case,

$$R = 35 \quad \text{and} \quad N = 150$$

Hence

$$PR = 100 - \frac{100 \times 35 - 50}{150}$$

$$= 100 - \frac{3450}{150} = 100 - 23 = 77$$

[**Ans.** Percentile rank is 77.]

From grouped data or frequency distribution

1st Method. (Direct method not needing any formula). For illustrating the working of this method, let us take the following distribution (same as taken for the computation of quartiles, deciles and percentiles) and calculate the percentile rank of the score 22.

Example 5.4

Scores	*f*
70–79	3
60–69	2
50–59	2
40–49	3
30–39	5
20–29	4
10–19	3
0–9	2
	$N = 24$

Solution. By adding frequencies from below, we see that upto the score 19.5, i.e. the upper limit of the class 10–19, 5 cases lie. Our problem is to find out the number of cases that lie below the score 22. The difference between the scores 19.5 and 22 is 22 – 19.5 = 2.5. Now, by observing the frequency distribution, we see that in the class interval 20–29, 10 scores are shared by 4 individuals. This knowledge may help us in our problem and we can proceed as under:

An interval of 10 is shared by 4 individuals. Therefore, an interval of 2.5 is shared by

$$\frac{4}{10} \times 2.5 = 1 \text{ individual}$$

Therefore, upto the score 22, 5 + 1 = 6 cases lie.

For expressing these cases on the scale of 100, we have to multiply them by $100/N$. In the present problem, $N = 24$.

Thus,

$$\text{Required percentile rank} = \frac{6 \times 100}{24} = 25$$

Note: By comparing these results with the value of the 1st quartile (Q_1) or 25th percentile (P_{25}) of this distribution, it can be easily concluded that percentile rank and percentiles are just opposite to each other.

Second Method. (Involving the use of a generalized formula). The percentile rank of a given score belonging to a grouped data, may be easily computed by employing the following formula:

$$PR = \frac{100}{N}\left[F + \left(\frac{X - L}{i}\right) \times f\right]$$

where

PR = Percentile rank for the desired score X

F = Cumulative frequency below the interval containing score X

X = Score for which we want the percentile rank

L = Actual lower limit of the interval containing X

i = Size of the class interval

f = Frequency of the interval containing X

N = Total number of cases in the given frequency distribution

Let us use this formula to calculate the percentile rank of the score 22.

Percentile rank for the score 22:

$$PR = \frac{100}{24}\left[5 + \frac{(22 - 19.5)}{10} \times 4\right]$$

$$= \frac{100}{24}\left(5 + \frac{2.5 \times 4}{10}\right)$$

$$= \frac{100 \times 6}{24} = 25$$

The answer 25 as percentile rank tallies with the answer computed through the direct method.

Third Method. (Use of cumulative percentage frequency curve or ogive). Percentile points and percentile ranks may both be read with a high degree of accuracy from an ogive accurately constructed on a graph sheet. A smoothed ogive (as given in Figure 5.1 which is a modified form of Figure 3.11) may provide better results.

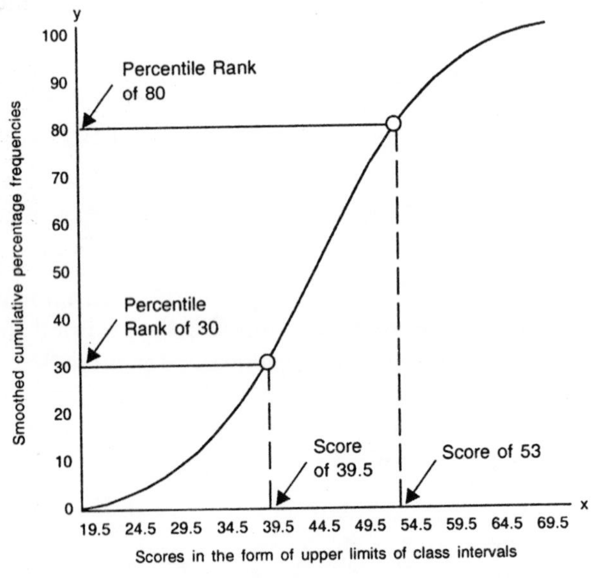

Figure 5.1 Computation of percentile points and percentile rank from an ogive.

Procedure.

1. To read a percentile points, a ruler is placed on the cumulative percentage column at the percentile point desired and a straight line is drawn from the rank to the curve. From this point on the curve, another line is drawn down to the score to make a right angle with the *x*-axis. The point where this vertical line meets the *x*-axis, indicates the desired percentile point on the score scale. In the above figure, the lines drawn show the values of P_{30} and P_{80}.

2. To read the percentile rank of a given score lying on the x-axis, a perpendicular line is drawn extending to the ogive curve. From this point where the perpendicular intersects the ogive, a line is drawn on the y-axis showing cumulative percentage frequencies. This point on the y-axis indicates the corresponding percentile rank of a given score. In Figure 5.1, a score of 39.5 has a percentile rank of 30 and a score of 53.00 has a percentile rank of 80.

Utility of Percentiles and Percentile Rank

Percentiles and percentile ranks may be used in the areas of education, psychology and sociology for the following purposes:

1. To indicate the relative position of an individual with respect to some attribute (achievement score, presence of some personality trait, etc.) in his own group.
2. For comparison, i.e., to compare
   (a) two or more individual students belonging to two or more sections, classes or schools,
   (b) the performance of two or more classes or schools, and
   (c) the performance of an individual if tested under two or more different testing conditions in terms of possession of some attributes or traits.

Illustration. Two boys studying in two different schools get the scores 35 and 40 in a weekly test in English. In this case, it is very difficult to compare their achievements. But if we say that the percentile rank is 90 in both the cases, then we can safely say that both are equal in terms of achievement in English in their respective schools.

3. To prepare the percentile norms for various standardized tests, inventories and scales for useful interpretations and classifications.

SUMMARY

Measurements in the field of education, psychology and sociology do not have an absolute zero like those found in natural sciences. Here, the useful interpretations can only be made if the performance of an individual is stated in relation to a reference group. Computation of percentiles and percentile ranks help in doing so.

Measures or statistics like quartiles, deciles, percentiles and the like indicate some fixed points like median, on the score scale below which a definite proportions of cases lie. While in the case of median, the series is divided into two equal halves by the median score, it is divided into 4, 10 and 100 equal parts respectively in the case of quartiles, deciles and percentiles. The formulae for the computation of quartiles, deciles and percentiles can be developed on the basis of the formula used for computation of median, i.e.

$$M_d = L + \frac{N/2 - F}{f} \times i$$

For percentiles we use the formula

$$P = L + \frac{(pN/100) - F}{f} \times i$$

Computation of a particular percentile, say p, gives us a point on the scale of measurement, i.e. a score below which p percent of the cases lie. Contrary to this, if we are provided with a specific score on the scale of measurement and are required to find out the percentage of cases lying below that score, then we are supposed to compute percentile rank of that specific score. In this way, percentile rank presents just the reverse picture of the percentile points.

Percentile rank, as the name suggests, is essentially a rank or the position of an individual on a scale of 100 decided on the basis of the individual's own score. For ungrouped data, it is given by the formula

$$PR = 100 - \frac{100R - 50}{N}$$

when R represents the rank position of the score whose percentile rank is to be determined.

In the case of grouped data, the percentile rank may be computed by (i) the direct method on the basis of interpolation without using a formula and (ii) by a generalized formula, i.e.

$$PR = \frac{100}{N}\left[F + \frac{X - L}{i}\right] \times f$$

Both percentile points and percentile ranks may be easily read from the cumulative percentage frequency curves (ogives) constructed from the respective frequency distributions by drawing perpendiculars on the curves.

The computation of percentiles and percentile ranks serves many purposes in the fields of education, psychology and sociology. It helps in indicating the clear-cut relative position of an individual with respect to some attribute in his own group. This knowledge further helps in drawing reliable comparison of the performance of two individuals or groups. The norms for useful interpretation, classification and comparison of various tests, scales and inventories can also be properly formulated with the help of these statistics.

EXERCISES

1. What do you understand by the term 'percentile' and 'percentile rank'? Illustrate the difference between them with the help of an example.
2. What is the need for the computation of percentiles and percentile ranks in the fields of education, psychology and sociology? Discuss in detail.
3. Define the terms percentile, quartile, decile and median. Discuss their mutual relationship.
4. Point out the process of computation of various quartiles, deciles and percentiles. Illustrate with the help of some hypothetical data.
5. Find out the values of the following from the distributions (c) and (d) given in problem 12 of Chapter 4.

   (a) 1st and 3rd quartiles (Q_1 and Q_3), (b) 1st decile (D_1), (c) 90th percentile (P_{90})
6. Compute the values of the following:

   (a) P_{30}, P_{70}, P_{85} and P_{90}

   (b) Percentile rank of the scores, 14, 20, 26 and 38, in the distributions given below:

Scores	*f*	*Scores*	*f*	*Scores*	*f*
37–39	2	27–29	1	70–74	3
34–36	10	24–26	3	65–69	4
31–33	15	21–23	6	60–64	7
28–30	19	18–20	10	55–59	12
25–27	16	15–17	9	50–54	14
22–24	8	12–14	11	45–49	21
19–21	9	9–11	10	40–44	17
16–18	7	6–8	3	35–39	15
13–15	3	3–5	3	30–34	10
10–12	1	0–2	1	25–29	2
	$N = 90$		$N = 57$		$N = 105$

7. In a particular group of 5 individuals, *A*, *B*, *C*, *D* and *E* get scores of 42, 60, 31, 50 and 71, respectively, on a certain test. Find their percentile ranks.

6

Measures of Variability

MEANING AND IMPORTANCE OF THE MEASURES OF VARIABILITY

Measures of central tendency—mean, median and mode—provide central value or typical representative of a set of scores as a whole. Through these measures we can represent the characteristic or the quality of the whole group by a single number. By comparing such typical representatives of different sets of scores, we can compare the achievement of two groups. These representative numbers merely give us an idea of the general achievement of the group as a whole. They do not show how the individual scores are spread out. Therefore, through measures of central tendency we are unable to know much about the distribution of scores in a series or characteristics items in a group. Therefore, measures of central tendency provide insufficient base for the comparison of two or more frequency distributions or sets of scores. This can be made clearer from the following example.

Let there be two small groups of boys and girls whose scores in an achievement test are such as the following:

Test scores of group *A* (boys): 40, 38, 36, 17, 20, 19, 18, 3, 5, 4.

Test scores of group *B* (girls): 19, 20, 22, 18, 21, 23, 17, 20, 22, 18.

Now the value of the mean in both the cases is 20 and, thus, so far as the mean goes, there is no difference in the performance of the two groups. Now the question arises as to whether we can take both sets of scores as identical. Definitely there is a lot of difference between the performance of two groups. Whereas the test scores of group *A* are found to range from 3 to 40, the scores in group *B* range from 18 to 23. The first group is composed of individuals who have wide individual differences. It consists of individuals who are very much capable or very poor in doing things. The second group, on the other hand, is composed of average individuals. Individuals in this latter group are less variable than those in the former. Thus there is a great need to pay attention to the variability or dispersion of scores in the sets of scores or series if we want to describe and compare them.

The above discussion may lead us to conclude that there is a tendency for data to be dispersed, scattered or to show variability around the average, consequently, the variability or dispersion may be defined in the following manner:

The tendency of the attributes of a group to deviate from the average or central value is known as *dispersion* or *variability*.

When we talk about the measures of variability or dispersion, our target is to find out simply the expected range of dispersion or variation above and below the average or central value for the given data.

TYPES OF MEASURES OF VARIABILITY

There are, chiefly, four measures for indicating variability or dispersion within the set of scores:

1. Range (R)
2. Quartile Deviation (Q)
3. Average Deviation (AD)
4. Standard Deviation (SD)

Each of the above measures of variability gives us the degree of variability or dispersion by the use of a single number and tells us how the individual scores are scattered or spread throughout the distribution or the given data. In what follows, we will discuss these measures in brief.

Range (R)

Range is the simplest measure of variability or dispersion. It is calculated by subtracting the lowest score in the series from the highest. But it is a very rough measure of the variability of a series. It takes only extreme scores into consideration and ignores the variation of individual items.

Quartile Deviation (Q)

It is computed by the formula

$$Q = \frac{Q_3 - Q_1}{2}$$

where Q_1 and Q_3 represent the 1st and 3rd quartiles of the distribution under consideration. The value $Q_3 - Q_1$ is the difference or range between the 3rd and 1st quartiles. It is called the *interquartile range*.

For computing quartile deviation, this interquartile range is divided by 2 and, therefore, quartile deviation is also named as semi-interquartile range. In this way, for computing Q, the values of Q_1 and Q_3 are first determined by the method explained earlier and then, applying the above formula, we get the value of the quartile deviation.

Average Deviation (*AD*)

Garrett (1971) defines Average Deviation (*AD*) as the mean of deviations of all the separate scores in the series taken from their mean (occasionally from the median or mode). It is the simplest measure of variability that takes into account the fluctuation or variation of all the items in a series.

Computation of average deviation from ungrouped data. In the case of ungrouped data, the average deviation is calculated by the formula

$$AD = \frac{\Sigma |x|}{N}$$

where $x = X - M$ = deviation of the raw score from the mean of the series and $|x|$ signifies that in the deviation values we ignore the algebraic signs +ve or –ve.

The use of this formula may be explained through the following example.

Example 6.1: Find the average deviation of the scores 15, 10, 6, 8, 11 of a series.

Solution. The mean of the given series is

$$\frac{15+10+6+8+11}{5} = \frac{50}{5} = 10$$

Scores X	*Deviation from the mean* ($X - M = x$)	$\lvert x \rvert$
15	$15 - 10 = 5$	5
10	$10 - 10 = 0$	0
6	$6 - 10 = -4$	4
8	$8 - 10 = -2$	2
11	$11 - 10 = 1$	1
$N = 5$		$\lvert x \rvert = 12$

By applying the formula

$$AD = \frac{12}{5} = 2.4$$

Computation of average deviation from grouped data. From the grouped data, *AD* can be computed by the formula

$$AD = \frac{\Sigma |fx|}{N}$$

Use of this formula can be understood by the following example.

Example 6.2:

Scores	*f*	*Mid-point X*	*fX*	*x* = (*X* – *M*)	*fx*	| *fx* |
110–114	4	112	448	11.94	44.76	44.76
105–109	4	107	428	6.94	27.76	27.76
100–104	3	102	306	1.94	5.82	5.82
95–99	0	97	0	–3.06	0	0
90–94	3	92	276	–8.06	–24.18	24.18
85–89	3	87	261	–13.06	–39.18	39.18
80–84	1	82	82	–18.06	–18.06	18.06
	N = 18		Σ*fX* = 1801			Σ | *fx* | = 162.76

Computation of Mean (*M*)

$$M = \frac{\Sigma fX}{N} = \frac{1801}{18} = 100.06$$

$$AD = \frac{\Sigma |fx|}{N} = \frac{162.76}{18} = 9.04$$

Standard Deviation (*SD*)

Standard deviation of a set of scores is defined as the square root of the average of the squares of the deviations of each score from the mean. Symbolically, we can say that

$$SD = \sqrt{\frac{\Sigma (X - M)^2}{N}} = \sqrt{\frac{\Sigma x^2}{N}}$$

where

X = Individual score
M = Mean of the given set of scores
N = Total No. of the scores
x = Deviation of each score from the mean.

Standard deviation is regarded as the most stable and reliable measure of variability as it employs the mean for its computation. It is often called *root mean square deviation* and is denoted by the Greek letter sigma (σ).

Computation of standard deviation (SD) from ungrouped data. Standard deviation can be computed from the ungrouped scores by the formula

$$\sigma = \sqrt{\frac{\Sigma x^2}{N}}$$

The use of this formula is illustrated in the following example:

Example 6.3: Calculate SD for the following set of scores:

52, 50, 56, 68, 65, 62, 57, 70.

Solution. Mean of the given scores

$$M = \frac{480}{8} = 60 \quad N = 8$$

Scores X	*Deviation from the mean* (X – M) or x	x^2
52	–8	64
50	–10	100
56	–4	16
68	8	64
65	5	25
62	2	4
57	–3	9
70	10	100
		Σx^2 = 382

Formula $$\sigma = \sqrt{\frac{\Sigma x^2}{N}} = \sqrt{\frac{382}{8}} = \sqrt{47.75} = 6.91$$

[**Ans.** Standard Deviation = 6.91]

Computation of SD from grouped data. Standard deviation in case of grouped data can be computed by the formula

$$\sigma = \sqrt{\frac{\Sigma fx^2}{N}}$$

The use of the formula can be illustrated with the help of the following example.

Example 6.4: Compute *SD* for the frequency distribution given below. The mean of this distribution is 115.

IQ Scores	f	X	M	x	x^2	fx^2
127–129	1	128	115	13	169	169
124–126	2	125	115	10	100	200
121–123	3	122	115	7	49	147
118–120	1	119	115	4	16	16
115–117	6	116	115	1	1	6
112–114	4	113	115	– 2	4	16
109–111	3	110	115	– 5	25	75
106–108	2	107	115	– 8	64	128
103–105	1	104	115	– 11	121	121
100–102	1	101	115	– 14	196	196
	$N = 24$					$\Sigma fx^2 = 1074$

Now,

$$\sigma = \sqrt{\frac{\Sigma fx^2}{N}} = \sqrt{\frac{1074}{24}} = \sqrt{44.75} = 6.69$$

Note: In the above example, if the value of the mean is not already given, then it is to be computed first with the help of the formula of mean, i.e.

$$M = \frac{\Sigma fX}{N}$$

Computation of SD from grouped data by short-cut method. Standard deviation from grouped data can also be computed by the following formula:

$$\sigma = i\sqrt{\frac{\Sigma fx'^2}{N} - \left(\frac{\Sigma fx'}{N}\right)^2}$$

where the notations have the same meaning as described earlier.

Example 6.5:

IQ Scores	f	X	$x' = X - A/i$	fx'	fx'^2
127–129	1	128	4	4	16
124–126	2	125	3	6	18
121–123	3	122	2	6	12
118–120	1	119	1	1	1
115–117	6	116	0	0	0
112–114	4	113	– 1	– 4	4
109–111	3	110	– 2	– 6	12
106–108	2	107	– 3	– 6	18
103–105	1	104	– 4	– 4	16
100–102	1	101	– 5	– 5	25
	$N = 24$			$\Sigma fx' = -8$	$\Sigma fx'^2 = 122$

Now putting the appropriate figures in the formula:

$$\sigma = i\sqrt{\frac{\Sigma fx'^2}{N} - \left(\frac{\Sigma fx'}{N}\right)^2} = 3\sqrt{\frac{122}{24} - \left(\frac{-8}{24}\right)^2}$$

$$= 3\sqrt{\frac{122}{24} - \frac{64}{24 \times 24}}$$

$$= \frac{3}{24}\sqrt{122 \times 24 - 64}$$

$$= \frac{1}{8}\sqrt{2864} = \frac{53.52}{8}$$

$$= 6.69$$

[**Ans.** Standard Deviation = 6.69.]

WHEN AND WHERE TO USE THE VARIOUS MEASURES OF VARIABILITY

Range

The computation of this measure of variability is recommended when

1. we need to know simply the highest and lowest scores of the total spread;
2. the group or distribution is too small;
3. we want to know about the variability within the group within no time;
4. we require speed and ease in the computation of a measure of variability; and
5. the distribution of the scores of the group is such that the computation of other measures of variability is not much useful.

Average Deviation

This measure is to be used when

1. distribution of the scores is normal or near to normal;
2. the standard deviation is unduly influenced by the presence of extreme deviations;

3. it is needed to weigh all deviations from the mean according to their size; and
4. a less reliable measure of variability can be employed.

Quartile Deviation

The use of this measure is recommended when

1. the distribution is skewed, containing a few very extreme scores;
2. the measure of central tendency is available in the form of median;
3. the distribution is truncated (irregular) or has some indeterminate end values;
4. we have to determine the concentration around the middle 50 per cent of the cases; and
5. the various percentiles and quartiles have been already computed.

Standard Deviation

The use of *SD* is recommended when

1. we need a most reliable measure of variability;
2. there is a need of computation of the correlation coefficients, significance of difference between means and the like;
3. measure of central tendency is available in the form of mean; and
4. the distribution is normal or near to normal.

In conclusion, it can be said that all the four measures of variability have their own strengths and weaknesses. The relative order of their applicability under different situations may be summarized as in the following table.

Situations	*Preferences*			
	I	II	III	IV
The need for a highly realiable variability measure	*SD*	*AD*	*Q*	*R*
The need for speed and ease in computation	*R*	*Q*	*AD*	*SD*
Median as the measure of central tendency	*Q*	*R*	—	—
Mean as the measure of central tendency	*SD*	*AD*	—	—
The need to compute further statistics from the measure of dispersion	*SD*	—	—	—

SUMMARY

There is a tendency for data to be dispersed, scattered or to show variability around the average or the central value. This tendency is known as *dispersion* or *variability*, which helps in knowing about the nature of the distribution of individual scores in a given series or a set of data. The overall comparison of two or more frequency distributions or sets of data may be more effectively made through the measures of variability.

Range is the simplest but a very rough measure of variability. It is the difference between the highest and the lowest scores of the series, and thus depends only on the position of two extreme scores and, as such, is not very reliable.

Quartile deviation is designed as the semi-inter-quartile range and is computed by the formula,

$$Q = \frac{Q_3 - Q_1}{2}$$

where Q_1 and Q_3 represent the 1st and 3rd quartiles of the distribution. It is more stable than the range, but it also fails to take into account the fluctuations or variations of all the items in a series.

Average deviation is the mean of the deviation of all the separate scores in the series taken from the mean or some other measure of central tendency. It takes into account the variation of all the items in a series. It is calculated by the formula

$$AD = \frac{\Sigma|x|}{N} \text{ in case of ungrouped data, and}$$

$$AD = \frac{\Sigma|fx|}{N} \text{ in case of grouped data.}$$

Here, $|x|$ signifies the deviation of the raw score (irrespective of +ve or –ve sign) from the mean of the series. The ignoring of algebraic signs constitutes a major weak point for this type of measure of variability.

Standard deviation, designated by σ, is the square root of the arithmetic average of the squared deviations of scores from the mean of the distribution. It is regarded as the most stable and reliable measure of variability as it employs mean for its computation and does not ignore algebraic signs. In case of ungrouped data, it is given by the formula

$$\sigma = \sqrt{\frac{\Sigma x^2}{N}}$$

and, in the case of grouped data, by the formula

$$\sigma = \sqrt{\frac{\Sigma fx^2}{N}}$$

Like mean, it also has a short-cut formula for its computation, i.e.

$$\sigma = i\sqrt{\frac{\Sigma fx'^2}{N} - \left(\frac{\Sigma fx'}{N}\right)^2}$$

In computation of further statistics from the measure of dispersion, we always prefer to compute standard deviation to all other measures of variability. But in case we need only a rough measure, range and quartile deviations serve our purpose very well.

EXERCISES

1. What do you understand by the term variability or dispersion of scores? Discuss the need of computation of the measure of variability.
2. What are the different measures of variability? Discuss them in brief.
3. Discuss the process of the computation of quartile and average deviations with the help of hypothetical data.
4. Discuss the process of the computation of standard deviation in the case of ungrouped and grouped data by taking some hypothetical data.
5. Point out the situations where the use of range, quartile deviation, average deviation and standard deviation is best recommended.
6. Which measure of variability would you prefer in the following situations?
   (a) The measure of central tendency is available in the form of median.
   (b) The distribution is badly skewed.
   (c) The coefficient of correlation is, subsequently, to be computed.
   (d) The variability is to be calculated easily within no time.
7. Calculate the quartile deviation and standard deviation for the frequency distributions (a), (b), (c) and (d) given under problems 12 and 13 in the exercises in Chapter 4.
8. Compute the average deviation and standard deviation from the following ungrouped data:

   30, 35, 36, 39, 42, 44, 46, 38, 34, 35.

9. Compute average deviation from the following distribution:

Scores	f
80–84	4
85–89	4
90–94	3
95–99	0
100–104	3
105–109	3
110–114	1
	$N = 18$

10. Given the following three frequency distributions, compute the standard deviation in each case:

(a)

Scores	f
125–129	1
120–124	5
115–119	7
110–114	6
105–109	9
100–104	9
95–99	6
90–94	4
85–89	1
80–84	1
	$N = 49$

(b)

Scores	f
21–22	1
19–20	0
17–18	2
15–16	2
13–14	5
11–12	9
9–10	4
7–8	3
5–6	2
3–4	1
1–2	1
	$N = 30$

(c)

Scores	f
90–94	1
85–89	2
80–84	3
75–79	5
70–74	11
65–69	12
60–64	10
55–59	14
50–54	11
45–49	11
40–44	16
35–39	8
30–34	5
25–29	2
20–24	1
	$N = 112$

7

Linear Correlation

In education and psychology, there are times when one needs to know whether there exists any relationship among the different attributes or abilities of the individual or they are independent of each other. Consequently, there are numerous questions like the following which need to be answered:

1. Does scholastic achievement depend upon the general intelligence of a child?
2. Is it true that the height of the children increases with the increase in their ages?
3. Is there any relationship between the size of the skull and the general intelligence of the individuals?
4. Is it true that dull children tend to be more neurotic than bright children?

Problems like the above in which there is a need to find out the relationship between two variables (age and height, intelligence and achievement and so on) can be tackled properly by the technique of correlation.

There are many types of correlation, like linear, curvilinear, biserial, partial or multiple correlation, that are computed in statistics. As we aim at providing an elementary knowledge of statistical methods, we shall confine ourselves here, to the method of linear correlation.

LINEAR CORRELATION—MEANING AND TYPES

This is the simplest kind of correlation to be found between two sets of scores or variables. Actually when the relationship between two sets of scores or variables can be represented graphically by a straight line, it is known as *linear correlation*. Such a correlation clearly reveals how the change in one variable is accompanied by a change in the other or to what extent increase or decrease in one is accompanied by the increase or decrease in the other.

The correlation between two sets of measures or variables can be positive or negative. It is said to be positive when an increase (or decrease) in one corresponds to an increase (or decrease) in the other. It is negative when an increase corresponds to a decrease and a decrease to an increase. There is also a possibility of a third type of correlation, i.e. zero correlation between the two sets of measures or variables, if there exists no relationship between them.

COEFFICIENT OF CORRELATION

For expressing the degree of relationship quantitatively between two sets of measures or variables, we usually take the help of an index that is known as *coefficient of correlation.* It is a kind of ratio which expresses the extent to which changes in one variable are accompanied by changes in the other variable. It involves no units and varies from –1 (indicating perfect negative correlation) to +1 (indicating perfect positive correlation). In case the coefficient of correlation is zero, it indicates zero correlation between two sets of measures.

Computation of Coefficient of Correlation

There are two different methods of computing coefficient of linear correlation:

1. Rank Difference Method
2. Product Moment Method

We now discuss these in some what detail.

Rank difference method. For computing the coefficient of correlation between two sets of scores achieved by individuals with the help of this method, we require rank, i.e. positions of merit of these individuals in possession of certain characteristics. The coefficient of correlation computed by this method, is known as the *rank correlation coefficient,* as it considers only the ranks of the individuals in the characteristics A and B. It is designated by the Greek letter ρ (rho). Sometimes, it is also known as Spearman's coefficient of correlation after the name of its inventor.

If we do not have scores and have to work with data in which differences between the individuals can be expressed only by ranks, rank correlation coefficient is the only correlation coefficient that can be computed. But this does not mean that it cannot be computed from the usual data given in raw scores. In case the data contains scores of individuals, we can compute ρ by converting the individual scores into ranks. For example, if the marks of a group of 5 students are given as

17, 25, 9, 35, 18, we will rank them as 4, 2, 5, 1 and 3. We determine the ranks or the positions of the individuals in both the given sets of scores. These ranks are then subjected to further calculation for the determination of the coefficient of correlation.

How is it done can be understood through the following examples.

Example 7.1

Individuals	*Marks in History (X)*	*Marks in Civics (Y)*	*Rank in History* (R_1)	*Rank in Civics* (R_2)	*Difference in ranks, irrespespective of +ve or –ve signs* $(R_1 - R_2 = \|d\|)$	*Difference squared* (d^2)
A	80	82	2	3	1	1
B	45	86	11	2	9	81
C	55	50	10	10	0	0
D	56	48	9	11	2	4
E	58	60	8	9	1	1
F	60	62	7	8	1	1
G	65	64	6	7	1	1
H	68	65	5	6	1	1
I	70	70	4	5	1	1
J	75	74	3	4	1	1
K	85	90	1	1	0	0
N = 11						$\Sigma d^2 = 92$

$$\rho = 1 - \frac{6\Sigma d^2}{N(N^2 - 1)}$$

$$= 1 - \frac{6 \times 92}{11(11^2 - 1)} = 1 - \frac{6 \times 92}{11 \times 120}$$

$$= 1 - \frac{23}{55} = 1 - 0.42$$

$$= 0.58$$

[**Ans.** Rank correlation coefficient = 0.58.]

Example 7.2

Individuals	*Scores in test (X)*	*Scores in test (Y)*	*Rank in X (R_1)*	*Rank in Y (R_2)*	$\lvert R_1 - R_2 \rvert = \lvert d \rvert$	d^2
A	12	21	8	6	2	4
B	15	25	6.5	3.5	3	9
C	24	35	2	2	0	0
D	20	24	4	5	1	1
E	8	16	10	9	1	1
F	15	18	6.5	8	0.5	0.25
G	20	25	4	3.5	0.5	0.25
H	20	16	4	9	5	25
I	11	16	9	9	0	0
J	26	38	1	1	0	0
$N = 10$						$\Sigma d^2 = 40.5$

$$\rho = 1 - \frac{6\Sigma d^2}{N(N^2-1)} = 1 - \frac{6 \times 40.5}{10\,(10^2-1)} = 1 - \frac{6 \times 40.5}{10 \times 99}$$

$$= 1 - \frac{8.1}{33} = 1 - 0.245 = 0.755$$

[**Ans.** Rank correlation coefficient = 0.755.]

Steps for the calculation of ρ:

Step 1. First, a position or a rank is assigned to each individual on both the tests. These ranks are put under column 3 (designated R_1) and column 4 (designated R_2), respectively. The task of assigning ranks, as in Example 1, is not difficult. But as in Example 2, where two or more individuals are found to have achieved the same score, some difficulty arises. In this example, in the first test, *X*, *B* and *F* are two individuals who have the same score, i.e. 15. Therefore, score 15 occupies the 6th position in order of merit. But now the question arises as to which one of the two individuals *B* and *F* should be ranked 6th or 7th. In order to overcome this difficulty we share the 6th and 7th rank equally between them and thus rank each one of them as 6.5.

Similarly, if there are three persons who have the same score and share the same rank, we take the average of the ranks claimed by these persons. For example, we can take score 20 in Example 2 which is shared by three individuals *D*, *G* and *H*. It is ranked third in the whole series. It will be difficult to assign ranks to individuals *D*, *G* and *H*. This can be overcome if ranks 3, 4 and 5 are shared equally by these individuals, and hence we can attribute rank 4 to each of them.

Step 2. After writing down the allocated ranks for all the individuals on both the tests, the differences in these ranks are calculated. In doing so, we do not consider the algebraic signs +ve or –ve of the difference. This difference is written under column 5 (designated $|d|$).

Step 3. In the next column (designated d^2), we square the rank difference or the values of *d* written in column 5.

Step 4. Now we calculate the total of all the values of d^2 and this sum is designated Σd^2.

Step 5. In the next step, the value of ρ is calculated by the formula

$$\rho = 1 - \frac{6\Sigma d^2}{N(N^2 - 1)}$$

where Σd^2 stands for the sum of the squares of differences between the ranks of the scores on the two tests and *N* for the number of individuals.

Product moment method. This method is also known as Pearson's product moment method in honour of the English statesman Karl Pearson, who is said to be the inventor of this method. The coefficient of correlation computed by this method is known as the *product moment coefficient of correlation* or Pearson's correlation coefficient and symbolically represented by *r*. The standard formula used in the computation of Pearson's product moment correlation coefficient is as follows:

$$r_{XY} = \frac{\Sigma xy}{N\sigma_x\sigma_y}$$

where

r_{XY} = Correlation between *X* and *Y* (two sets of scores)

x = Deviation of any *X*-score from the mean in test *X*

y = Deviation of the corresponding *Y*-score from the mean in test *Y*

$\Sigma\, xy$ = Sum of all the products of deviation (each x deviation multiplied by its corresponding y deviation)

σ_x = Standard deviation of the distribution of scores in test X

σ_y = Standard deviation of the distribution of scores in test Y

N = Total No. of scores of frequencies

In this formula, the basic quantity to determine the degree of correlation or correspondence between the two sets of variables x and y is $\Sigma\, xy/N$, i.e. the average of the sum of all the products of deviations. The higher its value, the larger will be the degree of correlation. This term $\Sigma\, xy/N$ is known as the product moment and the corresponding correlation is called the product moment correlation. According to Garrett, the name product moment is given to the term $\Sigma\, xy/N$ for the following reason:

In statistics, the formula for computing moments about the mean of a set of scores x is $(1/N)\ \Sigma\, x$. When corresponding deviations in terms of x and y are multiplied together, summed and divided by N to give $\Sigma\, xy/N$, the term product moment is used.

The value of the product moment $\Sigma\, xy/N$ is relatively unstable on account of its being dependent upon the units of measurement of two variable x and y. To get rid of this problem, x and y deviations are expressed as a ratio by converting them into σ scores (by dividing each x and y by its own standard deviation, σ_x and σ_y). Consequently, the formula for the computation of r becomes

$$r = \frac{\Sigma\, xy}{N\sigma_x\sigma_y}$$

Computation of r from ungrouped data. For computation of r from ungrouped data, the formula

$$r = \frac{\Sigma\, xy}{N\sigma_x\sigma_y}$$

may be simplified as follows:

$$r = \frac{\Sigma xy}{N\sigma_x\sigma_y} \qquad \text{(i)}$$

but $$\sigma_x = \sqrt{\frac{\Sigma\, x^2}{N}}, \qquad \sigma_y = \sqrt{\frac{\Sigma\, y^2}{N}}$$

Substituting these values of σ_x and σ_y in (i) we get

$$r = \frac{\Sigma xy}{N\sqrt{\frac{\Sigma x^2}{N}}\sqrt{\frac{\Sigma y^2}{N}}} = \frac{\Sigma xy}{\sqrt{\Sigma x^2 \, \Sigma y^2}} \quad \text{(ii)}$$

The use of this formula may be illustrated through the following example:

Example 7.3

Individuals	*Scores in test* X	*Scores in test* Y	x	y	xy	x^2	y^2
A	15	60	–10	10	–100	100	100
B	25	70	0	20	0	0	400
C	20	40	–5	–10	50	25	100
D	30	50	5	0	0	25	0
E	35	30	10	–20	–200	100	400
					$\Sigma xy = -250$	$\Sigma x^2 = 250$	$\Sigma y^2 = 1000$

Mean of series X, $M_X = 25$

Mean of series Y, $M_Y = 50$

$$r = \frac{\Sigma xy}{\sqrt{\Sigma x^2 \, \Sigma y^2}} = \frac{-250}{\sqrt{250 \times 1000}}$$

$$= \frac{-250}{\sqrt{250{,}000}} = \frac{-250}{500}$$

$$= -\frac{1}{2} = -0.5$$

[**Ans.** Product moment correlation coefficient = –0.5.]

Computation of r directly from raw scores when deviations are taken from zero (without calculating deviation from the means). In this case, product moment r is to be computed by the following formula:

$$r = \frac{N\,\Sigma XY - \Sigma X \, \Sigma Y}{\sqrt{\left[N\,\Sigma X^2 - (\Sigma X)^2\right]\left[N\,\Sigma Y^2 - (\Sigma Y)^2\right]}}$$

where

X and Y = Raw scores in the test X and Y.

XY = Sum of the products of each X score multiplied with its corresponding Y score

N = Total No. of cases or scores

The use of this formula may be understood through the following example:

Example 7.4

Subject	*Scores in test X*	*Scores in test Y*	*XY*	X^2	Y^2
A	5	12	60	25	144
B	3	15	45	9	225
C	2	11	22	4	121
D	8	10	80	64	100
E	6	18	108	36	324
$N = 5$	$\Sigma X = 24$	$\Sigma Y = 66$	$\Sigma XY = 315$	$\Sigma X^2 = 138$	$\Sigma Y^2 = 914$

$$r = \frac{N\Sigma XY - \Sigma X \Sigma Y}{\sqrt{\left[N\Sigma X^2 - (\Sigma X)^2\right]\left[N\Sigma Y^2 - (\Sigma Y)^2\right]}}$$

Here,

$$r = \frac{5\times 315 - 24\times 66}{\sqrt{(5\times 138 - 576)(5\times 914 - 66\times 66)}}$$

$$= \frac{1575 - 1584}{\sqrt{(690 - 576)(4570 - 4356)}}$$

$$= \frac{-75}{\sqrt{114\times 214}} = \frac{-75}{\sqrt{24396}}$$

$$= \frac{-75}{156.2} = -0.070$$

[**Ans.** Product moment correlation coefficient = –0.48.]

Computation of product moment r with the help of a scatter diagram or correlation table. Product moment r may be computed through a scatter diagram or correlation table. If this diagram or table is not given, then the need of its construction arises. Let us illustrate the construction of a scatter diagram or a correlation table with the help of some hypothetical data.

CONSTRUCTION OF SCATTER DIAGRAM

Example 7.5: Ten students have obtained the following scores on tests in History and Hindi. Express these scores through a scatter diagram.

Individuals	*A*	*B*	*C*	*D*	*E*	*F*	*G*	*H*	*I*	*J*
Scores in History (X)	13	12	10	8	7	6	6	4	3	1
Scores in Hindi (Y)	7	11	3	7	2	12	6	2	9	6

Procedure. To construct a scatter diagram from the given data, we usually proceed in the following manner:

1. First of all, the given X and Y scores in the two subjects are arranged into two frequency distributions by a suitable choice of size and the number of class intervals. In the present case, we can select these classes in the two distributions as under:

Scores in History		*Scores in Hindi*	
X	f	Y	f
13–14	1	11–12	2
11–12	1	9–10	1
9–10	1	7–8	2
7–8	2	5–6	2
5–6	2	3–4	1
3–4	2	1–2	2
1–2	1		
	$N = 10$		$N = 10$

2. A table is constructed with columns and rows. In the first row of the table, the class intervals for the variable X are to be written and along the left margin, the class intervals for the variable Y are to be written. In the present case, we begin the listing of class intervals belonging to X on the top from 1–2 and end with 13–14 and Y on the left margin from class intervals 1–2 to 11–12. Here, we have a correlation matrix of size equal to the number of class intervals in the X distribution multiplied by the number of class intervals in the Y distribution. We also add one column and one row to the matrix for the purpose of presenting the summation of the frequencies in the respective rows and columns.

3. Now we come again to the individual scores in test X and Y. We make one tally mark for each individual's X and Y scores. For example, for the individual C who scores 10 in test X and 3 in test Y, we place a tally mark in the cell at the intersection of the column for interval 9–10 in X and the row for interval 3–4 in Y. Similarly, for scores 1 and 6 of individual J, a tally mark is put in the cell at the intersection of the column for interval 1–2 and row for interval 5–6. All other individuals may be similarly tallied in their cells.
4. After completion of the task of tallying, these tally marks are translated into cell frequencies. These frequencies are written in each of the cells.
5. The cell frequencies in each of the rows will be summed up and sums will be written in the last column under the heading f_y. Similarly the cell frequencies in each of the columns may also be summed up and the sums are recorded in the bottom row under the heading f_x.
6. The frequencies recorded in the last column under the heading f_y are then summed up. This sum represents the total number of frequencies (N) for the distribution Y. Similarly, by summing up the frequencies recorded in the bottom row under the head f_x, we may get the total of all the frequencies (N) under the distribution X.

Table 7.1 Scatter Diagram for Data Given in Example 7.5

X Scores in History

Y Scores in Hindi

Class intervals	*1–2*	*3–4*	*5–6*	*7–8*	*9–10*	*11–12*	*13–14*	*fy*
11–12			/①			/①		2
9–10		/①						1
7–8				/①			/①	2
5–6	/①		/①					2
3–4					/①			1
1–2		/①		/①				2
fx	1	2	2	2	1	1	1	10

Example 7.6: In an entrance examination, 90 students earned the following scores on tests X and Y. Prepare a scatter diagram from this data.

Student's Roll No.	*Marks in X*	*Y*	*Roll No.*	*X*	*Y*	*Roll No.*	*X*	*Y*
1	80	45	31	53	26	61	58	46
2	52	30	32	51	30	62	56	48
3	56	36	33	64	35	63	52	45
4	45	26	34	63	37	64	50	40
5	67	30	35	62	28	65	66	42
6	70	48	36	66	25	66	65	44
7	64	46	37	68	30	67	46	43
8	55	36	38	75	32	68	55	35
9	53	32	39	72	36	69	54	30
10	63	31	40	43	46	70	53	28
11	64	34	41	56	32	71	78	46
12	76	54	42	58	30	72	76	50
13	74	46	43	55	42	73	65	52
14	58	37	44	45	22	74	55	35
15	57	32	45	44	28	75	54	30
16	53	30	46	33	16	76	53	32
17	46	34	47	76	56	77	70	45
18	48	26	48	66	36	78	69	46
19	47	20	49	65	46	79	68	47
20	72	46	50	68	40	80	57	36
21	46	22	51	67	48	81	56	35
22	71	50	52	71	58	82	55	34
23	46	28	53	72	57	83	45	26
24	44	30	54	80	59	84	46	28
25	42	22	55	79	54	85	41	24
26	60	50	56	78	56	86	52	34
27	62	42	57	66	46	87	58	36
28	65	38	58	64	52	88	62	40
29	55	36	59	63	53	89	66	46
30	52	42	60	60	50	90	60	42

Solution: *Construction of Frequency Distribution Tables*

Frequency distribution of scores on test X		*Frequency distribution of scores on test Y*	
Class intervals	*f*	*Class intervals*	*f*
80–84	2	55–59	5
75–79	7	50–54	9
70–74	8	45–49	17
65–69	15	40–44	10
60–64	13	35–39	14
55–59	16	30–34	18
50–54	13	25–29	10
45–49	10	20–24	7
40–44	6		
	$N = 90$		$N = 90$

Preparation of a Scatter Diagram

Table 7.2 Scatter Diagram for the Data Given in Example 7.6

→ *X scores* ←

Class intervals	*40–44*	*45–49*	*50–54*	*55–59*	*60–64*	*65–69*	*70–74*	*75–79*	*80–84*	*fy*
55–59							// (2)	// (2)	/ (1)	5
50–54					//// (4)	/ (1)	/ (1)	/// (3)		9
45–49	/ (1)		/ (1)	// (2)	/ (1)	𝍸 (6)	//// (4)	/ (1)	/ (1)	17
40–44		/ (1)	// (2)	/ (1)	/// (3)	/// (3)				10
35–39				𝍸 //// (9)	// (2)	// (2)	/ (1)			14
30–34	/ (1)		𝍸 /// (8)	//// (4)	// (2)	// (2)		/ (1)		18
25–29	/ (1)	𝍸 (5)	// (2)		/ (1)	/ (1)				10
20–24	/// (3)	//// (4)								7
fx	6	10	13	16	13	15	8	7	2	90

Computation of *r*

We know that the gereral formula for computing r is

$$r = \frac{\Sigma\, xy}{N \sigma_x \sigma_y}$$

Here x and y denote the deviations of X and Y scores from their respective means. When we take deviations from the assumed means of the two distributions, this formula is likely to be changed to the one below:

$$r = \frac{N \Sigma\, x'y' - \Sigma\, fx' \,\Sigma\, fy'}{\sqrt{\left[N \Sigma\, fx'^2 - (\Sigma\, fx')^2\right]\left[N \Sigma\, fy'^2 - (\Sigma\, fy')^2\right]}}$$

It may be observed that in computing r by the above formula, we need to know the values of $\Sigma\, x'y'$, $\Sigma fx'$, $\Sigma fy'$, $\Sigma fx'^2$ and $\Sigma fy'^2$. All these values may be conveniently computed through a scatter diagram. The process of determining these is illustrated through the extension of scatter diagrams constructed in Tables 7.1 and 7.2.

Now just look into the Table 7.3, here we can get the values

$$\Sigma\, x'y' = 5, \quad \Sigma fx' = -3, \quad \Sigma fy' = 5$$

$$\Sigma fx'^2 = 33, \quad \Sigma fy'^2 = 33$$

Putting these values in the formula for computing r, we get

$$r = \frac{(10 \times 5) - (-3)\,(5)}{\sqrt{[10 \times 33 - 9][10 \times 33 - 25]}}$$

$$= \frac{50 + 15}{\sqrt{[(330 - 9)][330 - 25]}}$$

$$= \frac{65}{\sqrt{321 \times 305}}$$

$$= \frac{65}{\sqrt{97905}}$$

$$= \frac{65}{312.9}$$

$$= 0.207$$

$$= 0.21 \text{ (approx.)}$$

[**Ans.** Product moment coefficient of correlation = 0.21.]

Table 7.3 Extension of Scatter Diagram of Table 7.1

← *X scores* →

↑ *Y scores* ↓ *Class intervals*	*1–2*	*3–4*	*5–6*	*7–8*	*9–10*	*11–12*	*13–14*	f_y	y'	fy'	fy'^2	x'	$x'y'$
11–12			−1 (1) 3			2 (1) 3		2	3	6	18	1	3
9–10		−2 (1) 2						1	2	2	4	−2	−4
7–8				0 (1) 1			3 (1) 1	2	1	2	2	3	3
5–6	−3 (1) 0		−1 (1) 0					2	0	0	0	−4	0
3–4					1 1 −1			1	−1	−1	1	1	−1
1–2		−4 (1) −2		0 (1) −2				2	−2	−4	8	−2	4
f_x	1	2	2	2	1	1	1	$N = 10$		$\Sigma fy' = 5$	$\Sigma fy'^2 = 33$	$\Sigma x' = -3$	$\Sigma x'y' = 5$
x'	−3	−2	−1	0	1	2	3						
fx'	−3	−4	−2	0	1	2	3	$\Sigma fx' = -3$					
fx'^2	9	8	2	0	1	4	9	$\Sigma fx'^2 = 33$					
y'	0	0	3	−1	−1	3	1	$\Sigma y' = 5$					
$x'y'$	0	0	−3	0	−1	6	3	$\Sigma x'y' = 5$					

Check: $\Sigma fx' = -3$ ↔ $\Sigma x' = -3$; Check: $\Sigma y' = 5$ ↔ $\Sigma fy' = 5$; Check: $\Sigma x'y' = 5$ ↔ $\Sigma x'y' = 5$

[illegible] Extension of Scatter Diagram Given in Table 7.2

→ *Scores in test X* ←

(Rows: → *Scores in test Y* ↓)

Class intervals	40–44	45–49	50–54	55-59	60–64	65–69	70–74	75–79	80–84	f_y	y'	fy'	fy'^2	x'	$x'y'$
55–59							4 (2) 8	6 (2) 8	4 (1) 4	5	4	20	80	14	56
50–54					0 (4) 12	1 (1) 3	2 (1) 3	9 (3) 9		9	3	27	81	12	36
45–49	−4 (1) 2		−2 (1) 2	−2 (2) 4	0 (1) 2	6 (6) 12	8 (4) 8	3 (1) 2	4 (1) 2	17	2	34	68	13	26
40–44		−3 (1) 1	−4 (2) 2	−1 (1) 1	0 (3) 3	3 (3) 3				10	1	10	10	−5	−5
35–39				−9 (9) 0	0 (2) 0	2 (2) 0	2 (1) 0			14	0	0	0	−5	0
30–34	−4 (1) −1		−16 (8) −8	−4 (4) −4	0 (2) −2	2 (2) −2		3 (1) −1		18	−1	−18	18	−19	19
25–29	−4 (1) −2	−15 (5) 10	−4 (2) −4		0 (1) −2	1 (1) −2				10	−2	−20	40	−22	44
20–24	−12 (3) −9	−12 (4) −12								7	−3	−21	63	−24	72
f_x	6	10	13	16	13	15	8	7	2	$N = 90$		$\Sigma fy' = 32$	$\Sigma fy'^2 = 360$	$\Sigma x'$ −36	$\Sigma x'y' = 248$
x'	−4	−3	−2	−1	0	1	2	3	4						
fx'	−24	−30	−26	−16	0	15	16	21	8	$\Sigma fx' = -36$					
fx'^2	96	90	52	16	0	15	32	63	32	$\Sigma fx'^2 = 396$					
y'	−10	−21	−8	1	13	14	19	18	6	$\Sigma y' = 32$					
$x'y'$	40	63	16	−1	0	14	38	54	24	$\Sigma x'y' = 248$					

Check ($\Sigma fx' = -36$ ↔ $\Sigma x' = -36$)

Check ($\Sigma y' = 32$ ↔ $\Sigma fy' = 32$)

Check ($\Sigma x'y' = 248$ ↔ $\Sigma x'y' = 248$)

Now putting the relevant values in the formula, we get

$$r = \frac{N \Sigma x'y' - \Sigma fx' \Sigma fy'}{\sqrt{\left[N \Sigma fx'^2 - (\Sigma fx')^2\right]\left[N \Sigma fy'^2 - (\Sigma fy')^2\right]}}$$

$$= \frac{(90 \times 248) - (-36 \times 32)}{\sqrt{\left[(90 \times 396) - (-36 \times -36)\right]\left[(90 \times 360) - (32 \times 32)\right]}}$$

$$= \frac{22320 + 1152}{\sqrt{(35640 - 1296)(32400 - 1024)}}$$

$$= \frac{23472}{\sqrt{34344 \times 31376}}$$

$$= \frac{23472}{\sqrt{1077577344}}$$

$$= \frac{23472}{32826.3}$$

$$= 0.715 = 0.73 \text{ (approx).}$$

[**Ans.** Pearson's correlation coefficient = 0.73]

Explanation of the process of computation of r from scatter diagrams. Let us consider the process of the computation of the values of Σfx, Σfy, $\Sigma fx'^2$, $\Sigma fy'^2$ and $\Sigma x'y'$ with the help of the scatter diagram computed above in Tables 7.3 and 7.4 and then the determination of r from the formula. The various steps involved are as follows:

Step 1. (Completion of the scatter diagram). The scatter diagram in its complete form must have one row and one column designated f_x and f_y respectively for the total of the frequencies belonging to each class interval of the scores in test X and Y. If the totals are not given (in the assigned scatter diagram) then they are to be computed and written in the row and column headed by f_x and f_y. The grand total of these rows and columns should tally with each other. There grand totals were 10 and 90 respectively in our problem.

Step 2. (Extension of the scatter diagram). The scatter diagram is now extended by 5 columns designated y', fy', fy'^2, x' and $x'y'$ and 5 rows designated x', fx', fx'^2, y', and $x'y'$. At the end of each of these columns and rows, the provision for the sum (Σ values) is also to be kept.

Step 3. (Determining the values x', fx', fx'^2 and y', fy', fy'^2). x' and y' for the scores of tests X and Y represent the values.

$$\frac{X - \text{Assumed mean for } X \text{ distribution}}{\text{Class interval of the } X \text{ distribution}}, \text{ i.e. } \frac{X - A_X}{i_x}$$

$$\frac{Y - \text{Assumed mean for } Y \text{ distribution}}{\text{Class interval of the } Y \text{ distribution}}, \text{ i.e. } \frac{Y - A_Y}{i_y}$$

These assumed means are located and values of x', fx', fx'^2 and y', fy', fy'^2 are computed in the same way as already done in Chapters 4 and 6 for computing the mean and standard deviation by short-cut methods.

Step 4. (Determining the value of $\Sigma x'y'$). To obtain this value, we have to compute the values for the columns under x' and rows under y'. Let us proceed by concentrating on the following main points:

1. Check that in each cell, the cell frequencies have been written exactly in the centre of the cell.
2. Now begin with the values of x' (–4, –3, –2, –1, 0, 1, 2, 3 and 4) written in one of the bottom rows adjacent to f_x. Take one value, say –4, at a time and multiply it with all the cell frequencies lying in the column headed by the interval 40–44 of the X scores and write the product on the top left of the respective cell (above the frequency number written in the cell), e.g. $-4 \times 1 = -1$ is to be written on the top of the column in front of the class interval 45–49 of the Y scores and $-4 \times 1 = -4$ on the top of the column in front of the class interval 25–29 of the Y scores and $-4 \times 3 = -12$ on the top of the column in front of the class interval 20–24. Similarly, we take the value –3 and write the products –3, –15, –12 on the top of the cells lying in the IInd column headed by the intervals 45–49 of the X scores in front of the class interval 40–44, 25–29, and 20–24 of the Y scores. The other product values calculated from –2, –1 and the like are written on the top of the cells column as shown in Table 7.4
3. The next task begins with the values of y' (4, 3, 2, 1, 0, –1, –2, and –3) written in the column lying adjacent to f_y. We take each of these values one by one and multiply them with each of the cell frequencies lying in each row. For example, if we take the value 4 of y', we will have the products $4 \times 2 = 8$, $4 \times 2 = 8$, $4 \times 1 = 4$. These products are to be recoreded in the bottom (towards right) of each of the cells lying in the 1st row. Similarly, by taking the value 3 of y', we get the products as $4 \times 3 = 12$, $3 \times 1 = 3$, $3 \times 1 = 3$ and $3 \times 3 = 9$. It is

recorded at the bottom of the respective cells of the IInd row. Proceeding in the same way, the cross products of the remaining values of x' with the cell frequencies lying in other rows may be found and recorded in their due places as illustrated in Table 7.4.

4. The cross products written on the top left of each row cells will be summed up. This algebraic sum of each row cells provides the desired values of x' (14, 12, 13, –5, –5, –19, –22 and –24). The sum of all these values is called $\Sigma x'$. It tallies with the value of $\Sigma fx'$ (shown in Table 7.4 as –36).
5. The cross products written towards the right of the bottom of each cell in the different columns are then summed up. This algebraic sum of each column cell provides us the desired values of y'. Here these values are –10, –21, –8, 1, 13, 14, 19, 8 and 6 respectively. The sum of all these values are called $\Sigma y'$. It tallies with the values of $\Sigma fy'$ (shown in Table 7.4 as 32).
6. In the last column, designated $x'y'$, we have products of the respective values of columns y' and x' (e.g. $4 \times 14 = 56$, $3 \times 12 = 36$, ...) After summing up, the algebraic sum provides the desired values of $\Sigma x'y'$ (248 in the table).

Similarly, in the last row, designated $x'y'$, the product values are computed by multiplying the values of y' with the respective values of x'. The algebraic sum of these products provides us the value of $\Sigma x'y'$. It tallies with the value of $\Sigma x'y'$ determined earlier.

Step 5. (Computation of r using formula). In the last step, the obtained values of Σxy, $\Sigma fx'$, $\Sigma fx'^2$, $\Sigma fy'$ and $\Sigma fy'^2$ are put in the formula for the computation of the desired product moment r. For further understanding of the above computation process of the product moment r, we are giving two more solved examples.

Example 7.7:

	Scores in the subject X							
Class intervals (*Scores in the subject Y*)	12–13	14–15	16–17	18–19	20–21	22–23	24–25	Total
35–37					1		1	2
32–34					6	3		9
29–31		1	2	6	8	1		18
26–28		4	4	6	11	4	1	30
23–25	2	1	6	5	4	1		19
20–22	3	2	1	1				7
Total	5	8	13	18	30	9	2	85

Solution: For solving the above given problem we will first work for the extension of correlation table of the Example 7.7 and then calculate the needed values of $\Sigma x'y'$, $\Sigma fx'$, $\Sigma fy'$, $\Sigma fx'^2$, $\Sigma fy'^2$ etc. finally for computing r. The extended table with the needed computation work has been shown in Table 7.5.

Computation of r

$$r = \frac{N\Sigma x'y' - \Sigma fx' \cdot \Sigma fy'}{\sqrt{\left[N\Sigma fx'^2 - (\Sigma fx')^2\right]\left[N\Sigma fy'^2 - (\Sigma fy')^2\right]}}$$

$$= \frac{85 \times 78 - 10 \times 9}{\sqrt{(85 \times 174 - 10 \times 10)(85 \times 119) - (9 \times 9)}}$$

$$= \frac{6630 - 90}{\sqrt{(14{,}790 - 100)(10115 - 81)}}$$

$$= \frac{6540}{\sqrt{146{,}90 \times 10034}}$$

$$= \frac{6540}{\sqrt{147{,}399{,}460}}$$

$$= \frac{6540}{12{,}140.8} = 0.538$$

$$= 0.54 \text{ (approx.)}$$

[**Ans.** Pearson's correlation coefficient = 0.54.]

Table 7.5 Extension of Correlation Table of Example 7.7

→ *Scores in the subject X* ←

(↑ *Scores in the subject Y* ↓ — rows. Each cell shows: upper number, circled frequency in parentheses, lower number.)

Class interval	12–13	14–15	16–17	18–19	20–21	22–23	24–25	f_y	y'	fy'	fy'^2	x'	$x'y'$
35–37					1 (1) 3		3 (1) 3	2	3	6	18	4	12
32–34					6 (6) 12	6 (3) 6		9	2	18	36	12	24
29–31		−2 (1) 1	−2 (2) 2	0 (6) 6	8 (8) 8	2 (1) 1		18	1	18	18	6	6
26–28		−8 (4) 0	−4 (4) 0	0 (6) 0	11 (11) 0	8 (4) 0	3 (1) 0	30	0	0	0	10	0
23–25	−6 (2) −2	−2 (1) −1	−6 (6) −6	0 (5) −5	4 (4) −4	2 (1) −1		19	−1	−19	19	−8	8
20–22	−9 (3) −6	−4 (2) −4	−1 (1) −2	0 (1) −2				7	−2	−14	28	−14	28
f_x	5	8	13	18	30	9	2	$N = 85$		$\Sigma fy' = 9$	$\Sigma fy'^2 = 119$	$\Sigma x' = 10$	$\Sigma x'y' = 78$
x'	−3	−2	−1	0	1	2	3						
fx'	−15	−16	−13	0	30	18	6	$\Sigma fx' = 10$					
fx'^2	45	32	13	0	30	36	18	$\Sigma fx'^2 = 174$					
y'	−8	−4	−6	−1	19	6	3	$\Sigma y' = 9$					
$x'y'$	24	8	6	0	19	12	9	$\Sigma x'y' = 78$					

Check: $\Sigma fx' = 10$ ↔ $\Sigma x' = 10$; Check: $\Sigma y' = 9$ ↔ $\Sigma fy' = 9$; Check: $\Sigma x'y' = 78$ ↔ $\Sigma x'y' = 78$

Example 7.8:

→ *Scores in the subject X* ←

↑ *Scores in the subject Y* ↓

Class intervals	*30–34*	*35–39*	*40–44*	*45–49*	*50–54*	*55–59*	*60–64*	*65–69*	*Total*
130–139				1		1		1	3
120–129			1		1	2	1		5
110–119	1	2	5	6	11	6	3	2	36
100–109	3	7	9	17	13	5	1	1	56
90–99	4	10	16	12	5	1			48
80–89	4	9	8	2	2				25
Total	12	28	39	38	32	15	5	4	173

Solution: We will have extension of correlation table given in Example 7.8 along with the computation of the needed values $\Sigma x'y'$, $\Sigma fx'$, $\Sigma fy'$, $\Sigma fx'^2$, $\Sigma fy'^2$, as provided in Table 7.6.

Computation of r

$$r = \frac{N\Sigma x'y' - \Sigma fx' \, \Sigma fy'}{\sqrt{\left[N\Sigma fx'^2 - (\Sigma fx')^2\right]\left[N\Sigma fy'^2 - (\Sigma fy')^2\right]}}$$

$$= \frac{(173 \times 173) - (-38 \times -43)}{\sqrt{\left[(173 \times 460) - (-38 \times -38)\right]\left[(173 \times 231) - (-43 \times -43)\right]}}$$

$$= \frac{29{,}929 - 1634}{\sqrt{(79{,}580 - 1444)(39{,}963 - 1849)}}$$

$$= \frac{28{,}295}{\sqrt{78{,}136 \times 38{,}114}}$$

$$= \frac{28{,}295}{\sqrt{29{,}78{,}075{,}504}}$$

$$= \frac{28{,}295}{54{,}571.7}$$

$$= 0.518$$

$$= 0.52 \text{ (approx.)}$$

[**Ans.** Pearson's correlation coefficient = 0.52.]

Table 7.6 Extension of Scatter Diagram of Example 7.8

→ *Scores in the subject X* ←

(↑ *Scores in the subject Y* ↓ — rows. In each cell: upper value, circled frequency in parentheses, lower value.)

Class intervals	*30–34*	*35–39*	*40–44*	*45–49*	*50–54*	*55–59*	*60–64*	*65–69*	f_y	y'	fy'	fy'^2	x'	$x'y'$
130–139				0 (1) 3		2 (1) 3		4 (1) 3	3	3	9	27	6	18
120–129			–1 (1) 2		1 (1) 2	4 (2) 4	3 (1) 2		5	2	10	20	7	14
110–119	–3 (1) 1	–4 (2) 2	–5 (5) 5	0 (6) 6	11 (11) 11	12 (6) 6	9 (3) 3	8 (2) 2	36	1	36	36	28	28
100–109	–9 (3) 0	–14 (7) 0	–9 (9) 0	0 (17) 0	13 (13) 0	10 (5) 0	3 (1) 0	4 (1) 0	56	0	0	0	–2	0
90–99	–12 (4) –4	–20 (10) –10	–16 (16) –16	0 (12) –12	5 (5) –5	2 (1) –1			48	–1	–48	48	–41	41
80–89	–12 (4) –8	–18 (9) –18	–8 (8) –16	0 (2) –4	2 (2) –4				25	–2	–50	100	–36	72
f_x	12	28	39	38	32	15	5	4	N = 173		$\Sigma fy'$ = – 43	$\Sigma fy'^2$ = 231	$\Sigma x'$ = –38	$\Sigma x'y'$ = 173
x'	–3	–2	–1	0	1	2	3	4						
fx'	–36	–56	–39	0	32	30	15	16	$\Sigma fx'$ = –38					
fx'^2	108	112	39	0	32	60	45	64	$\Sigma fx'^2$ = 460					
y'	–11	–26	–25	–7	4	12	5	5	$\Sigma y'$ = –43					
$x'y'$	33	52	25	0	4	24	15	20	$\Sigma x'y'$ = 173					

Check: $\Sigma fx'$ = –38 ↔ $\Sigma x'$ = –38; $\Sigma y'$ = –43 ↔ $\Sigma fy'$ = –43; $\Sigma x'y'$ = 173 ↔ $\Sigma x'y'$ = 173.

An alternative method for the computation of r. The calculation of the values of $\Sigma\, x'y'$ presents a serious problem to most beginners. Therefore, an alternative method is hereby suggested by employing the following formula:

$$r = \frac{A + B - D}{2\sqrt{AB}}$$

where

$$A = \Sigma\, fx'^2 - \frac{(\Sigma\, fx')^2}{N}$$

$$B = \Sigma\, fy'^2 - \frac{(\Sigma\, fy')^2}{N}$$

$$D = \Sigma\, fd^2 - \frac{(\Sigma\, fd)^2}{N}$$

The values of $\Sigma fx'$, $\Sigma fx'^2$, $\Sigma fy'$ and $\Sigma fy'^2$ may be easily computed through the extended scatter diagram as done in all the previous examples concerning the computation of r. The only new thing is the calculation of the values of $\Sigma\, fd$ and $\Sigma\, fd^2$ through the distribution of diagonal frequencies. The diagonal frequencies are located in different cells as is evident from the diagonal dotted lines drawn in the following scatter diagram of Example 7.7.

Example 7.9:

Table 7.7 Extended Scatter Diagram of Example 7.7 Showing Diagonal Frequencies

→ *Score in the subject X* ←

(Rows: → *Score in the subject Y* ←)

Class intervals	*12–13*	*14–15*	*16–17*	*18–19*	*20–21*	*22–23*	*24–25*	f_y	y'	fy'	fy'^2
35–37					1		1	2	3	6	18
32–34					6	3		9	2	18	36
29–31		1	2	6	8	1		18	1	18	18
26–28		4	4	6	11	4	1	30	0	0	0
23–25	2	1	6	5	4	1		19	–1	–19	19
20–22	3	2	1	1				7	–2	–14	28
f_x	5	8	13	18	30	9	2	N = 85		$\Sigma fy'$ = 9	$\Sigma fy'^2$ = 119
x'	–3	–2	–1	0	1	2	3				
fx'	–15	–16	–13	0	30	18	6	$\Sigma\, fx'$ = 10			
fx'^2	45	32	13	0	30	36	18	Σfx^2 =174			

The frequencies in the respective diagonal cells may be easily located along the dotted lines of the above scatter diagram and the process of the computation of the values of Σfd and Σfd^2 may be carried out as follows:

Diagonal frequency f	d	fd	fd^2
1	3	3	9
9	2	18	36
20	1	20	20
16	0	0	0
18	–1	–18	18
9	–2	–18	36
2	–3	–6	18
$N = 85$		$\Sigma fd = -1$	$\Sigma fd^2 = 137$

The values of A, B and D can now be calculated as follows

$$A = \Sigma fx'^2 - \frac{(\Sigma fx')^2}{N} = 174 - \frac{100}{85}$$

$$= 174 - 1.18 = 172.82$$

$$B = \Sigma fy'^2 - \frac{(\Sigma fy')^2}{N} = 119 - \frac{81}{85}$$

$$= 119 - 0.95 = 118.05$$

$$D = \Sigma fd^2 - \frac{(\Sigma fd)^2}{N} = 137 - \frac{1}{85} = 137 - 0.01$$

$$= 136.99$$

$$r = \frac{A + B - D}{2\sqrt{AB}} = \frac{172.82 + 118.05 - 136.99}{2\sqrt{172.82 \times 118.05}}$$

$$= \frac{153.88}{2 \times 142.83}$$

$$= \frac{76.94}{142.83} = 0.539 = 0.54 \text{ (approx.)}$$

[**Ans.** Product moment correlation coefficient = 0.54.]

Example 7.10

Table 7.8 Extended Scatter Diagram of Example 7.8 Showing Diagonal Frequencies

← *Score in subject X* →

← *Score in subject Y* →

Class intervals	*30–34*	*35–39*	*40–44*	*45–49*	*50–54*	*55–59*	*60–64*	*65–69*	*fy*	*y′*	*fy′*	*fy′²*
130–139				1		1		1	3	3	9	27
120–129			1		1	2	1		5	2	10	20
110–119	1	2	5	6	11	6	3	2	36	1	36	36
100–109	3	7	9	17	13	5	1	1	56	0	0	0
90–99	4	10	16	12	5	1			48	–1	–48	48
80–89	4	9	8	2	2				25	–2	–50	100
fx	12	28	39	38	32	15	5	4	*N* =173		$\Sigma fy'$ =–43	$\Sigma fy'^2$ =231
x′	–3	–2	–1	0	1	2	3	4				
fx′	–36	–56	–39	0	32	30	15	16	$\Sigma fx'$ =–38			
fx′²	108	112	39	0	32	60	45	64	$\Sigma fx'^2$ =460			

Computation of $\Sigma\, fd$ and $\Sigma\, fd^2$

Diagonal frequency f	*d*	*fd*	*fd²*
1	4	4	16
7	3	21	63
16	2	32	64
31	1	31	31
55	0	0	0
41	–1	–41	41
15	–2	–30	60
6	–3	–18	54
1	–4	–4	16
		$\Sigma fd = -5$	$\Sigma fd^2 = 345$

Computation of the values A, B and D

$$A = \Sigma fx'^2 - \frac{(\Sigma fx')^2}{N} = 460 - \frac{38 \times 38}{173}$$

$$= 460 - \frac{1444}{173} = 460 - 8.35 = 451.65$$

$$B = \Sigma fy'^2 - \frac{(\Sigma fy')^2}{N} = 231 - \frac{43 \times 43}{173}$$

$$= 231 - 10.69 = 220.31$$

$$D = \Sigma fd^2 - \frac{(\Sigma fd)^2}{N} = 345 - \frac{25}{173}$$

$$= 345 - 0.14 = 344.86$$

Now

$$r = \frac{A + B - D}{2\sqrt{AB}}$$

$$= \frac{451.65 + 220.31 - 344.86}{2\sqrt{451.65 \times 220.31}}$$

$$= \frac{327.10}{2 \times 315.44} = \frac{163.55}{315.44} = 0.518$$

$$= 0.52 \text{ (approx.)}$$

It can be seen that the value of r computed in the above two examples tallies with the values of r computed through the use of the general formula given earlier.

Assumptions underlying the use of Pearson's product moment method in the computation of the correlation coefficient. The use of the product moment method for the computation of correlation coefficient between two variables is based upon the following assumptions:

Linearity of relationship. The relationship between the two variables should be linear (described by a straight line). In other words, the best fitting regression lines (to be discussed later in this chapter) joining the means of columns or means of the rows of the scatter diagrams should fall nearly in straight lines.

Homoscedasticity. The standard deviation of the scores in the different columns and rows should be equal and fairly homogeneous.

Continuity of the variables. The two variables for which correlation is to be computed should be continuous variables in terms of measurement.

Normality of distributions. Distributions in two variables should be fairly symmetrical and unimodal. In other words the distributions should be fairly normal or at least not badly skewed.

Interpretation of the computed correlation coefficient. When we have computed a correlation coefficient between two variables, the next thing is to consider what it tells us. In fact it is computed to tell us about the following important things:

First, it tells us whether there is any correlation between two variables and if any such relationship exists, then to indicate the type of relationship. Finally, it indicates the degree of closeness or significance of this relationship. Now let us see what should be kept in mind for interpreting computed correlation for the purposes given above.

1. First of all the signs of correlation coefficient should be taken into consideration. A positive sign tells about the existence of positive correlation between two variables while the negative sign indicates the negative correlation.
2. It should be clearly understood that the coefficient of correlation is an index number, not a measurement, on a linear scale of equal units. Therefore, it is not wise to interpret a r of 0.60 as two times the relationship shown by r of 0.30.
3. Computed correlation coefficient may be understood by summarizing it as follows:

The range of computed correlation coefficient	*Interpretation*
0 (zero value)	Zero relation, absolutely no relationship.
From 0.00 to ± 0.20	Slight, almost negligible relationship.
From ± 0.21 to ± 0.40	Low correlation, definite but small relationship.
From ± 0.41 to ± 0.70	Moderate correlation, substantial but small relationship.
From ± 0.71 to ± 0.90	High correlation, marked relationship.
From ± 0.91 to 0.99	Very high correlation, quite dependable relationship.
± 1	Perfect correlation, almost identical or opposite relationship.

4. The above verbal interpretation of the correlation coefficient is arbitrary. The task of interpretation should not be considered as simple. The question regarding significance of the size of the coefficient of correlation cannot be fully answered without referring to the particular purposes and situtations under which the coefficient of correlation has been computed. Consequently, we have to interpret coefficient of correlation in the way we aim to use it for different purposes like the following:

   (a) in the form of a reliability coefficient for testing the reliability of a test:

   (b) in the form of a validity coefficient for studying the predictive validity of a test:

   (c) in the form of a purely descriptive device for describing the nature of relationship between two variables.

   For example, if an intelligence test is adminstered today and again, after a month from today to the same individuals. The correlation between these two set of scores will help in determining the reliability of the intelligence test. In this situation, we will require correlation coefficient as high as .90 and above. But in the case of using correlation coefficient for predicting validity of a test we will not require the value of correlation coefficient as much high.

5. Finally, the question arises as to how low a correlation coefficient may be and still be of value. The answer to this question requires the knoweldge of the techniques for testing the significance of rank correlation coefficient or Pearson's product moment r. All these techniques will be discussed in Chapter 9.

SUMMARY

Linear correlation represents the simplest kind of correlation to be found between two sets of scores or variables. It reveals how the change in one variable is accompanied by a change in the other in terms of direction as well as magnitude. The relationship is generally expressed by a ratio known as coefficient of correlation. It involves no units and varies form −1 to +1 (perfect postive to perfect negative correlation). A zero value indicates absolutely no relationship between two variables.

In computing coefficient of correlation between two sets of scores achieved by the individuals with the help of rank difference method, ranks, i.e. positions of merit of these individuals in possession of certain characteristics, are employed. The coefficient of correlation in this case is known as Rank correlation coefficient or Spearman's coefficient of correlation and is designated by the Greek letter ρ (rho). The formula employed is

$$\rho = 1 - \frac{6 \Sigma d^2}{N(N^2 - 1)}$$

where d is the difference between the rank of the scores on two different tests and N is number of individuals whose scores are under consideration for computing.

Product moment method, also known as Pearson's product moment method, is another good method for computing correlation between any two sets of data. The product moment coefficient computed by this method is symbolically represented by r. Its standard formula is

$$r = \frac{\Sigma xy}{N \sigma x \, \sigma y}$$

In the case of ungrouped data, this formula is changed to

$$r = \frac{\Sigma xy}{\sqrt{\Sigma x^2 \, \Sigma y^2}}$$

With grouped data (using scatter diagram or correlation table), it takes the following form:

$$r = \frac{N \Sigma x'y' - \Sigma fx' \, \Sigma fy'}{\sqrt{\left[N \Sigma fx'^2 - (\Sigma fx')^2\right]\left[N \Sigma fy'^2 - (\Sigma fy')^2\right]}}$$

While in the case of raw scores it is given as:

$$r = \frac{N \Sigma XY - \Sigma X \, \Sigma Y}{\sqrt{\left[N \Sigma X^2 - (\Sigma X)^2\right]\left[N \Sigma Y^2 - (\Sigma Y)^2\right]}}$$

For computing r with grouped data, a scatter diagram or a correlation table is usually used. However, if needed, they may be constructed directly from the results of tests or experiments by forming two frequency distributions of appropriate size. These scatter diagrams are further extended to give the necessary values for the computation of r.

An alternative method for computing r without involving the computation of the value $\Sigma x'y'$ is given by the formula

$$r = \frac{A + B - D}{2\sqrt{AB}}$$

The use of Pearson's product method rests with the assumptions of linearity of relationship, homoscedasticity, continuity and normality of the distributions of the two variables.

Both direction and magnitude are taken into account while interpreting a coefficient of correlation in view of the situation or purpose to be served by its computation.

EXERCISES

1. Enumerate the need and importance of computing correlation in the fields of education and psychology.
2. What do you mean by linear correlation? Discuss the various types of linear correlation.
3. What is coefficient of correlation? Discuss in brief the two important methods of computing coefficient of linear correlation.
4. What is Rank difference method of computing coefficient of correlation? Why is this method given this name? Discuss the process of its computation with the help of some hypothetical data.
5. What is Pearson's Product Moment Method of computing correlation? Why has it been named so?
6. What do you understand by a scatter diagram? Discuss its preparation with the help of some hypothetical data.
7. Point out the formulae and process employed in computing product moment r in the following cases:
   (a) From ungrouped data (by taking deviation from the mean).
   (b) Directly from raw scores.
   (c) From scatter diagram data.
8. What do you understand by the term coefficient of correlation? Discuss the ways and means for the interpretation of a computed coefficient of correlation.
9. Discuss in brief the various assumptions underlying the use of Pearson's Product Moment Method for the computation of correlation coefficient.

10. Find rank correlation coefficient from the following data and interpret the results.

(a)

Individuals	*A*	*B*	*C*	*D*	*E*	*F*	*G*	*H*
Marks in Hindi	30	40	50	20	10	45	22	18
Marks in English	55	75	60	12	11	38	25	15

(b)

Individuals	*A*	*B*	*C*	*D*	*E*	*F*	*G*	*H*	*I*	*J*
Marks in *X*	19	16	16	12	11	11	10	9	8	7
Marks in *Y*	16	17	14	13	12	12	9	9	6	7

(c)

Individuals	*A*	*B*	*C*	*D*	*E*	*F*	*G*	*H*	*I*	*J*
Rating by one observer	18	14	15	17	12	13	10	9	7	6
Rating by another observer	15	16	14	13	9	10	8	7	11	6

11. Find the correlation coefficient between the following two sets of scores using the product moment method and also, interpret these coefficients.

(a)

Subjects	*a*	*b*	*c*	*d*	*e*	*f*	*g*	*h*
Test *X*	15	18	22	17	19	20	16	21
Test *Y*	40	42	50	45	43	46	41	41

(b)

Subjects	*a*	*b*	*c*	*d*	*e*	*f*	*g*	*h*	*i*	*j*
Test *X*	13	12	10	10	8	6	6	5	3	2
Test *Y*	11	14	11	7	9	11	3	7	6	1

12. Find the correlation between the following two sets of raw scores directly without computing deviations from the mean. Interpret the results.

(a)

Individuals	*A*	*B*	*C*	*D*	*E*	*F*	*G*	*H*	*I*	*J*
Test *X*	13	12	10	8	7	6	6	4	3	1
Test *Y*	7	11	3	7	2	12	6	2	9	6

(b)

Individuals	*A*	*B*	*C*	*D*	*E*	*F*	*G*	*H*	*I*	*J*
Variable *X*	24	20	18	17	15	12	10	8	6	4
Variable *Y*	13	9	12	20	11	16	5	2	7	1

13. Find the Pearson's product moment r from the following scatter diagram (correlation table) and interpret the results:

(a) *Scores on Test X*

Class intervals (Scores on Test Y)	*0–4*	*5–9*	*10–14*	*15–19*	*20–24*	*25–29*	*30–34*	*Total*
15–17			1			1	2	4
12–14		1	1	3	1	2	1	9
9–11		1	4	5	5	1		16
6–8	2	3	5	4	5	2		21
3–5	2	5	1		1	1		10
0–2	2	1		1				4
Total	6	11	12	13	12	7	3	64

(b) *Scores on Test X*

Class intervals (Scores on Test Y)	*11–20*	*21–30*	*31–40*	*41–50*	*51–60*	*61–70*	*71–80*
45–49					1		1
40–44					7	4	
35–39		1	2	7	9	1	
30–34		4	5	7	12	4	1
25–29	2	1	7	6	5	1	
20–24	4	2	1	1			

(c) *Scores on Test X*

Class intervals (Scores on Test Y)	*100–109*	*110–119*	*120–129*	*130–139*	*140–149*	*150–159*	*160–169*	*Total*
70–71			1	3	3	4	2	13
68–69			4	11	6	3	2	26
66–67		2	9	11	8	2	1	33
64–65	1	5	7	10	3			26
62–63	1	2	6	1	2			12
Total	2	9	27	36	22	9	5	110

8

The Normal Curve and its Applications

WHAT IS A NORMAL CURVE?

The literal meaning of the term normal is average. We make use of this term while computing the average in data related to education, psychology or sociology. In these areas, those who are able to reach a particular fixed level in qualification or characteristics are termed as normal, while there who are above or below this point are abnormal. Nature has been kind enough to distribute quite equally most of the things and attributes like wealth, beauty, intelligence, height, weight and the like. As a result, a majority among us possess average beauty, wealth, intelligence, height and weight. There are quite a few persons who deviate noticeably from average, either be above or below it. This is equally true for data in terms of achievement scores, intelligence scores, rating scores, etc. collected through tests, surveys and experiments performed in education, psychology and sociology on a randomly selected sample or population.

If we plot such a distribution of data on graph paper (Figure 8.1),

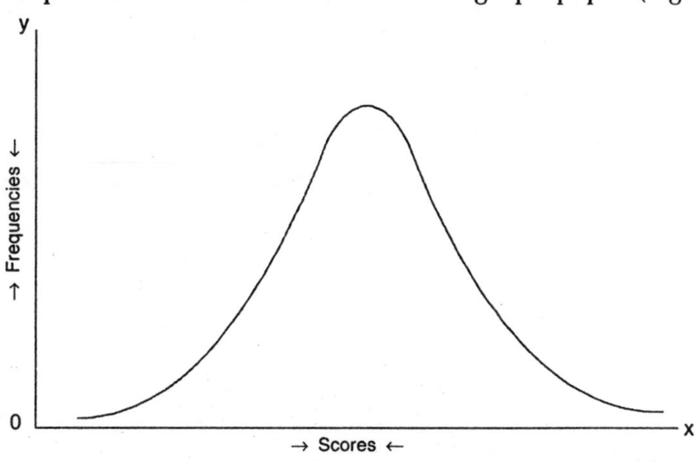

Figure 8.1 Normal curve.

we would get an interesting typical curve often resembling a vertical cross-section of a bell. This bell-shaped curve is called a *normal curve.*

The data from a certain coin or a dice-throwing experiment involving a chance success or probability, if plotted on a graph paper, give a frequency curve which closely resembles the normal curve. It is because of this reason and because of its origin from a game of chance that the normal curve is often called the normal probability curve.

Laplace and Gauss (1777–1855) derived this curve independently. They worked on experimental errors in Physics and Astronomy and found the errors to be distributed normally. This is the reason why the curve representing the normal characteristics is also named as normal curve of error or simply the curve of error where 'error' is used in the sense of a deviation from the true value. Because of its discovery by Laplace and Gauss, the curve is also named as Gaussian curve in the honour of Gauss.

The normal curve takes into account the law which states that the greater a deviation from the mean or average value in a series, the less frequently it occurs. This is satisfactorily used for describing many distributions which arise in the fields of education, psychology and sociology.

However, it is not at all essential for a normal distribution to be described by an exactly perfect bell shaped curve as shown in Figure 8.1. Such a perfect symmetrical curve rarely exists in our actual dealings as we usually cannot measure an entire population. Instead, we work on representative samples of the population. Therefore, in actual practice, the slightly deviated or distorted bell-shaped curve is also accepted as the normal curve on the assumption of normal distribution of the characteristics measured in the entire population.

From the above account, it should not be assumed that the distributions of the data in all cases will always lead to normal or approximately normal curves. In cases where the scores of individuals in the group seriously deviate from the average, the curves representing these distributions also deviate from the shape of a normal curve. This deviation or divergence from normality tends to vary in two ways:

In Terms of Skewness

Skewness refers to the lack of symmetry. A normal curve is a perfectly symmetrical curve. In case the curve is folded along the vertical middle line (perpendicular drawn from the highest point of the curve to its base line) the two sides of the base line will overlap. Also, for this curve, mean, median and mode are the same. In many distributions which deviate from the normal, the values of mean, median and mode are different and there is no symmetry between the right and the left halves of the curve. Such distributions are said to be skewed, being inclined more towards the left or the right to the centre of the curve as shown in Figures 8.2 and 8.3. For comparison, a normal (symmetrical) curve is also provided in Figure 8.4.

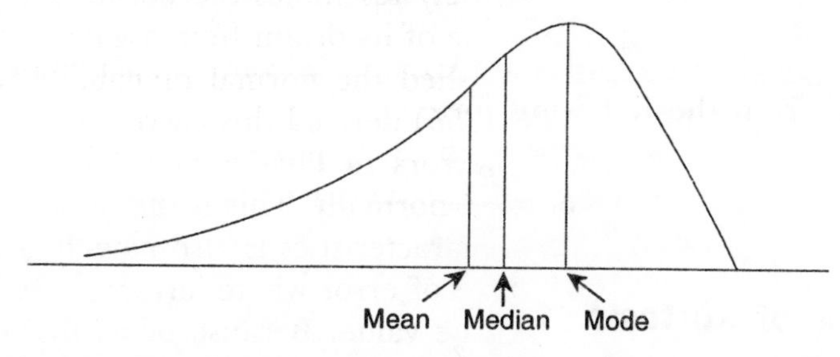

Figure 8.2 Negative skewness (the curve inclines more to the left).

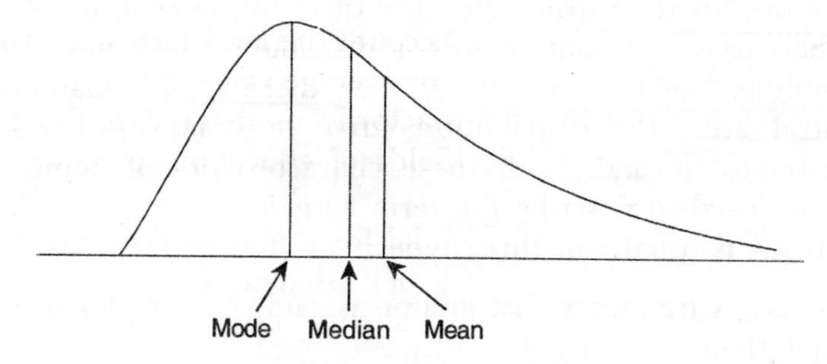

Figure 8.3 Positive skewness (the curve inclines more to the right).

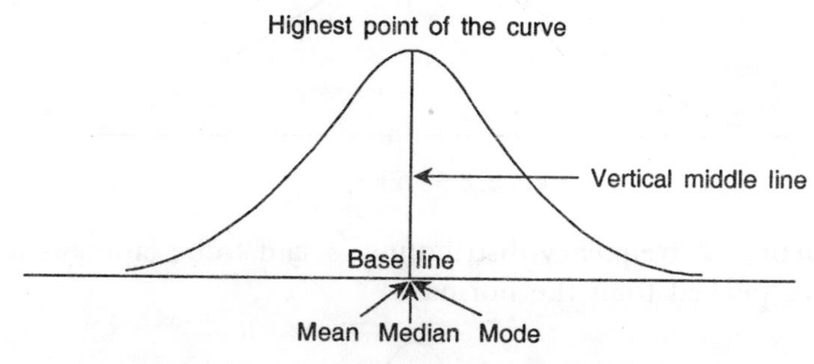

Figure 8.4 Normal (symmetrical) curve.

As illustrated in the given figures, there are two types of skewed distributions. The distributions are said to be skewed negatively when there are many individuals in a group with their scores higher than the average score of the group. Similarly, the distributions are said to be skewed positively when there are more individuals in a group who score less than the average score for their group.

Skewness in a given distribution may be computed by the following formula:

$$\text{Skewness} = \frac{3\,(\text{Mean} - \text{Median})}{\text{Standard deviation}}$$

or

$$S_k = \frac{3\,(M - M_d)}{\text{SD}}$$

In case when the percentiles are known, the value of skewness may be computed from the following formula:

$$S_k = \frac{P_{90} + P_{10}}{2} - P_{50}$$

In Terms of Kurtosis

When there are very few individuals whose scores are near to the average score for their group (too few cases in the central area of the curve) the curve representing such a distribution becomes 'flattened' in the middle. On the other hand, when there are too many cases in the central area, the distribution curve becomes too 'peaked' in comparison to normal. Both these characteristics of being flat or peaked, are used to describe the term *kurtosis*.

Kurtosis is usually of three types:

Platykurtic. A frequency distribution is said to be platykurtic, when it is flatter than the normal.

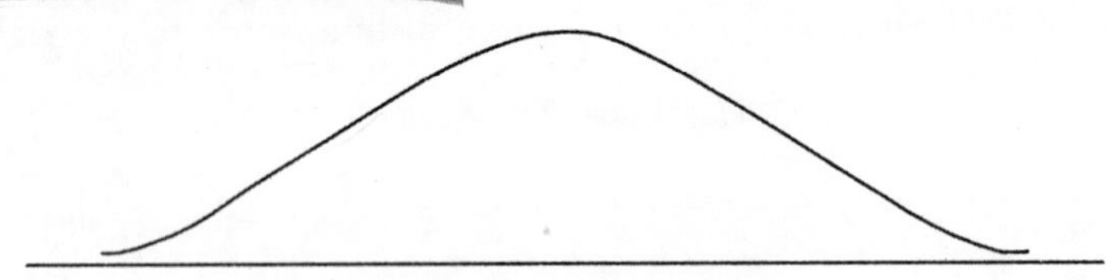

Figure 8.5 Platykurtic.

Leptokurtic. A frequency distribution is said to be laptokurtic, when it is more peaked than the normal.

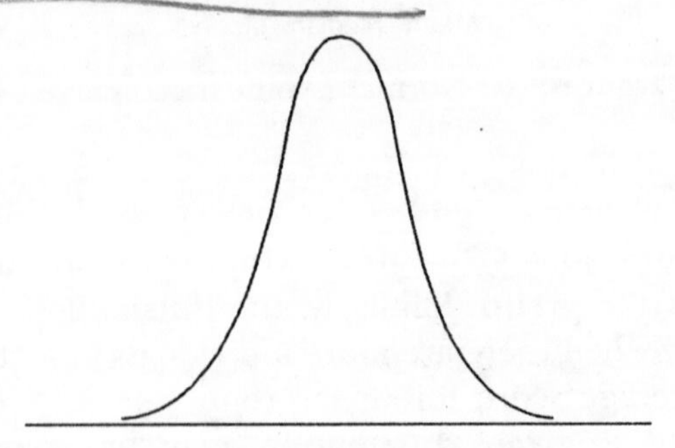

Figure 8.6 Leptokurtic.

Mesokurtic. A frequency distribution is said to be mesokurtic, when it almost resembles the normal curve (neither too flattened nor too peaked).

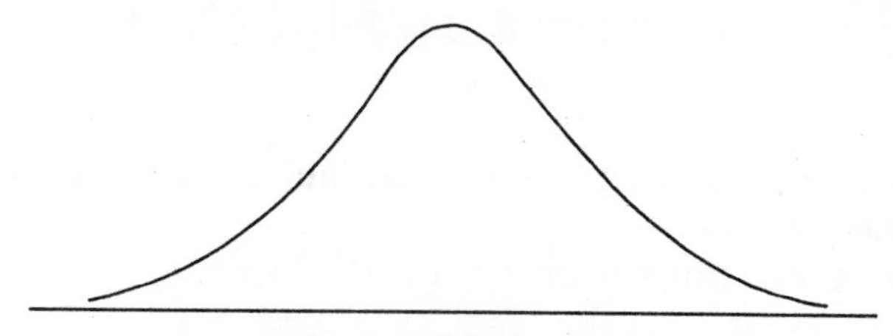

Figure 8.7 Mesokurtic.

The value of kurtosis for a given curve may be computed through the following formula:

$$\text{Kurtosis} = \frac{\text{Quartile deviation}}{\text{90th percentile} - \text{10th percentile}}$$

or

$$K_u = \frac{Q}{P_{90} - P_{10}}$$

In the case of a normal curve, this value is equal to 0.263. Consequently, if the value of kurtosis is greater than 0.263, the distribution is said to be platykurtic; if less than 0.263, the distribution is leptokurtic.

CHARACTERISTICS AND PROPERTIES OF A NORMAL CURVE

1. For this curve, mean, median and mode are the same.
2. The curve is perfectly symmetrical. In other words, it is not skewed. The value of the measure of skewness computed for this curve is zero.
3. The normal curve serves as a model for describing the peakedness or flatness of a curve through the measure of kurtosis. For the normal curve, the value of kurtosis is 0.263. If for a distribution the value of kurtosis is more than 0.263, the distribution is said to be more flat at the top than the normal curve. But in case the value of kurtosis is less than 0.263, the distribution is said to be more peaked than the normal.
4. The curve is asymptotic. It approaches but never touches the base line at the extremes because of the possibility of locating in the population, a case which scores still higher than our highest score or lower than our lowest score. Therefore, theoretically, it extends from minus infinity to plus infinity.

5. As the curve does not touch the base line, the mean is used as the starting point for working with the normal curve.
6. The curve has its maximum height or ordinate at the starting point, i.e. the mean of the distribution. In a unit normal curve, the value of this ordinate is equal to .3989.
7. To find the deviations from the point of departure (i.e. mean), standard deviation of the distribution (σ) is used as a unit of measurement.
8. The curve extends on both sides -3σ distance on the left to $+3\sigma$ distance on the right.
9. The points of inflection of the curve occur at ±1 standard deviation unit ($\pm 1\sigma$) above and below the mean. Thus the curve changes from convex to concave in relation to the horizontal axis at these points.
10. The total area under the curve extending from -3σ to $+3\sigma$ is taken arbitrarily to be 10,000 because of the greater ease in the computation of the fractional parts of the total area found for the mean and the ordinates erected at various distances from the mean. The computation of such fractional parts of the total area for travelling desired σ distances from the mean may be conveniently made with the help of Table B given in the appendix of this textbook.
11. We may find that 3413 cases out of 10,000 or 34.13% of the entire area of the curve lies between the mean and $+1\sigma$ on the base line of the normal curve. Similarly, another 34.13% cases lie between the mean and -1σ on the base line. Consequently, 68.26% of the area of the curve falls within the limits ±1 Standard deviation ($\pm 1\sigma$) unit from the mean. Going further it may be found out that 95.44% cases lie from -2σ to $+2\sigma$ and 99.74% cases lie from -3σ to $+3\sigma$. Consequently only 26 cases in 10,000 (10,000 – 9974) should be expected to lie beyond the range $\pm 3\sigma$ in a large sample as shown in Figure 8.8.

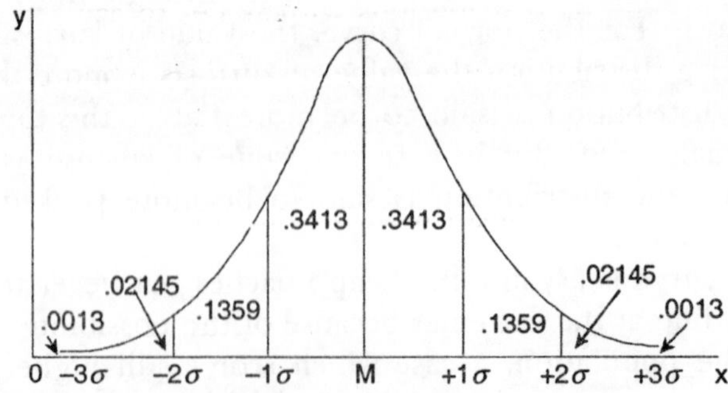

Figure 8.8 Normal curve showing areas at different distances from the mean.

12. In this curve, the limits of the distances $\pm 1.96\sigma$ include 95% and the limits $\pm 2.58\sigma$ include 99% of the total area of the curve, 5% and 1% of the area, respectively falling beyond these limits as shown in Figure 8.9.

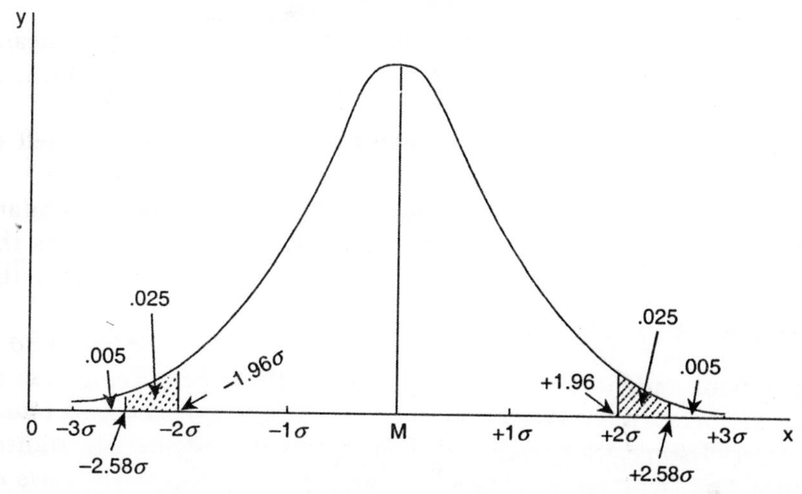

Figure 8.9 Normal curve showing 5% and 1% cases lying beyond the limits $\pm 1.96\sigma$ and $\pm 2.58\sigma$, respectively.

APPLICATIONS OF THE NORMAL CURVE

Normal curve has wide significance and applications in the field of measurement concerning education, psychology and sociology. Some of its main applications are discussed in the following sections:

Use as a Model

Normal curve represents a model distribution. It can be used as a model to

1. compare various distributions with it i.e. to say, whether the distribution is normal or not and if not, in what way it diverges from the normal;
2. compare two or more distributions in terms of overlapping; and
3. evaluate students' performance from their scores.

Computing Percentiles and Percentile Ranks

Normal probability curve may be conveniently used for computing percentiles and percentile ranks in a given normal distribution.

Understanding and Applying the Concept of Standard Errors of Measurement

The normal curve as we have pointed out earlier, is also known as the normal curve of error or simply the curve of error on the grounds that it helps in understanding the concept of standard errors of measurement. For example, if we compute mean for the distributions of various samples taken from a single population, then, these means will be found to be distributed normally around the mean of the entire population. The sigma distance of a particular sample mean may help us determine the standard error of measurement for the mean of that sample.

Ability Grouping

A group of individuals may be conveniently grouped into certain categories as A, B, C, D, E (Very good, good, average, poor, very poor) in terms of some trait (assumed to be normally distributed), with the help of a normal curve.

Transforming and Combining Qualitative Data

Under the assumption of normality of the distributed variable, the sets of qualitative data such as ratings, letter grades and categorical ranks on a scale may be conveniently transformed and combined to provide an average rating for each individual.

Converting Raw Scores into Comparable Standard Normalized Scores

Sometimes, we have records of an individual's performance on two or more different kinds of assessment tests and we wish to compare his score on one test with the score on the other. Unless the scales of these two tests are the same, we cannot make a direct comparison. With the help of a normal curve, we can convert the raw scores belonging to different tests into standard normalized scores like sigma (or z scores) and T-scores. For converting a given raw score into a z score, we subtract the mean of the scores of the distribution from the respective raw scores and divide it by the standard deviation of the distribution $\left(\text{i.e., } z = \frac{X - M}{\sigma}\right)$. In this way, a standard z score clearly indicates how many standard deviation units a raw score is above or below the mean and thus provides a standard scale for the purpose of valuable comparison. Sinze z values may carry negative signs and decimals, they are converted into T values by multiplying by some constant and added to a second constant, i.e. using the formula T score = $10z + 50$.

Determining the Relative Difficulty of Test Items

Normal curve provides the simplest rational method of scaling test items for difficulty and therefore, may be conveniently employed for determining the relative difficulty of test questions, problems and other test items.

ILLUSTRATION OF THE APPLICATIONS OF THE NORMAL CURVE

Now, let us study some of the applications of the normal curve discussed so far, with the help of a few examples. Solutions to these problems require:

1. a knowledge of the conversion of raw scores into z scores and vice versa, and
2. the use of the normal curve Table B (Appendix) showing the fractional parts of the total area of the curve in relation to sigma distances.

Converting Raw Scores into z Scores and Vice Versa

The relationship between z scores and raw scores can be expressed by the formula

$$z = \frac{X - M}{\sigma}$$

where

X = a given raw score
M = Mean of the distribution of X scores
σ = SD of the distribution of X scores

Example 8.1: Given Mean = 49.5 and SD = 14.3 for a distribution, change the score of 80 into z or sigma score.

Solution

$$z = \frac{X - M}{\sigma}$$

where

$X = 80, \quad M = 49.5, \quad \text{SD} = 14.3$

Putting these values in the formula, we get

$$z = \frac{80 - 49.5}{14.3} = \frac{30.5}{14.3} = 2.13$$

Example 8.2: Given $M = 48$, $\sigma = 8$, for a distribution, convert a z score (σ score) of the value 0.625 into a raw score.

Solution

$$z = \frac{X - M}{\sigma}$$

Putting known values in the given formula, we get

$$0.625 = \frac{X - 48}{8}$$

or

$$X = 0.625 \times 8 + 48 = 5.0 + 48 = 53$$

Making Use of the Table of Normal Curve

Table B of the normal curve (given in the Appendix) provides the fractional parts of the total area (taken as 10,000) under the curve in relation to the respective sigma distances from the mean. This table may therefore be used to find the fractional part of the total area when z scores or sigma scores are given and also to find the sigma or z scores, when the fractional parts of the total area are given. Let us illustrate it with the help of examples.

Example 8.3: From the table of the normal distribution, read the areas from mean to 2.73σ.

Solution. We have to look for the figure of the total area given in the table corresponding to 2.73σ score. For this we have to first locate 2.7 sigma distance in the first column headed by

$$z = \frac{X - M}{\sigma}$$

(σ scores) and then move horizontally in the row against 2.7 until we reach the place below the sigma distance .03 (lying in column 4). The figure 4968 gives the fractional parts of the total area (taken as 10000) corresponding to the 2.73σ distance (lying on the right side) from the mean of the curve. Consequently, 4968/10000 or 49.68 percent of the cases may be said to lie between the mean and 2.73σ.

Example 8.4: From the table of the normal distribution read the value of sigma score from the mean for the corresponding fractional area 3729.

Solution. The figure of the area 3729 located in the table lies in front of the row of the σ distance 1.1 and below the column headed by the σ distance .04. Consequently, the corresponding sigma distance from the area 3729 may be computed as 1.14.

Examples of Application of the Normal Curve

Case I: Comparing scores on two different tests

Example 8.5: A student obtains 80 marks in Maths and 50 in English. If the mean and SD for the scores in Maths are 70 and 20 and for the scores in English are 30 and 10 find out in which subject, Maths or English, he did better?

Solution. Here, from the given data, direct comparison of his status in Maths and in English cannot be made because the marks achieved do not belong to the same scale of measurement. For putting them into a common scale, let us convert these two raw scores into z scores. Here,

Raw scores in maths $(X_1) = 80$, $\quad M_1 = 70$ and $\sigma_1 = 20$,

and

Raw score in English $(X_2) = 50$, $\quad M_2 = 30$ and $\sigma_2 = 10$

Therefore,

$$z \text{ score in Maths} = \frac{X_1 - M_1}{\sigma_1} = \frac{80 - 70}{20} = 0.5$$

and

$$z \text{ score in English} = \frac{X_2 - M_2}{\sigma_2} = \frac{50 - 30}{10} = 2.0$$

We can thus conclude that he did better in English than in Maths.

Case II: To determine percentage of the individuals whose scores lie between two given scores

Example 8.6: In a sample of 1000 cases, the mean of test scores is 14.5 and standard deviation is 2.5. Assuming normality of distribution how many individuals scored between 12 and 16?

Solution. Both the raw scores 12 and 16 have to be converted into z scores (sigma scores)

$$z \text{ score equivalent to raw score } 12 = \frac{X - M}{\sigma}$$

$$= \frac{12 - 14.5}{2.5}$$

$$= \frac{-2.5}{2.5} = -1\sigma$$

z score equivalent to raw score 16 $= \frac{16 - 14.5}{2.5} = \frac{1.5}{2.5}$

$$= 0.6\sigma$$

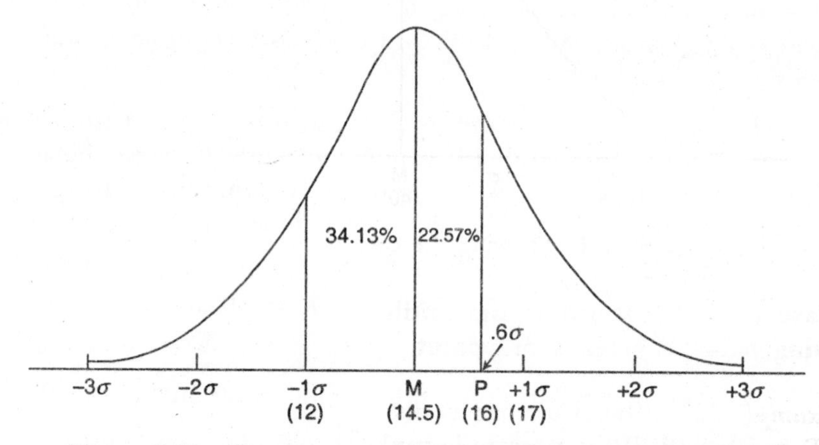

Figure 8.10 Showing cases lying between scores 12 and 16.

From the normal curve table, we see that 2257 (out of 10000), i.e. 22.57% cases lie between mean and 0.6σ. Similarly, between -1σ and mean, 3413, i.e. 34.13% cases lie. In this way, it may be easily concluded that 22.57 + 34.13 = 56.7% or 567 individuals out of 1000 score between 12 and 16.

Case III: To determine percentage of the individuals scoring above a given score point

Example 8.7: In a sample of 500 cases, the mean of the distribution is 40 and standard deviation 4. Assuming normality of distribution, find how many individuals score above 47 score point.

Solution. z score equivalent to the raw score 47 is given by

$$\frac{X - M}{\sigma} = \frac{47 - 40}{4} = \frac{7}{4} = 1.75\ \sigma$$

From the normal curve table, it may be found that 4599 out of 10,000 or 45.99 percent cases lie between mean and 1.75σ. It is also known that a total of 50 percent cases lie on both sides of the mean.

Therefore, it may be easily concluded that in all 50 – 45.99 = 4.01 or 4% individuals or 20 individuals out of 500 score above the score point 47 (shown as P in Figure 8.11).

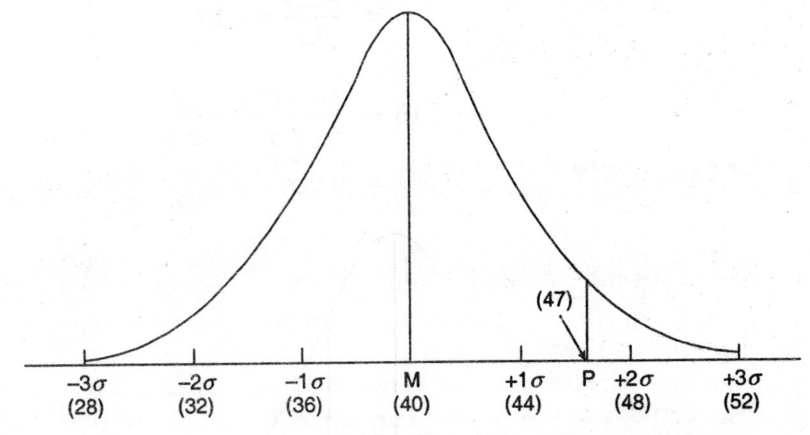

Figure 8.11 Showing the cases above 47 score point.

Case IV: To determine percentile rank, i.e. percentages of cases lying below a given score point

Example 8.8: Given a normal distribution N = 1000, Mean = 80, SD = 16; find (i) the percentile rank of the individual scoring 90 and (ii) the total number of individuals whose scores lie below the score point 40.

Solution. (i) The percentile rank is essentially a rank or the position of an individual (on a scale of 100) decided on the basis of the individual's score. In other words, here we have to determine the percentage of cases lying below the score point 90. For this, let us first transform the raw score into the standard z score with the help of the formula

$$z = \frac{X - M}{\sigma} = \frac{90 - 80}{16} = \frac{10}{16}$$

$$= 0.625 \text{ sigma score } = 0.625\,\sigma$$

Now, we have to determine the total percentage of cases lying below 0.625σ (standard scores).

The sigma score 0.625 is halfway between 0.62 and 0.63. Therefore, we have to interpolate the area lying between M and 0.625 from the given normal curve table as

$$2324 + \frac{2357 - 2324}{2} = 2324 + \frac{33}{2} = 2340.5 \text{ or } 2341$$

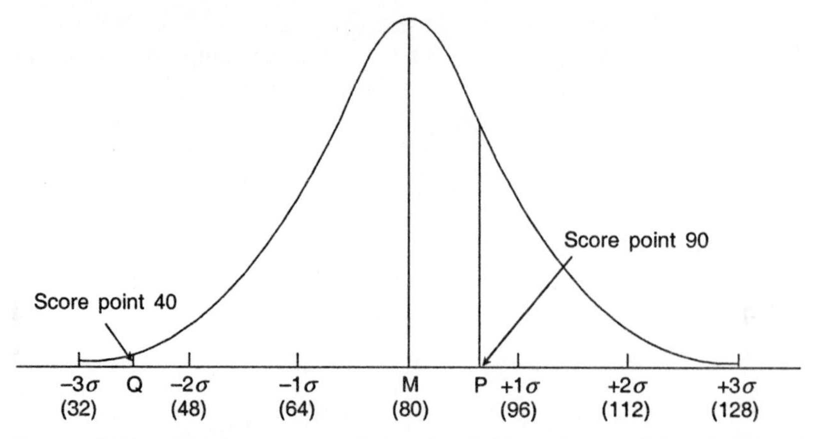

Figure 8.12 Showing percentile rank of 90 and cases lying below 40.

We can say that 23.41% cases lie between M and 0.625σ distance. But 50% of cases lie up to the Mean. Therefore, it may be concluded that there are 50 + 23.41 = 73.41% of the individuals whose scores lie below the score point 90 (shown as point P in the figure) or we may say that percentile rank of the individual scoring 90 is 73.

(ii) The z score equivalent to the raw score 40 is

$$\frac{X - M}{\sigma} = \frac{40 - 80}{16} = \frac{-40}{16} = -2.5\sigma$$

From the normal curve table, we may find that 4938 out of 10,000 or 49.38 percent cases lie between M and -2.5σ. Therefore, it may be easily concluded that, in all, 50 − 49.38 = 0.62 percent of the cases lie below the given score point 40 (shown by Q in the figure), or

$$\frac{0.62}{100} \times 1000 = 6.2$$

i.e. 6 individuals achieve below the score point 40.

Case V: To determine the limits of the scores between which a certain percentage of the cases lie

Example 8.9: If a distribution is normal with M = 100 and SD = 20, find out the two points between which the middle 60 percent of the cases lie.

Solution. It may be seen from the figure that the middle 60% of the cases are distributed in such a way that 30% (or 3000 out of 10,000) of the cases lie to the left and 30% to the right of the mean.

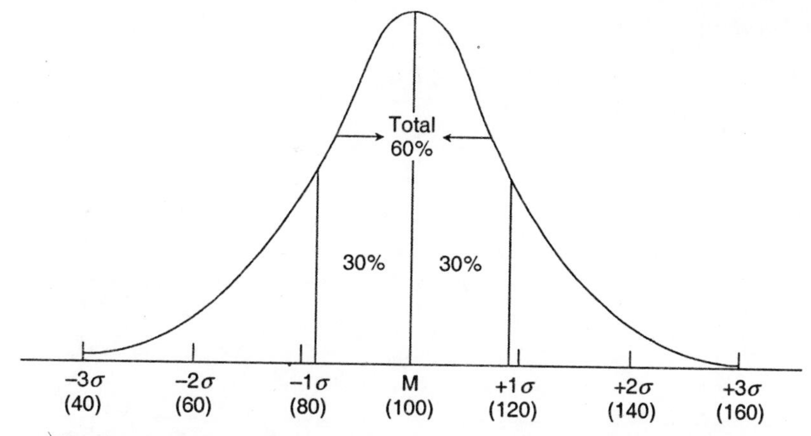

Figure 8.13 Showing the area covered by middle 60 percent.

From the normal curve (Table B in the Appendix), we have to find out the corresponding σ distance for the 3000 fractional parts of the total area under the normal curve. There is a figure of 2995 for area in the table (very close to 3000) for which we may read sigma value as 0.84σ. It means that 30% of the cases lie on the right side of the curve between M and 0.84σ and similarly 30% of the cases lie on the left side of the figure between M and -0.84σ. The middle 60% of the cases, therefore, fall between the mean and standard score $+0.84\sigma$. We have to convert the standard z scores to raw scores with the help of the formulae

$$z = \frac{X_1 - M}{\sigma_1}, \qquad z = \frac{X_2 - M}{\sigma_2}$$

or

$$0.48 = \frac{X_1 - 100}{20} \quad \text{and} \quad -0.84 = \frac{X_2 - 100}{20}$$

or

$$X_1 = 16.8 + 100 \text{ and } X_2 = 100 - 16.8$$

or

$$X_1 = 116.8 \quad \text{and} \quad X_2 = 83.2$$

After rounding the figures, we have the scores 117 and 83 that include the middle 60 percent of the cases.

Case VI: To find out the limits in terms of scores which include the highest given percentages of the cases

Example 8.10: Given a normal distribution with a mean of 120 and SD of 25, what limits will include the highest 10% of the distribuution (see Figure 8.14).

Solution.

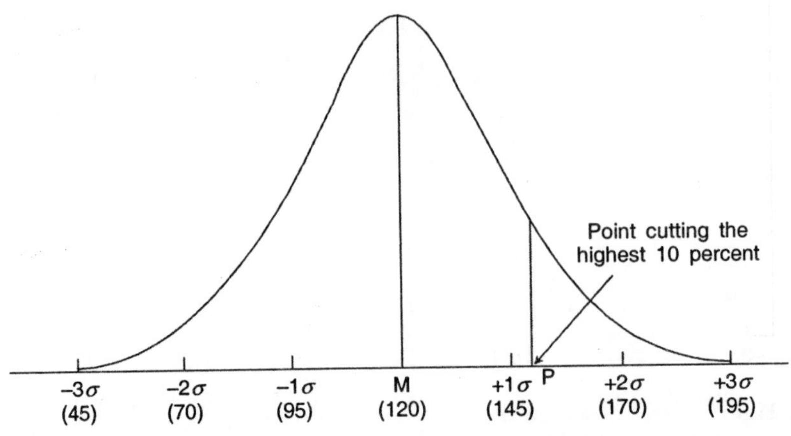

Figure 8.14 Showing the area covered by highest 10%.

Since 50% of the cases of a normally distributed group lie in the right half of the distribution, the highest 10% of the cases will have 40% of the cases between its lower limits and the mean of the distribution. From Table B, of the normal curve, we know that 3997 cases in 10,000 or 40% of the distribution are between the mean and 1.28σ. Therefore, the lower limit of the highest 10% of the cases is $M + 1.28\sigma$ or $120 + 1.28 \times 25$ (as here in the present example, $M = 120$ and $\sigma = 25$). Thus, the lower limit of the highest 10% of the cases is $120 + 32 = 152$ and the upper limit of the highest 10% of the cases will be the highest score in this distribution.

Case VII: To determine the percentile points or the limits in terms of scores which include the lowest given percentages of the cases

Example 8.11: Given a normal distribution, $N = 1000$, $M = 80$ and $\sigma = 16$, determine the percentile P_{30}.

Solution. In determining percentile P_{30}, we have to look for a score point on the scale of measurement below which 30 percent of the cases lie.

It may be clearly observed from Figure 8.15 that such a score point on the scale of measurement will have 20% of the cases lying on the left side of the mean. From the table of the normal curve, let us try to find out the corresponding σ distances from the mean for the 20% or 2000 out of 1000 cases. By interpolation, it may be taken as 0.525σ and its sign will be negative since it lies on the left side of the distribution. Therefore, the required score here will be:

$$M - 0.525\sigma \text{ or } 80 - 0.525 \times 16 = 80 - 8.4 = 71.6 \text{ or } 72$$

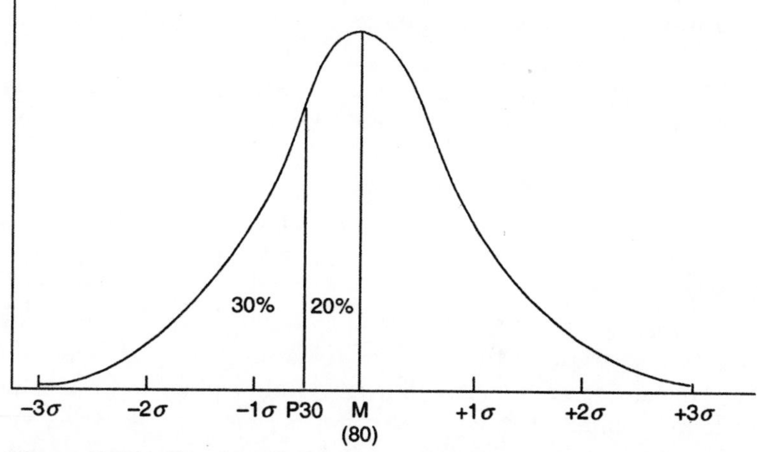

Figure 8.15 Showing the area covered by the lowest 30 percent.

Here, we can say about the limits in terms of scores which include the lowest 30% of the cases. The upper limit of these cases may now be given by the score point 71.6 and the lower limit will be the lowest score of the distribution.

Case VIII: To determine the relative difficulty value of the test items

Example 8.12: Four problems *A*, *B*, *C*, and *D* have been solved by 50%, 60%, 70%, and 80% respectively of a large group. Compare the difference in difficulty between *A* and *B* with the difference between *C* and *D*.

Solution.

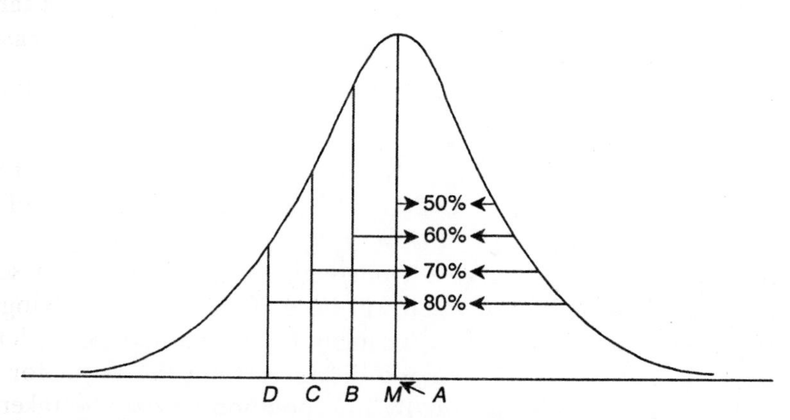

Figure 8.16 Showing the problems solved by different percentages of the cases.

In the case of a large group, the assumption about normal distribution of the ability of a group in terms of the achievement or a test, holds good. The percentage of the students who are able to solve a particular problem are counted from the extreme right. Therefore, while starting on the base line of the curve from the extreme right, up to the point *M* (mean of the group), we may cover the 50% of the cases who can solve a particular problem. For the rest 60, 70 or 80 percent (more than 50%) we have to proceed on the left side of the baseline of the curve. Figure 8.16 represents well, the percentage of cases who are able to solve a particular problem.

For problem *A*, we see that it has been solved by 50% of the group. It is also implied that 50% of the group has not been able to solve it. Therefore, we may say that it was an average problem having zero difficulty value.

In the case of problem *B*, we see that it has been solved by 60% of the group. It has been a simple problem, in comparison to *A* as 10% more individuals in the group are able to solve it. For determining the difficulty value of this problem, we have to find the σ distance from the mean of these 10% of the individuals. From the normal curve table we see that 10% (1000 out of 10,000) cases fall at a sigma distance of 0.253 from the mean. Here we have to interpolate as the given table contains $0.25\sigma = 0987$ and $0.26\sigma = 1026$; therefore, $0.253\sigma = 1000$ (approx.). Therefore, the difficulty value of problem *B* will be taken as -0.253σ.

Similarly, we may determine the difficulty value of problem *C* passed by 70% of the group (20% more individuals of the group than the average). From the table, we know that 20% (2000 out of 10,000) cases fall at a sigma distance of 0.525 from the mean. Therefore, the difficulty value of problem *C* will be taken as -0.525σ and the difficulty value of problem *D* passed by 80% (30% more individuals than the average) will be -0.840σ.

Let us represent all the determined difficulty values as under:

Problem	*Solved by* (%)	*Difficulty value*	*Relative difficulty value* (σ *differences*)
A	50	-0	
B	60	-0.253σ	-0.253σ
C	70	-0.525σ	
D	80	-0.840σ	-0.315σ

It may be seen that problem *B* is simpler than problem *A* by having 0.253σ less difficulty value and similarly problem *D* is simpler than the problem *C* by having 0.315σ less difficulty value.

Example 8.13: Three questions are solved by 20%, 30% and 40% respectively of a large unrelated group. If we assume the ability measured by the test questions to be distributed normally, find out the relative difficulty value of these questions.

Solution.

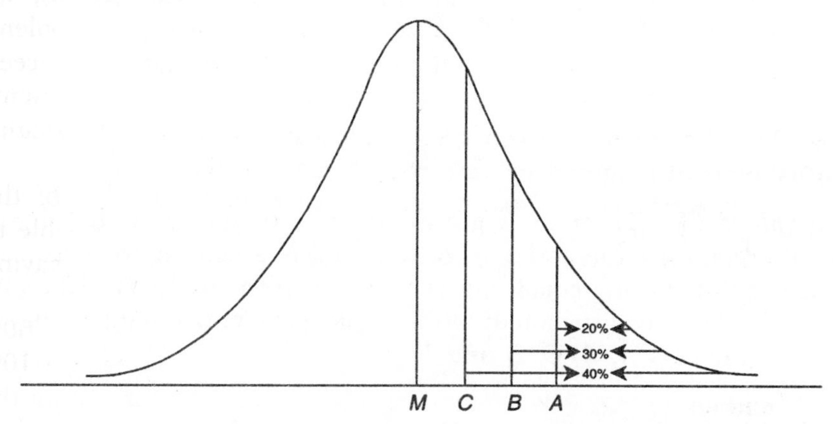

Figure 8.17 Showing problems passed by different percentages of the students.

Questions *A*, *B* and *C* are solved by 20%, 30% and 40% of the group. Therefore, from the point of view of difficulty, question *A* is the most difficult one in comparison to questions *B* and *C*. Question *A* has been solved by only 20% of the group. Our first task is to find for question *A*, a point on the base line such that 20% of the entire group (who has solved this question) lies below this point. The highest 20% in a normal curve as shown in Figure 8.17 must have 30% of the cases between its lower limit and the mean. From Table B of the normal curve, we find that 30% or 3000 out of 10,000 cases must fall between *M* and 0.844σ. For finding out the σ value for 3000, we have to interpolate between the values 2985 and 3023 respectively for 0.84σ and 0.85σ. In this way, the difficulty value for question *A* is 0.844σ.

Similarly, the difficulty value for question *B*, solved by 30% of the group may be determined by locating a point on the baseline above and below which 30% and 70% cases lie. The highest 30% as shown in Figure 8.17 must have 20% of the cases between its lower limit and mean. From Table B, we find that 20% (2000 out of 10,000) cases must fall between *M* and 0.525σ. Therefore, the difficulty value of question *B* will be 0.525σ.

Question *C* has been solved by 40% and failed by 60% of the entire group. The point on the base line separating the individuals who have passed and failed may be located such that it has 10% (1000 out of 10,000) cases lying between its lower limit and the mean. From Table B, we find the corresponding σ value for 10% or 1000 cases which is 0.253σ. Hence the difficulty value of question *C* is 0.253σ.

We may summarize the results as follows:

Question	*Solved by %*	*Difficulty value*
A	20	0.844σ
B	30	0.525σ
C	40	0.253σ

Case IX: To divide a given group into categories according to an ability or trait assumed to be distributed normally

Example 8.14: There is a group of 200 students that has to be classified into five categories, *A, B, C, D* and *E*, according to ability, the range of ability being equal in each category. If the trait counted under ability is normally distributed; tell how many students should be placed in each category *A, B, C, D* and *E*.

Solution.

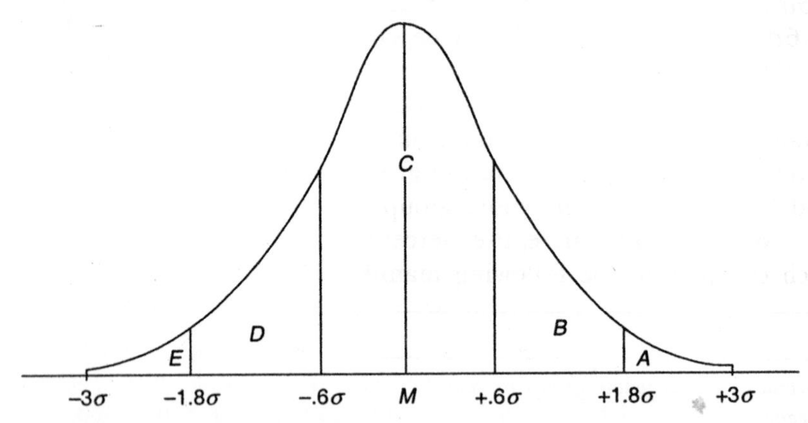

Figure 8.18 Division of the area into five equal categories.

As the trait under measurement is normally distributed, the whole group divided into five equal categories may be represented diagramatically as shown in Figure 8.18. It shows that the base line of the curve, considered to extend from -3σ to $+3\sigma$, i.e. over a range of 6σ, may be divided into five equal parts. It gives 1.2σ as the portion of the base line to be allotted to each category. This allotment may be made in the manner as shown in Figure 8.18 with the various categories demarcated by erecting perpendiculars. Here, group *A* covers the upper 1.2σ segment (falling between 1.8σ and 3σ), group *B* the next 1.2σ group *C* lies 0.6σ to the right and 0.6σ to the left of the mean groups *D* and *E* covers the same relative positions on the left side of the mean as covered by the groups *B* and *A* on the right side of the mean.

After the area of the curve occupied by the respective categories is demarcated the next problem is to find out from the normal curve table the percentage of cases lying within cach of these areas.

Let us begin the task with area *A*. It extends from 1.8σ to 3σ. To know the percentage of cases falling within this area, we read from the table the cases lying between mean and 3σ (4986 or 49.86%) and then between *M* and 1.8σ (4641 or 4641%). The difference (49.86 – 46.41 = 3.45%) will yield the required percentage of the whole group belonging to category *A*. Therefore, group *A* may be said to comprise 3.45% or 3.5% of the whole group.

Similarly, group *B* will cover the cases lying between 0.6σ and 1.8σ. We find from the table that the percentage of the whole group lying between *M* and 1.8σ is 46.41 and between *M* and 0.6σ is 22.57. Therefore, group *B* may be said to comprise 46.41 – 22.57 = 23.84% of the entire group.

Group *C* extends from -0.6σ to 0.6σ on both sides of the mean. The normal curve table tells us that 22.57% cases lie between *M* and 0.6σ and a similar percentage of cases, i.e. 22.57, lies between *M* and -0.6σ. Therefore, group *C* may be said to comprise 22.57 × 2 = 45.14 or 45% of the entire group.

Groups *D* and *E*, as can be seen from Figure 8.18, are identical to groups *B* and *A* and, therefore, may be found to consist of the same percentage of cases as covered in groups *B* and *A*, respectively, i.e. 23.8 and 0.5 percent of the whole group.

We may summarize the percentage and number of students in each category in the following manner:

	A	*B*	*C*	*D*	*E*
Percentage of the whole group in each category	3.5	23.8	45.0	23.8	3.5
Number of students in each category out of the total 200 students	7.0	47.6	90.0	47.6	7.0
Number of students in whole number	7	48	90	48	7

SUMMARY

The literal meaning of the term normal is average. Most of the things and attributes in nature are distributed in a normal way. There are quite a few persons who deviate noticeably from average and a very few who markedly differ from average. If the data in terms of the results of tests, surveys and experiments performed on a randomly selected sample or population are plotted on a graph paper, we are likely to get a typical curve often resembling a vertical cross-section of a bell. This bell-shaped curve is named as normal curve. It is a perfectly symmetrical curve along the vertical middle line. Where the scores of individuals in the group seriously deviate from the average, the curves representing these distributions also deviate from the shape of a normal curve. This deviation from the normality tends to vary either in terms of skewness or in terms of kurtosis.

Skewness refers to the lack of symmetry. In a distribution showing skewness, there is no symmetry between the right and left halves of the curve. There are two types of skewed distributions—negative and positive—indicating the inclination of the curve more towards left or right. It is computed by the formulae

$$S_k = \frac{3(M - M_d)}{\sigma}$$

$$S_k = \frac{P_{90} + P_{10}}{2} - P_{50}$$

Kurtosis refers to the flatness or peakedness of a frequency distribution as compared with the normal. If it is more flat than the normal, it is named as platy-kurtic and if more peaked, then it is called as lepto-kurtic. Kurtosis is computed by the formula

$$K_u = \frac{Q}{P_{90} + P_{10}}$$

A normal curve shows interesting properties and typical characteristics like the following:

1. Mean, median and mode are the same.
2. The value of the measure of skewness is zero.
3. The value of the measure of kurtosis is 0.263.
4. It approaches but never touches the base line at the extremes.
5. The mean of the distribution is used as the starting point. The curve has its maximum height at this point. The distance travelled along the base line from this point is measured in the unit of the Standard deviation of the distribution (σ).
6. The curve extends from -3σ to $+3\sigma$ covering a total area of 10,000 (taken arbitrarily). 68.26 percent of this area falls within the limits $\pm 1\sigma$, 95.44 percent within $\pm 2\sigma$ and 99.74 percent within $\pm 3\sigma$, thus leaving 26 cases in 10,000 beyond the range $\pm 3\sigma$.
7. Limits of the distances $\pm 1.96\sigma$ include 95 percent and the limits $\pm 2.58\sigma$ include 99 percent of the total cases.

Normal curve has a wide significance and applicability and may be used

1. as a model for comparing various distributions and distributing school marks and categorical ratings;
2. to compute percentiles and percentile ranks;
3. to understand and apply the concept of standard errors of measurement;
4. for the purpose of ability grouping;
5. for transforming and combining qualitative data;
6. for converting raw scores into comparable standard normalized scores; and
7. for determining the relative difficulty of test items.

EXERCISES

1. What is a normal curve? Why is it named as normal probability curve, normal curve of error or Gaussian curve?
2. What do you understand by the term divergence from normality? Point out the main types of such divergent curves and throw light on the concepts of skewness and kurtosis.
3. Define and explain the terms skewness and kurtosis along with their main types.
4. Discuss the chief characteristics and properties of a normal curve.
5. What do you understand by the terms normal distribution and normal curve? Bring out the main applications of the concept of normal curve in the fields of education, psychology and sociology.
6. Given the following data regarding two distributions,

	Mathematics	*Physics*
M	60	33
SD	8	9
Achievement scores of a student	70	67

find out whether the student did better in Maths or Physics.

7. Given a normal distribution with a mean of 50 and standard deviation of 15,

    (a) What percent of the cases will lie between the scores of 47 and 60,

    (b) What percent of the cases will lie between 40 and 47, and

    (c) What percent of the group is expected to have scores greater than 68?

8. In a normal distribution with a mean of 54 and SD of 5, calculate the following:
   (a) Q_1 and Q_3 (P_{25} and P_{75})
   (b) Two scores between which lies the middle 50% cases.
   (c) Number of persons out of 600 who score below 57.

9. Given N = 100, M = 28.52, SD = 4.66; assuming normality of the given distribution find
   (a) What percent of cases lie between 23–25 and
   (b) What limits include the middle 60%?

10. On the assumption that IQ's are normally distributed in the population with mean of 100 and standard deviation of 15, what percentage of the cases fall
    (a) above 135 IQ
    (b) above 120 IQ
    (c) below 90 IQ
    (d) between 75 and 125 IQ

11. Assuming a normal distribution of scores, a test has a mean score of 100 and a standard deviation of 15. Compute the following:
    (a) Score that cuts off the top 10%,
    (b) Score that cuts off the lower 40%,
    (c) Percentage of cases above 90,
    (d) Score that occupies the 68th percentile rank, and
    (e) Score limits of the middle 68%.

12. Four tests are passed by 15%, 50%, 60% and 75% respectively of a large unrelated group. Assuming normality, find the relative difficulty value of each problem.

13. Given three test items. 1, 2 and 3 passed by 50%, 40% and 30% respectively of a large group. On the assumption of normality of distribution, what percentage of this group must pass test item 4 in order for it to be as much more difficult than 3 as 2 is more difficult than 1?

14. There is a group of 1000 individuals to be divided into 10 sub-groups, i.e. *A, B, C, D, E, F, G, H, I* and *J* respectively according to a trait supposed to be distributed normally. What number of individuals should be placed in each of these sub-groups?

15. Scores on a particular psychological test are normally distributed with a mean of 50 and SD of 10. The decision is made to use a letter grade system, as follows: A 10%, B 20%, C 40%, D 20% and E 10%. Find the score intervals for the five letter grades.

9

Significance of the Mean and Other Statistics

WHY IS SAMPLING NEEDED?

In education and psychology, we have to compute mean and several other representative values for studying the characteristics of a certain population. But it is neither feasible nor practicable to approach each and every element of the population. For example, if we wish to know about the average height of the Indian male of 25 years of age, then, we have to catch hold of all the young men of 25 years of age (necessarily identified as citizens of India), measure their heights and compute the average. This average will yield a true value of the desired population mean. But to do so is not a simple task. It is quite impracticable as well as inessential to approach every Indian male of 25 years of age. The convenient as well as practical solution lies in estimating the population mean from the sample means. Here, we may take a few representative samples of appropriate size from the randomly selected districts and states in India. Suppose that we have taken 100 such samples. Then, the means of these samples may yield the desired average height of the whole population of the Indian male of 25 years of age.

SIGNIFICANCE OF THE SAMPLE MEAN AND OTHER STATISTICS

The representative values like mean, median, standard deviation, etc. calculated from the samples are called statistics and those directly computed from the population are named as parameters. The statistics computed from the samples may be used to draw inferences and estimates about the parameters. In an ideal situation, we expect any sample statistic to give a true estimate of the population statistic. The degree to which a sample mean (or other statistics) represents its parameter, is an indication of the significance of the computed sample mean.

Therefore, in a situation in which we approach the element of a representative sample rather than the element of the entire population and compute the sample mean and other statistic , for the estimation of related parameters, we have to make sure of the significance or trustworthiness of the computed sample statistics. In other words, we have to say how far we can rely on the computed mean or some other statistic, to predict or estimate the value of the related parameter (the true mean).

Concept of Standard Error in Computing the Significant Value of the Mean or Other Statistics

Assume that we have knowledge of the true mean (mean of the population). Also suppose that we have taken 100 representative samples from the population and computed their respective sample means. If we analyze the distribution of these sample means, we will come to know that a majority of these sample means are clustered around the population mean and in the case of a large sample (number of cases more than 30), the distribution will be found normal as shown in Figure 9.1. The mean of the sample will be a fairly good or a somewhat true estimate of the population mean. Some of these sample means will deviate from the population mean either on the positive or the negative side, while most of them will show negligibly small deviations.

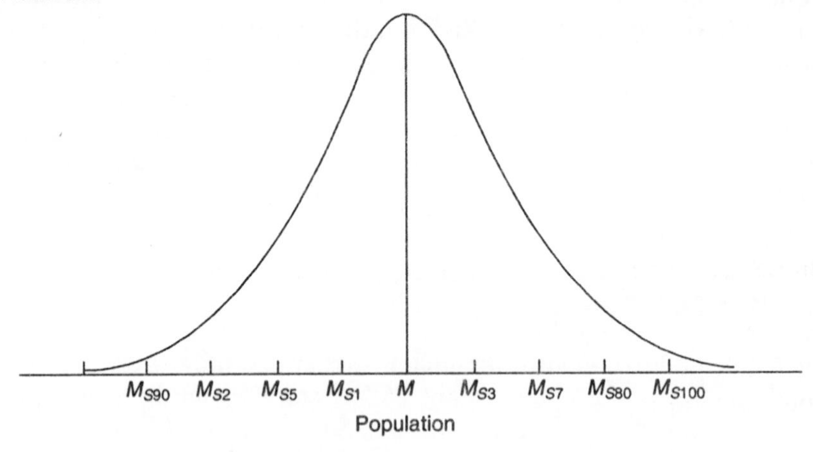

Figure 9.1 Normal distribution of the means of the samples.

The measure of dispersion or deviation of these sample mean scores, may also be calculated in the form of standard deviation. In an ideal case, a sample mean must represent the population mean (or true mean) but on application, a sample mean is likely to differ from its parameter or true value. This difference is known as the possible error that may occur in estimating the true mean from a given sample mean. The curve representing the distribution of sample means possessing lesser or greater error of estimation for the population mean is called the curve of the error and the standard deviation of this distribution of sample means is known as the standard error of the mean.

In a large sample, the standard error of the mean may be computed with the help of the following formula:

$$\text{Standard Error of the Mean, } SE_M \text{ or } \sigma_M = \frac{\sigma}{\sqrt{N}}$$

where N stands for total No. of cases in the sample and σ for standard deviation of the distribution of the sample means.

In the true sense, σ must represent the standard deviation of the population. But as we seldom know this value, the SD of the given sample, the significance of whose mean we have to estimate, may be used in this formula.

Confidence Intervals

As said earlier, a sample mean is employed to estimate the population mean. In the actual sense, it is very difficult to say categorically that a sample mean is, or is not, a trustworthy estimate of the population mean. All the sample means drawn from the same population deviate in one way or the other from the population mean and the distribution of these sample means (in the case of large samples, $N > 30$) is a normal distribution. The standard error of the mean (SE_M or σ_M) represents a measure by which the sample means deviate from the overall population mean. Now the question arises as by how much should a sample mean deviate from the population mean so that it may be taken as a trustworthy estimate of the population mean. The answer lies in the limits of confidence intervals fixed on the basis of degree of confidence or trustworthiness required in a particular situation.

Usually, we make use of 0.95 (or 0.05) and 0.99 (or 0.01) percentage of probability as the two known degrees of confidence for specifying the interval within which we may assert the existence of the population mean.

In the case of normal distribution we know from the table of normal curve that 95% cases lie within the limits $M \pm 1.96\sigma$ and 99 percent cases lie within the limits $M \pm 2.58\sigma$ (this fact has already been emphasized in Chapter 8 (vide Figure 8.9). Hence, from the normal distribution of the sample means, it may be safely concluded that there are 95 chances out of 100 for a sample mean to deviate from the population mean by $\pm 1.96\sigma_M$ (± 1.96 times the standard error of the mean) and only 5 chances out of 100 that the population mean will lie beyond the limits $M \pm 1.96\sigma_M$. Similarly, it may be generalized that there are 99 chances out of 100 for a sample mean to deviate from the population mean by $\pm 2.58\sigma_M$ and only 1 chance out of 100 that the population mean will lie beyond the limits $M \pm 2.58\sigma_M$.

The values in terms of scores of the limits $M \pm 1.96\sigma_M$ and $M \pm 2.58\sigma_M$ are called confidence limits and the interval they contain is called the confidence interval for a known and a fixed degree or a level of confidence.

In this text, we will be using the term 5% and 1% level of confidence in defining the limits ($M \pm 1.96\sigma_M$ and $M \pm 2.58\sigma_M$) beyond which the population mean may be estimated to lie. At 5% level of confidence, we will say that our population mean may lie within the range of $M \pm 1.96\sigma_M$ and at 1% level of confidence, we will say that the population mean may lie within the range of $M \pm 2.58\sigma_M$.

The concept of confidence intervals does not help in locating the population mean exactly, however, it does give some idea about where the population mean is likely to be. This information is quite useful and less expensive for an appropriate estimation of the population mean on the basis of practically available and easily computed sample means.

Computation of Significance of Mean in Case of Large Samples

Example 9.1: In a psychological test, a sample of 500 pre-University students of Rohtak city is found to possess the mean score of 95.00 and SD of 25. Test the significance of this mean. In other words how far can this mean be trusted to estimate the mean of the entire population of the pre-University students studying in the colleges of Rohtak.

Solution. We have seen that means of large samples randomly drawn from the same population produce a normal distribution. In the present case a sample of 500 students is quite a large sample. Therefore, the standard error of the mean may be computed by the formula

$$SE_M \text{ or } \sigma_M = \frac{\sigma}{\sqrt{N}} = \frac{25}{\sqrt{500}} = \frac{25}{\sqrt{5\times 10\times 10}} = \frac{25}{10\sqrt{5}} = 1.12$$

Significance of the given mean at 5% and 1% levels of confidence may be given through the following confidence limits.

At 5% level of confidence

$$\begin{aligned} M \pm 1.96\sigma_M &= 95 \pm 1.96 \times 1.12 \\ &= 95 \pm 2.2 \\ &= 92.8 \text{ to } 97.2 \end{aligned}$$

It means that there are only 5 chances out of 100 that the population mean or true mean will lie beyond the limit 92.8–97.2.

At 1% level of confidence

$$\begin{aligned} M \pm 2.58\sigma_M &= 95 \pm 2.58 \times 1.12 \\ &= 95 \pm 2.89 \\ &= 92.11 \text{ to } 97.89 \end{aligned}$$

It means that there is only 1 chance out of 100 that the true mean will lie beyond the limit 92.11–97.89.

Significance of Mean for Small Samples

Concept of *t* distribution. We usually (however, quite arbitrarily) take a sample of 30 cases or more as a large sample and a sample of less than 30 as small. We have seen that the means of large samples randomly drawn from the same population produce a normal distribution (Figure 9.1). However, when samples are less than 30 in size, the distribution does not take the shape of a normal curve. It is symmetrical but leptokurtic. In other words, it becomes more peaked in the middle and has relatively more area in its tails. Such a distribution is known as the *t* distribution. It was developed originally in 1908 by W.S. Gosset, who wrote under the pen name "Student". *t* distribution is sometimes called "Student" distribution in honour of its discoverer.

It should be clearly understood that *t* distribution is not a single curve (as in the case of a perfect normal curve) but a whole family of curves, the shape of each being a function of sample size. As the size of the sample increases and includes about 30 cases, the *t* distribution takes the shape of a normal curve.

The nature of the *t* distribution is also linked to the number of degrees of freedom. A different *t* distribution exists for each number of degrees of freedom. As the number of degrees of freedom increases, the *t* distribution takes the shape of a normal curve. This fact may be well illustrated through Table C of the *t* distribution given in the Appendix. In this table, we find the values of *t* in relation to the given degrees of freedom and level of confidence. We observe that, as the number of degrees of freedom increases and approaches infinity, *t* approaches the values 1.96 and 2.58, respectively, at 5% and 1% levels of confidence (it is seen that these are the values of sigma scores at the 5% and 1% levels of confidence in the case of a normal distribution).

Concept of degrees of freedom. The number of independent variables is usually called the number of degrees of freedom. This term has been borrowed from Coordinate Geometry and Mechanics where the position of a point or a body is specified by a number of independent variables, i.e. the coordinates. Each coordinate corresponds to one degree of freedom of movement. Constraints on the body reduces the number of degrees of freedom.

The concept of degrees of freedom is widely used in dealing with small sample statistics. The symbol *df* is frequently used to represent the degrees of freedom. The 'freedom' in the term degrees of freedom signifies 'freedom to vary'. Therefore, the degrees of freedom associated with a given sample are determined by the number of observations (the number of values of the variables) that are free to vary. The degrees of freedom are reduced through the constraints or restrictions imposed upon the observations or variables. As a general rule one degree of freedom is lost for each constraint or restriction imposed. The number of degrees of freedom in any case, is given by the formula

No. of degrees of freedom = No. of observations or variables – No. of constraints or restrictions

Let us illustrate it with the help of some examples.

If we have five scores as 12, 10, 7, 6 and 5, the mean is 8 and the deviations of these scores from their mean are 4, 2, –1, –2, and –3 respectively. The sum of these deviations is zero. In consequence, if any four deviations are known, the remaining deviation may be automatically determined. In this way, out of the five deviations, only four (i.e. $N - 1$) are free to vary as the condition that "the sum equal to zero" suddenly imposes restriction upon the independence of the 5th deviant. Thus, we may observe that in a sample for the given set of observations or scores (N), one degree of freedom is lost when we employ the mean of the scores for computing the variance of standard deviation (by calculating deviation of the scores from the mean). Originally there were 5 ($N = 5$) degrees of freedom in computing the mean because all the observations or scores were quite independent. But as we made use of the mean for computing variance and standard deviation, we lost one degree of freedom.

Let us now take the case of the sampling distribution of means and decide about the degrees of freedom. For the purpose of illustration, let us assume that there are only three samples in our sampling distribution of means. The means of these samples are M_1, M_2 and M_3. The mean of these means, say M, will be our population mean. We know that the sum of the deviations around the mean of any distribution is zero. Therefore, in this case $(M - M_1) + (M - M_2) + (M - M_3)$ will be equal to zero. We see that up to the point of computation of M, we had M_1, M_2 and M_3 as independent observations, but after computing M, we lose one degree of freedom as the value of M_1, M_2 and M_3 is automatically fixed in the light of the value of M. In this way, we may find that when we employ the sample mean as an estimate of the parameter (population mean), one degree of freedom is lost and we are left with $N - 1$ degrees of freedom for estimating the population variance and standard deviation.

However, the degrees of freedom are not always $N - 1$ in all cases. It varies with the nature of the problem and the restriction imposed. For example, in the case of correlation between two variables where we need to compute deviations from two means, the number of restrictions imposed goes up to two and consequently, the number of degrees of freedom becomes $N - 2$. Similarly (as we would see in Chapters 11 and 12 of this text), in the case of contingency tables of Chi square test and analysis of variance, we may have some other different formulae for the computation of number of degrees of freedom. However, in all cases, we will always have a common feature conveying that the number of observations or values in a given data minus the number of restrictions imposed upon this data, constitute the number of degrees of freedom for that data.

Process of Determining the Significance of Small Sample Means

It may be summarized under the following steps:

Determining the standard error of the mean. In small samples (N less than 30), the standard error of the mean is computed by the formula:

$$SE_M \quad \text{or} \quad s_m = \frac{s}{\sqrt{N}}$$

where N is the size of the sample and s is the standard deviation.

Here the value of s is calculated using the formula

$$s = \sqrt{\frac{\Sigma x^2}{N-1}}$$

(where x = deviation scores from the mean) instead of the formula

$$\sigma = \sqrt{\frac{\Sigma x^2}{N}}$$

used for computing SD in large samples.

Use of *t* distribution in place of normal distribution. As we discussed earlier, the distribution of sample means in the case of small samples takes the shape of a t distribution instead of a normal distribution. Therefore we try to make use of the t distribution.

Determining the degrees of freedom. As we know, the shape of a t distribution depends upon the number of degrees of freedom. The number of degrees of freedom thus have to be determined by using the formula

$$df = N - 1$$

where N stands for the number of cases in the samples.

Using the *t* distribution table. Like the normal curve table, t distribution table is also available. Table C given in the appendix represents such a table. From this table, we can read the value of t for the given degrees of freedom at the specific level of probability (5% or 1%) decided at the beginning of the experiment or collection of data.

Determining the confidence interval. After locating the values of t at the 5% and 1% levels of confidence with known degrees of freedom, we may proceed to determine the range or confidence interval for the population mean, indicated as follows:

1. From the first value of t, say t_1 read from the table, we can say that 95% of the sample means lie between the limits $M \pm t_1 \times$ Standard error of the mean and the remaining 5% fall beyond these limits.
2. From the second value of t, say t_2, read from the table, we can say that 99% of the sample means lie between the limits $M \pm t_2 \times$ Standard error of the mean and that only 1% fall beyond these limits.

Let us illustrate the above process through an example.

Example 9.2: In a particular test there were 16 independent observations of a certain magnitude with a mean of 100 and SD of 24. Find out (at both 0.05 and 0.01 levels of confidence) the limits of the confidence interval for the population (or true) mean.

Solution. The sample consists of 16 observations and hence may be regarded as a small sample. Therefore,

$$SE_M \text{ or } s_m = \frac{s}{\sqrt{N}} = \frac{24}{\sqrt{16}} = \frac{24}{4} = 6$$

Number of degrees of freedom $= N - 1 = 16 - 1 = 15$. From Table C, we read the value of t for 15 degrees of freedom at the points 0.05 and 0.01 (5% and 1% levels of confidence). These values are 2.13 and 2.95. Therefore, the limits of confidence interval at the 0.05 level is

$$M \pm 2.13 \times SE_M = 100 \pm 2.13 \times 6 = 100 \pm 12.78$$

or

from 87.22 to 112.78

The limits of confidence interval at .01 level are

$$M \pm 2.95 \times SE_M = 100 \pm 2.95 \times 6 = 100 \pm 17.70$$

or

from 82.30 to 117.70

SIGNIFICANCE OF SOME OTHER STATISTICS

Like mean, the significance of some other statistics like median, standard deviation, quartile deviation, percentages, correlation coefficient, etc. may also be determined by computing the standard errors of these estimates. For large samples ($N > 30$) the respective formulae are given below:

Standard Error of a Median

$$\sigma_{Md} = \frac{1.253\sigma}{\sqrt{N}} \quad \text{(in terms of } \sigma)$$

$$\sigma_{Md} = \frac{1.858Q}{\sqrt{N}} \quad \text{(in terms of } Q)$$

where σ and Q represent the standard deviation and quartile deviation respectively of the given sample.

Standard Error of a Quartile Deviation

$$SE_Q \text{ or } \sigma_Q = \frac{0.786\sigma}{\sqrt{N}} \quad \text{(in terms of } \sigma)$$

$$\sigma_Q = \frac{1.17Q}{\sqrt{N}} \quad \text{(in terms of } Q)$$

Standard Error of a Standard Deviation

$$SE_\sigma \text{ or } \sigma_\sigma = \frac{\sigma}{\sqrt{2N}}$$

Standard Error of the Coefficient of Correlation

$$SE_r \text{ or } \sigma_r = \frac{1-r^2}{\sqrt{N}}$$

$$\text{SE}_\rho \text{ or } \sigma_\rho = \frac{1.05(1-\rho)^2}{\sqrt{N}}$$

After determining the standard error of the required statistics with the help of these formulae, we determine their significance at 5% or 1% level of confidence by computing the limits of the respective confidence intervals. Let us illustrate it through the following example.

Example 9.3: The performance on an intelligence test of 225 students of grade X is as follows:

$$\text{Median} = 90.8 \text{ and SD} = 3.5$$

Determine the confidence limits at the 0.05 and 0.01 levels for estimation of the population median.

Solution. Standard error of the median

$$\sigma_{\text{Md}} = \frac{1.253\sigma}{\sqrt{N}}$$

Here,

$$\sigma = 3.5, \quad N = 225$$

Substituting the respective values in the formula, we obtain

$$\sigma_{\text{Md}} = \frac{1.253 \times 3.5}{\sqrt{225}} = \frac{4.3855}{15} = 0.292$$

The confidence interval at 5% level of confidence is

$$M_d \pm 1.96\sigma_{\text{Md}} = 90.8 \pm 1.96 \times 0.292 = 90.8 \pm 0.572$$

or

$$\text{from } 85.08 \text{ to } 91.372$$

The confidence interval at 1% level of confidence is

$$M_d \pm 2.58\sigma_{\text{Md}} = 90.8 \pm 2.58 \times 0.292 = 90.8 \pm 0.753$$

or

$$\text{from } 87.27 \text{ to } 91.553$$

Coefficient of Correlation r

Case I: When the sample is large (preferably N = 100 or more) and value of r close to ± .50. In all such cases the significance of r may be tested through the computation of its standard error by the following formula:

Standard error of r,

$$\sigma_r = \frac{1-r^2}{\sqrt{N}}$$

Let us take Example 7.8 as an illustration.

Example 9.4: Here, $r = 0.52$ and $N = 173$. Therefore,

$$\sigma_r = \frac{1-(.52)^2}{\sqrt{173}} = \frac{1-0.2704}{13.15}$$

$$= \frac{0.7296}{13.15} = 0.055$$

By assuming the sampling distribution of r to be normal we have the following confidence intervals at 5% and 1% level for delimiting our population r.

Interval at 5% level of confidence is

$$r \pm 1.96 \times \sigma_r = 0.52 \pm 1.96 \times 0.055 = 0.52 \pm 0.108$$

or

from 0.412 to 0.628

The interval at 1% level of confidence is

$$r \pm 2.58 \times \sigma_r = 0.52 \pm 2.58 \times 0.055 = 0.52 + 0.142$$

or

from 0.378 to 0.662

In this way, we may conclude that the estimated r is at least as large as 0.378 and no larger than 0.662.

Case II: When we have a large sample (N is 30 or greater) and any value of r (whether too high or too low). In all the above cases, we have converted this value into z function for testing the significance of a given value r. (This conversion may be done with the help of Table D given in the Appendix.) After this, using the following formula, we find the standard error of z

$$\sigma_z = \frac{1}{\sqrt{N-3}}$$

Subsequently, confidence interval at the 5% and 1% levels of confidence may be found by using formulae $z \pm 1.96 \times \sigma_z$ and $z \pm 2.58 \times \sigma_z$. These values are again converted into r function with the help of the conversion Table D.

The whole process can be better understood through the following illustration.

Example 9.5: Given $r = 0.78$ and $N = 84$, find the confidence interval at 0.05 and 0.01 levels of confidence for estimating true r.

Solution. The z value for the given r (as read from Table D given in the Appendix) is 1.05.

The standard error of z, i.e.

$$\sigma_z = \frac{1}{\sqrt{N-3}} = \frac{1}{\sqrt{84-3}} = \frac{1}{\sqrt{81}} = \frac{1}{9} = 0.11$$

The confidence interval at the 5% level for the true z is

$$z \pm 1.96 \times \sigma_z = 1.05 \pm 1.96 \times 0.11 = 1.05 \pm 0.2156$$

$$= 1.05 \pm 0.216 \text{ (up to three decimals)}$$

from 0.834 to 1.266, i.e.

or

from 0.83 to 1.27 (rounded to two decimals)

These values of z are again converted into r values with the help of Table D. Thus, the confidence interval at 5% level for the true r = from 0.68 to 0.85.

The confidence interval at 1% level for the true z is

$$z \pm 2.58 \times \sigma_z = 1.05 \pm 2.58 \times 0.11 = 1.05 \pm 0.2838$$

$$= 1.05 \pm 0.28 \text{ (rounded to two decimals)}$$

or

from 0.77 to 1.33

Converting these z values back into r values from Table D. We get confidence interval at the 1% level for the true r, as 0.645 to 0.87.

Case III: When we make use of the null hypothesis to test *r*. This method of testing the significance of r developed by R.A. Fisher by making use of the t distribution and testing the significance of an obtained r against the null t hypothesis, shows that the population r is, in fact, zero.

Fisher in his work demonstrated that when the population r is zero, a parameter t can be estimated by the formula,

$$t = \frac{r\sqrt{N-2}}{\sqrt{1-r^2}}$$

The values of t for different samples are distributed as in a t distribution. However, in actual practice, there is no need to compute the value of (t ratio) from a given r. It can be done with the help of Table E given in the Appendix. From this table, we can read directly, given the degrees of freedom, the values of r that would be significant at 0.05 and 0.01 levels of confidence and then take the appropriate decision about the significance of the given r.

This method may be employed in the case of large as well as small samples with any obtained value of r. The procedure can be understood through the following illustration.

Example 9.6: Given $r = 0.52$ and $N = 72$ test the significance of the given r.

Solution. Let us set up a null hypothesis saying that the population r is in fact zero and see whether it is accepted or rejected in view of the given data.

Here, $N = 72$. Therefore, the number of degrees of freedom will be $N - 2 = 72 - 2 = 70$. We read the values of r at 0.05 and 0.01 levels of confidence from Table E (given in the Appendix) for $df = 70$. These are 0.232 and 0.302 respectively. Therefore, the given value of r, i.e. 0.52 (being much higher than 0.232 or 0.302) is highly significant at both 5% and 1% levels. The hypothesis that population r is in fact, zero, is rejected and we may take the computed value of r as quite trustworthy and significant.

SUMMARY

In studying the characteristics of a certain population, it is neither feasible nor practical to approach each and every element of the population. Therefore, we usually resort to sampling. A sample of the appropriate size is drawn from the population and the desired statistics, mean, median, SD, and the like are calculated. These sample statistics are then used to draw an estimate about the parameters, i.e. the mean, median, SD, correlation coefficient and so on of the whole population. The degree to which a sample statistics represents its parameter is an index of the significance of trustworthiness of the computed sample statistic—mean, median and so on.

Testing the significance or trustworthiness of the computed sample mean and of other statistics requires the computation of standard error of the sample mean and other statistics. Suppose we take a number of samples from the same population and compute means for these samples. The distribution of these sample means in case of large samples, i.e. $N>30$, will be normal and may be shown by a normal curve. Standard deviation of this distribution will be known as the standard error of the mean.

In the case of a large sample, the standard error of mean may be computed by the formula

$$\sigma_M = \frac{\sigma}{\sqrt{N}}$$

of median by the formula

$$\sigma_{\text{Md}} = \frac{1.253\sigma}{\sqrt{N}}$$

of SD by
$$\sigma_\sigma = \frac{\sigma}{\sqrt{2N}}$$

of quartile deviation by
$$\sigma_Q = \frac{0.786\sigma}{\sqrt{N}}$$

and of r by
$$\sigma_r = \frac{1 - r^2}{\sqrt{N}}$$

In all these formulae, N represents the total number of cases in the sample and σ, the SD of the distribution of the given sample.

In the case of small samples ($N<30$), standard error of mean may be computed by the formula

$$SE_M \text{ or } s_m = \frac{s}{\sqrt{N}}$$

where s is the SD of the sample which may be computed by using the formula

$$s = \sqrt{\frac{\Sigma x^2}{N - 1}}$$

where x represents deviation scores from the mean.

After computing the standard error of the mean (or of other statistics), testing of the significance of the mean (or of other statistic) requires the computation of the limits of confidence intervals fixed on the basis of levels of confidence or significance (degree of confidence or trustworthiness required in a particular situation). 0.05 and 0.01 are the two levels of confidence or significance that are usually employed.

The values in terms of the scores of the limits $M \pm 1.96\sigma_M$ and $M \pm 2.58\sigma_M$ are called *confidence limits* and the interval they contain is called *confidence interval* at the 0.05 and 0.01 levels of confidence respectively.

The limits of the confidence intervals given by the values $M \pm 1.96\sigma_M$ and $M \pm 2.58\sigma_M$ tell us how far a sample mean should miss the population mean so that it may be taken as a trustworthy estimate of the population mean. The same thing may also be said about the trustworthiness or significance of other statistics, median, SD, etc. In this way, we can point out the significance of the mean and of other statistics, first by computing SE and then determining the limits of confidence intervals at 0.05 or 0.01 levels of significance.

In the case of small samples, the distribution of sample means takes the shape of a t distribution, and not normal as in the case of large samples. Here we have to read the values of t from a table of t distribution, for given degrees of freedom (computed by the formula $df = N - 1$ in the case of mean, median, SD, etc.) at the specific level of confidence 0.05 or 0.01. To determine the limits of confidence interval, we use the formula $M \pm t \times$ Standard error of the mean.

Testing the significance of coefficient of correlation when the sample is quite large (N = 100 or more) and value of r close to ±0.05 requires the use of the formula

$$\sigma_r = \frac{1 - r^2}{\sqrt{N}}$$

for computing SE of r. If we have a large sample (N = 30 or > 30) and any value of r, too high or too low, use of z function is appropriate. Conversion of r into z or vice versa is made possible through a conversion table, and standard error of z is computed by the formula

$$\sigma_z = \frac{1}{\sqrt{N - 3}}$$

Another suitable method for testing the significance of r is provided by Fisher by making use of the t distribution and testing the significance of an obtained r against the null hypothesis that the population is, in fact, zero.

EXERCISES

1. What do you understand by the terms population and sampling? Define the terms statistics and parameter. How do we use statistics for estimating the parameters?
2. Explain the concept of standard error for determining the significance of the mean and other statistics.
3. What do we mean by the term significance of sample mean? Explain in detail.
4. Explain the concept of confidence interval and confidence limits as used in determining the significance of mean and other statistics.
5. How would you proceed to determine the significance of a given sample mean in a large sample? Illustrate with the help of a hypothetical example.

6. How does the procedure for determining the significance of the mean of a small sample differ from the mean of a large sample? Illustrate with the help of a hypothetical example the process of determining the significance of a small sample mean.

7. Discuss in brief the process of determining the significance of the statistics like median, standard deviation and quartile deviation.

8. Discuss the different methods used to determine the significance of a correlation coefficient between two variables of a given sample.

9. From the following data, compute the standard of mean and establish the confidence intervals for the location of true mean at .05 and .01 levels.

	Sample A	*Sample B*	*Sample C*	*Sample D*	*Sample E*	*Sample F*
Mean	40	45	60	50	30	80
SD	4	6	2	8	3	12
N	125	400	16	900	25	626

10. Are the following values of r significantly different from zero?

    (a) $r = 0.30$ for $N = 25$

    (b) $r = 0.60$ for $N = 15$

11. Given $r = 0.48$ and $N = 25$

    (a) find the standard error of r and determine the limits of confidence intervals at 0.05 and 0.01 levels.

    (b) convert the given r into a z function; σ_z and determine the limits of the confidence intervals at 0.05 and 0.01 levels.

    (c) by using the concept of null hypothesis, find whether the given r is significant at 0.05 or 0.01 levels.

12. On an attitude scale, the performance of a group of 36 student teachers was recorded as below:

    $$M_d = 30.4, \qquad SD = 2.4$$

    How well does this median represent the median of the population from which this sample was drawn?

10

Significance of the Difference between Means

NEED AND IMPORTANCE

In the fields of education and psychology, there are many occasions when we are more interested in knowing about the significance of the difference between two sample means (independent or correlated), drawn from the same or different populations rather than merely knowing the significance of the computed sample means.

Let us illustrate a few such occasions:

1. A teacher wants to test the relative effectiveness of two teaching methods. For this he divides the IX class students into two random groups. One group is taught by him with method A and the other with method B. After a few months, he administers an achievement test to both of these groups and computes the means of the respective achievement scores of the two groups, say M_1 and M_2. The difference between these two means, i.e. $M_1 - M_2$ is then determined. Now the question arises as to how significant this difference should be to help decide whether method A or B is better.
2. A research worker wants to study the effect of anxiety on the computational and reasoning ability in Mathematics. For this purpose, he may test a group of students on some achievement test in Mathematics and derive the mean value of their achievement scores. Then he may induce a state of anxiety, re-administer the achievement test to the same group and compute the mean of the achievement scores. Now to decide whether the anxiety factor has affected the achievement of the group, he has to take a decision about the significance of the difference between two means.
3. A person wants to study the effect of a certain medicine or a yoga exercise in promoting intelligence. For this purpose, he

divides the students of a class in two equal random groups. One group called the experimental group, is treated with medicine or yoga exercises while with the other called the control group, nothing is done. The IQ scores of these two groups may, then, be determined with the help of some group mental ability test. The significance of the difference between the mean scores of experimental and control group will, then, help him decide whether the given medicine or yoga exercises is contributing factor in the promotion of intelligence.

In all the above situations, the problem is the determination of significance of the difference between two computed means. One is bound to question whether the difference, if any, between the two sample means is the result of sample fluctuations which have occurred incidentally or indicates some really valid differences which will help in drawing some useful interpretations.

FUNDAMENTAL CONCEPTS IN DETERMINING THE SIGNIFICANCE OF THE DIFFERENCE BETWEEN MEANS

Concept of Standard Error

In Chapter 9, we have seen that in determining the significance of a sample mean, if we successfully draw random samples from a given population, compute their means, and arrange these means into a frequency distribution, the result is a normal curve (t distribution curve in the case of small sample means). Going further, the standard deviation of the distribution of these sample means called the standard error of the mean was taken as the yardstick for testing the significance of a given sample mean.

Proceeding on the same lines, if we have data related to differences between means of a number of samples, the sampling distribution of these difference between means will also look like a normal curve, in large samples (and t distribution curve in the case of small samples). The standard deviation of this distribution called standard error of the differences between means then, may be taken as the yardstick against which we may safely test the obtained difference between any two sample means.

The standard error of the difference between independent and correlated means in the case of both large and small samples is computed with the help of some particular formulae.

Concept of Null Hypothesis

Null hypothesis is the starting point of solving a problem related to the significance of difference between means. The first task of a research worker of an experimenter is to establish this hypothesis. Such a hypothesis always emphasizes that there exists no real difference between two population means and that the difference found between sample means is therefore, insignificant.

In the course of a study or an experiment, the null hypothesis is stated, so that it can be tested for possible rejection under the assumption that it is true. For example in the case of studying the superiority of one method of teaching over the other, we divide the students of a class into two equal random groups, teach them using different methods, test them with the help of an achievement test and compute the mean and SD of the scores of each of these groups. In this experimental study, the null hypothesis may be stated thus:

There exists no significant difference between the achievements of two groups taught by different methods. If this null hypothesis is rejected, then it is possible to make statements with a certain probability level regarding the superiority of one method over the other. In this way, the central point in the course of an experiment or a study regarding the testing of significance of difference between two sample means is the testing of an established null hypothesis for its possible rejection.

The task of rejection of a null hypothesis rests on some of the following points:

Setting up the Level of Confidence or Significance

The experimenter has to take a decision about the level of confidence or significance at which he is going to test, his hypothesis. At times he may decide to use 0.05 or 5% level of significance for rejecting a null hypothesis (when a hypothesis is rejected at the 5% level it is said that the chances are 95 out of 100, that the hypothesis is not true and only 5 chances out of 100 that it is true). At other times, he may prefer to make it more rigid and therefore, use the 0.01 or 1% level of significance. If a hypothesis is rejected at this level, the chances are 99 out of 100, that the hypothesis is not true and that only 1 chance out of 100 is true. This level on which we reject the null hypothesis, is established before doing the actual experiment (before collecting data). Later we have to adhere to it.

Size of the Sample

The sampling distribution of the differences between means may look like a normal curve or *t* distribution curve depending upon the size of the samples drawn from the population. If the samples are large

(N = 30 or greater than 30), then the distribution of differences between means will be a normal one. If it is small (N is less than 30), then the distribution will take the form of a t distribution and the shape of the t curve will vary with the number of degrees of freedom. In this way, for large samples, statistics advocating normal distribution of the characteristics in the given population will be employed, while for small samples, the small sample statistics will be used.

Hence in the case of large samples possessing a normal distribution of the differences of means, the value of standard error used to determine the significance of the difference between means will be in terms of standard sigma (z) scores. On the other hand, in the case of small samples possessing a t distribution of differences between means, we will make use of t values rather than z scores of the normal curve. Accordingly, in the case of large samples, we make use of the normal curve of Table B (Appendix) to decide the critical value of the z scores of the standard error to reject a null hypothesis at the 0.05 or 0.01 level. From the normal curve table we see that 95% and 99% cases lie at the distance of 1.96σ and 2.58σ. Therefore, the sigma or z scores of 1.96 and 2.58 are taken as critical values for rejecting a null hypothesis.

If a computed z value of the standard error of the differences between means approaches or exceeds the values 1.96 and 2.58, then we may safely reject a null hypothesis at the 0.05 and 0.01 levels.

To test the null hypothesis in the case of small sample means, we first compute the t ratio in the same manner as z scores in case of large samples. Then we enter the table of t distribution (Table C in the Appendix) with $N_1 + N_2 - 2$ degrees of freedom and read the values of t given aganist the row of $N_1 + N_2 - 2$ degrees of freedom and columns headed by 0.05 and 0.01 levels of significance. If our computed t ratio approaches or exceeds the values of t read from the table, we will reject the established null hypothesis at the 0.05 and 0.01 levels of significance, respectively.

Two-Tailed and One-Tailed Tests of Significance

Two-tailed test. In making use of the two-tailed test for determining the significance of the difference between two means, we should know whether or not such a difference between two means really exists and how trustworthy and dependable this difference is. In all such cases, we merely try to find out if there is a significant difference between two sample means; whether the first mean is larger or smaller than the second, is of no concern. We do not care for the direction of such a difference, whether positive or negative. All that we are interested in, is a difference. Consequently, when an experimenter wishes to test the null hypothesis, H_0: $M_1 - M_2 = 0$, against its possible rejection and finds that it is rejected, then he may conclude that a difference really exists between the two means. But he does not make any assertion about the direction of the difference. Such a test is a non-directional test. It is also named as two-tailed test, because it employs both sides, positive and negative, of the distribution (normal or t distribution) in the estimation of probabilities. Let us consider the probability at 5% significance level in a two-tailed test with the help of Figure 10.1.

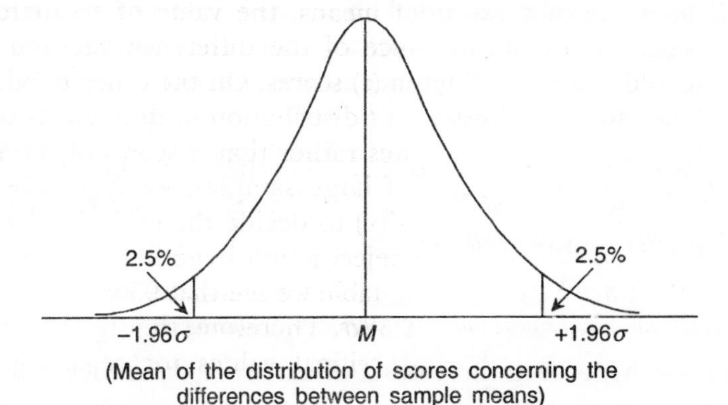

Figure 10.1 Two-tailed test at the 5% level.

Therefore, while using both the tails of the distribution we may say that 2.5% of the area of the normal curve falls to the right of 1.96 standard deviation units above the mean and 2.5% falls to the left of 1.96 standard deviation units below the mean. The area outside these limits is 5% of the total area under the curve. In this way, for testing the significance at the 5% level, we may reject a null hypothesis if the computed error of the difference between means reaches or exceeds the yardstick 1.96. Similarly, we may find that a value of 2.58 is required to test the significance at the 1% level in the case of a two-tailed test.

One-tailed test. As we have seen, a two-tailed or a non-directional test is appropriate, if we are only concerned with the absolute magnitude of the difference, that is, with the difference regardless of sign.

However, in many experiments, our primary concern may be with the direction of the difference rather than with its existence in absolute terms. For example, if we plan an experiment to study the effect of coaching work on computational skill in mathematics, we take two groups—the experimental group, which is provided an extra one hour coaching work in mathematics, and the control group, which is not provided with such a drill. Here, we have reason to believe that the experimental group will score higher on the mathematical computation ability test which is given at the end of the session. In our experiment we are interested in finding out the gain in the acquisition of mathematical computation skill (we are not interested in the loss, as it seldom happens that coaching will decrease the level of computation skill).

In cases like these, we make use of the one-tailed or directional test, rather than the two-tailed or non-directional test to test the significance of difference between means. Consequently, the meaning of null hypothesis, restricted to an hypothesis of on difference with two-tailed test, will be somewhat extended in a one-tailed test to include the direction—positive or negative—of the difference between means.

Let us illustrate the difference in the situations where we use the two-tailed or one-tailed tests:

Null hypothesis. There is no difference between the mean IQ's of athletes and non-athletes. In this situation, we use a two-tailed test.

If we change the *Null Hypothesis* as

Athletes do not have higher IQ's than non-athletes. or
Athletes do not have lower IQ's than non-athletes.

Each of these hypothesis indicates a direction of difference rather than the mere existence of difference, and hence, we have to use a one-tailed test. In other words, in a one-tailed test we have to set up the hypothesis that M_1 is greater than M_2 or M_1 is less than M_2 ($M_1 > M_2$ or $M_1 < M_2$) instead of $M_1 = M_2$ as in the case of a two-tailed test. In such a situation, we are concerned only with one tail (left or right) of the distribution (normal or t distribution) as shown in Figure 10.2.

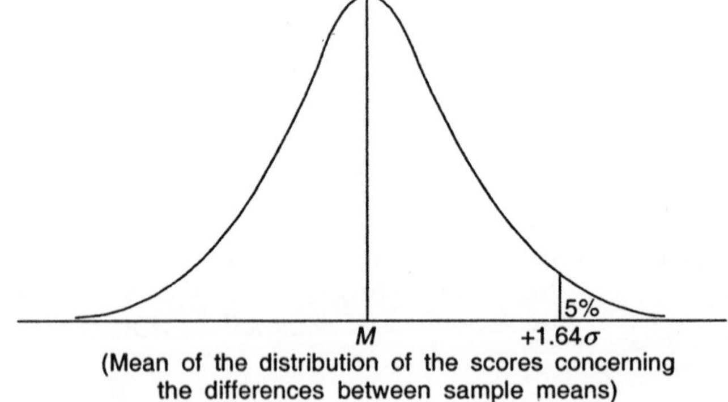

Figure 10.2 One-tailed test at the 5% level.

Thus at the 5% level of significance we will have 5% of the area, all in one tail (at the 1.64 standard deviation unit above the mean rather than having it equally divided into two tails as shown in Figure 10.1, for a two-tailed test. Consequently, in a one-tailed test for testing the difference between large sample means, z score of 1.64 will be taken as a yardstick at the 5% level of significance for the rejection of the null hypothesis instead of 1.96 in the case of a two-tailed test. Similarly, a z score of 2.33 will be taken as a yardstick to test the significance of the difference between means of large samples at 1% level of significance.

In the case of a t distribution of small sample means, in making use of the one-tailed test we have to look for the critical t values, written in Table C of the Appendix, against the row $(N_1 + N_2 - 2)$ degrees of freedom under the columns labelled 0.10 and 0.02 (instead of 0.05 and 0.01 as in the case of two-tailed test) to test the significance at 0.05 and 0.01% levels of significance, respectively.

HOW TO DETERMINE THE SIGNIFICANCE OF DIFFERENCE BETWEEN TWO MEANS

The process of determining the significance of difference between two given sample means varies with respect to the largeness or smallness of the samples as well as the relatedness or unrelatedness (independence) of the samples. Consequently, we should deal with the following types of situations for discussing the process of determining the significance of difference between two means. (Here, by a large sample we mean the samples having 30 or more cases and by a small sample, the sample consisting less than 30 cases. We call the samples independent when they are drawn at random from the totally different and unrelated groups or when we administer non-correlated tests on the same sample to collect relevant data.)

Case I: Large but independent samples.

Case II: Small but independent samples.

Case III: Large but correlated samples.

Case IV: Small but correlated samples.

In all these cases, the experimenter has to set up a null hypothesis and take a decision about the level of significance at which he wishes to test his null hypothesis. Then, he has to determine the SE of the difference between the two means and compute the z score or t ratio, take a decision about the significance of these standard scores at a given level of significance and finally reject or retain the null hypothesis.

The procedure listed so far, however is followed with somewhat different formulae and steps in each of the four cases as may be evident from the following.

Case I: Significance of difference between two means for large but independent samples

Step 1. To determine the SE of the difference between the means of two samples. The formula for determining standard error of the difference between means of two large but independent (non-correlated) samples is:

$$SE_D \text{ or } \sigma_D = \sqrt{\sigma_{M_1}^2 + \sigma_{M_2}^2}$$

where

σ_{M_1} = SE of the means of the first sample

σ_{M_2} = SE of the means of the second sample

As we already know, σ_{M_1} and σ_{M_2} may be calculated by the formula

$$\sigma_{M_1} = \frac{\sigma_1}{\sqrt{N_1}}$$

where σ_1 is the SD of the first sample and N_1 is the size of the first sample.

$$\sigma_{M_2} = \frac{\sigma_2}{\sqrt{N_2}}$$

where σ_2 is the SD of the second sample and N_2 is the size of the second sample. In this way, the formula becomes

$$\sigma_D = \sqrt{\frac{\sigma_1^2}{N_1} + \frac{\sigma_2^2}{N_2}}$$

Step 2. To compute the z value for the difference in sample means. The sampling distribution of difference between means in the case of large samples is a normal distribution. This difference represented on the base line of the normal curve may be converted into standard sigma scores (*z* values) with the help of the following formula:

$$z = \frac{M_1 - M_2}{\sigma_D} = \frac{\text{Difference between means}}{\text{Standard error of difference between means}}$$

In this way, *z* represents the ratio of difference between the means to the standard error of the difference between the means.

Step 3. Testing the null hypothesis at some pre-established level of significance. At this stage, the null hypothesis, i.e. there exists no real difference between the two sample means, is tested against its possible rejection at 5% or 1% level of significance in the following manner.

1. If the computed *z* value [i.e. $z = (M_1 - M_2)/\sigma_D$] is equal to 19.6 or greater than 1.96 (equal to or greater than 1.65 in the case of a one-tailed test), we declare it significant for the rejection of the null hypothesis at 5% level of significance.

2. In case the computed z value is equal to 2.58 or greater than 2.58 (equal to or greater than 2.33 in a one-tailed test), we declare it significant for the rejection of null hypothesis at 1% level of significance.
3. If the computed z value is greater than 1.96 but less than 2.58 (greater than 1.65 and less than 2.33 in the case of a one-tailed test) we say that the null hypothesis is rejected at 5% level of significance but not rejected at 1% level of significance.

The rejection of a null hypothesis then, helps in concluding that the difference found between the two sample means is real and trustworthy and not merely on account of some chance factors or due to sampling fluctuations.

Let us illustrate the entire process through some examples.

Example 10.1: (Two-tailed test). A science teacher wanted to know the relative effectiveness of lecture-cum-demonstration method over the traditional lecture method. He divided his class into equal random groups A and B and taught group A by the lecture-cum-demonstration method and group B by the lecture method. After teaching for three months, he administered an achievement test to both groups. The data collected were as under:

	Group A	*Group B*
Mean	43	30
SD	8	7
No. of students	65	65

From this data, what do you conclude about the effectiveness or supremacy of one method of teaching over the other?

Solution. Here, the teacher has first, to establish a null hypothesis, i.e. there exists no real difference between the means of two samples. This hypothesis, then, will be tested in the following way. The difference between means,

$$M_1 - M_2 = 43 - 30 = 13$$

The standard error of the difference between means,

$$SE_D \text{ or } \sigma_D = \sqrt{\sigma_{M_1}^2 + \sigma_{M_2}^2} = \sqrt{\frac{\sigma_1^2}{N_1} + \frac{\sigma_2^2}{N_2}} = \sqrt{\frac{8 \times 8}{65} + \frac{7 \times 7}{65}}$$

$$= \sqrt{\frac{64 + 49}{65}} = \sqrt{\frac{113}{65}} = 1.32$$

Converting the obtained difference between means into standard sigma (z) scores:

$$z = \frac{M_1 - M_2}{\sigma_D} = \frac{13}{1.32} = 9.85$$

Our computed z value is much greater than 1.96 as well as 2.58, the critical values required to reach 5% and 1% levels of significance, respectively. Thus, we may safely conclude that the difference between the means of two samples cannot be attributed to a chance factor. This difference is quite trustworthy and dependable to say that the lecture-cum-demonstration method is more effective as a method of teaching than the traditional-lecture method.

Example 10.2: (One-tailed test). A mathematics teacher divides his class into two random groups. He provides special coaching in computation skill for an hour daily to the experimental group hoping that such a drill will promote the computation skill of the students of this group. The control group is not provided any such drill. At the end of the session, he administers an achievement test and collects data as under.

	Experimental group	*Control group*
Mean	35	30
SD	4	3
N	48	45

Is the gain (difference between means) significant enough to indicate that a drill in mathematics promotes computation skill?

Solution. In this test, the teacher is interested to know the significance of difference between means in terms of a particular direction, i.e. gain from the special coaching. Therefore, to determine the significance of difference between means, a one-tailed test (in place of the two-tailed test) will be used.

In this case, the process of testing the null hypothesis will be the same as in the case of two-tailed test, illustrated in example 10.1, except that the critical value of z will be taken as 1.65 and 2.33 (in place of 1.98 and 2.68) at the 5% and 1% levels of significance, respectively. The computation work will be as follows:

Difference between means $= M_1 - M_2 = 35 - 30 = 5$

Standard error of the difference between means:

$$\sigma_D = \sqrt{\frac{\sigma_1^2}{N_1} + \frac{\sigma_2^2}{N_2}} = \sqrt{\frac{4 \times 4}{48} + \frac{3 \times 3}{45}} = \sqrt{\frac{16}{48} + \frac{9}{45}}$$

$$= \sqrt{\frac{8}{15}} = \sqrt{0.5333} = 0.73$$

Converting the difference between means into standard sigma scores (z), we get the corresponding z values.

$$z = \frac{M_1 - M_2}{\sigma_D} = \frac{5}{0.73} = 6.85$$

We may say that our computed value of z exceeds the critical value of 1.65 and 2.33. Therefore, it may be taken as significant at both 5% and 1% levels. Hence the null hypothesis is rejected at the 5% and 1% levels and we may say that (99 times out of 100) the gain is significant and drill work may be taken as a significant factor for the promotion of computation skill.

Case II: Significance of the difference between two means for small but independent samples

Step 1. Computation of the standard error of the difference between two means. In the case of large sample means, we used the formula

$$\sigma_D = \sqrt{\frac{\sigma_1^2}{N_1} + \frac{\sigma_2^2}{N_2}}$$

for the computation of the standard error of difference means. We made use of two separate standard deviations σ_1 and σ_2 from each of the samples. But in the case of small samples, we may make use of a single standard deviation σ called pooled SD for the computation of the standard error of difference as shown in the following formula:

$$SE_D \text{ or } \sigma_D = \sigma\sqrt{\frac{1}{N_1} + \frac{1}{N_2}} \qquad \text{(i)}$$

where σ = pooled SD of the samples. Let us see how this pooled SD (σ) can be computed from the data of two sample means.

For testing the significance of the mean in the case of small samples, we have seen in Chapter 9 that SD of sample is computed by the formula $\sqrt{\Sigma x^2/(N-1)}$ instead of the usual formula $\sqrt{\Sigma x^2/N}$. If we have two small samples, then their SD's will be expressed as follows:

$$\sigma_1 = \sqrt{\frac{\Sigma x_1^2}{N_1 - 1}}, \qquad \sigma_2 = \sqrt{\frac{\Sigma x_2^2}{N_2 - 1}} \qquad \text{(ii)}$$

It has also been established that when two samples are small, we can get a better estimate of the true SD (σ in the population) by pooling the sum of squares of deviations taken around the means of the two groups and compute a rough or pooled SD by using the following formula:

$$\text{Pooled SD or } \sigma = \sqrt{\left[\frac{\Sigma x_1^2 + \Sigma x_2^2}{(N_1 - 1) + (N_2 - 1)}\right]} \qquad \text{(iii)}$$

where

$x_1 = X_1 - M_1$ (deviation of scores of first samples from its mean).

$x_2 = X_2 - M_2$ (deviation of scores of second sample from its mean).

When we are given the values of σ_1 and σ_2 instead of raw scores or the mid-points of the intervals X_1, and X_2, then we have to compute the values of Σx_1^2 and Σx_2^2 with the help of the following formula (derived from formula (ii) given above):

$$\Sigma x_1^2 = \sigma_1^2 (N_1 - 1)$$

$$\Sigma x_2^2 = \sigma_2^2 (N_2 - 1)$$

Hence, for the computation of the standard error of difference between the means of two small samples, we must first, try to compute a value of the pooled SD (σ) by formula (iii) and then compute σ_D with the help of formula (i), i.e.

$$\sigma_D = \sqrt{\frac{1}{N_1} + \frac{1}{N_2}}$$

Step 2. To compute the t value for the difference in sample means. The sampling distribution of the difference between means in small samples is t distribution. Therefore, here we make use of t values instead of z values to convert the difference between means into a standard score. The formula used to determine the standard t values is:

$$t = \frac{M_1 - M_2}{\sigma_D} = \frac{\text{Difference between means}}{\text{Standard error of difference between means}}$$

Step 3. Testing the null hypothesis at some pre-established level of significance. Here, we proceed as follows:

1. Number of degrees of freedom is calculated by using the formula

$$df = N_1 + N_2 - 2$$

2. We then refer to Table C of t distribution (Appendix) with the calculated degrees of freedom, df, and read the t values given under columns 0.05 and 0.01 (0.10 and 0.02 for one-tailed test) for the critical t values used to test the null hypothesis at 5% and 1% levels of significance.
3. If our t value (computed in Step 2) is equal to or greater than the critical t value read from table C for 5% and 1% levels of significance, then we take the computed value of t as significant and consequently reject the null hypothesis at 5% or 1% levels of significance.

Let us illustrate the whole process now with the help of a few examples.

Example 10.3: Two groups of 10 students each got the following scores on an attitude scales:

Group I : 10, 9, 8, 7, 7, 8, 6, 5, 6, 4
Group II : 9, 8, 6, 7, 8, 8, 11, 12, 6, 5

Compute the means for both groups and test the significance of the difference between these two means.

Solution

First sample				*Second sample*			
X_1	M_1	x_1	x_1^2	X_2	M_2	x_2	x_2^2
10	7	3	9	7	8	1	1
9	7	2	4	8	8	0	0
8	7	1	1	6	8	–2	4
7	7	0	0	7	8	–1	1
7	7	0	0	8	8	0	0
8	7	1	1	8	8	0	0
6	7	–1	1	11	8	3	9
5	7	–2	4	12	8	4	16
6	7	–1	1	6	8	–2	4
4	7	–3	9	5	8	–3	9
Total 70		$\Sigma x_1^2 = 30$		Total 80		$\Sigma x_2^2 = 44$	
$M_1 = 70/10 = 7$				$M_2 = 80/10 = 8$			

$$\text{Pooled SD or } \sigma = \sqrt{\frac{\Sigma x_1^2 + \Sigma x_2^2}{(N_1 - 1) + (N_2 - 1)}} = \sqrt{\frac{30 + 44}{9 + 9}}$$

$$= \sqrt{\frac{74}{18}} = \sqrt{4.1111} = 2.03$$

$$\text{SE}_D \text{ or } \sigma_D = \sigma\sqrt{\frac{1}{N_1} + \frac{1}{N_2}} = 2.03\sqrt{\frac{1}{10} + \frac{1}{10}} = 2.03\sqrt{\frac{1}{5}}$$

$$= \frac{2.03}{2.2361} = 0.908$$

$$t = \frac{M_1 - M_2}{\sigma_D} = \frac{7 - 8}{0.908} = \frac{-1}{0.908} = -1.1$$

$$df = N_1 + N_2 - 2 = 10 + 10 - 2 = 18$$

We find from Table C that the critical value of t with 18 degrees of freedom at 5% level of significance is 2.10. Our computed value of t, i.e. 1.1 is quite smaller than the critical table value 2.10 and hence is not significant. Therefore, the null hypothesis cannot be rejected and as a result, the given difference in sample means being insignificant, can only be attributed to some chance factors or sampling fluctuations.

Example 10.4: It is generally known that the habit of reading newspapers and magazines is helpful in bringing about an increase in language vocabulary. A language teacher divides his class into two groups—experimental and control. Under the assumption that newspaper reading will increase the vocabulary, the experimental group was given two hours daily to read English newspapers and magazines, while no such facility was provided to the control group. After six months, both the groups were given a vocabulary test. The scores obtained are detailed below.

Experimental group	115, 112, 109, 112, 137
Control group	110, 112, 95, 105, 111, 97, 112, 102

Interpet the data and say whether the gain in vocabulary is significant.

Solution.

Experimental group				*Control group*			
X_1	M_1	x_1	x_1^2	X_2	M_2	x_2	x_2^2
115	113	2	4	110	105.5	4.5	20.25
112	113	–1	1	112	105.5	6.5	42.25
109	113	–4	16	95	105.5	–10.5	110.25
112	113	–1	1	105	105.5	–0.5	.25
117	113	4	16	111	105.5	5.5	30.25
				97	105.5	–8.5	72.25
				112	105.5	6.5	42.25
				102	105.5	–3.5	12.25
Total 565			$\Sigma x_1^2 = 38$	Total 844			$\Sigma x_2^2 = 330$

$N_1 = 5$ $\quad$ $N_2 = 8$

$M_1 = \dfrac{565}{5} = 113$ $\quad$ $M_2 = \dfrac{844}{8} = 105.5$

$$\text{Pooled SD or } \sigma = \sqrt{\frac{\Sigma x_1^2 + \Sigma x_2^2}{(N_1 - 1) + (N_2 - 1)}}$$

$$= \sqrt{\frac{38 + 330}{(5-1) + (8-1)}}$$

$$= \sqrt{\frac{368}{4+7}} = \sqrt{\frac{368}{11}} = 5.79$$

$$\text{SE}_D \text{ or } \sigma_D = \sigma\sqrt{\frac{1}{N_1} + \frac{1}{N_2}} = 5.79\sqrt{\frac{1}{5} + \frac{1}{8}}$$

$$= 5.79\sqrt{0.200 + 0.125} = 5.79 \times 0.57$$

$$= 3.30$$

$$t = \frac{M_1 - M_2}{\sigma_D} = \frac{113 - 105.5}{3.30} = 2.27$$

Here, the teacher has to use a one-tailed test because he has every reason to believe that his treatment (the practice of reading newspapers and magazines daily) will produce an effect in the positive direction only (it will increase the vocabulary). Therefore, we will refer the t table with $N_1 + N_2 - 2$, i.e. 11 degrees of freedom and locate the

t value under the column .10 for determining the critical value of t at the 0.05 level. Consequently at 5% level of significance the critical value of t = 1.80. Our computed value of t, i.e. 2.28, crosses 1.80. Hence it is to be taken as significant at the 5% level. As as result, with 5% level of confidence, we can reject the null hypothesis and say the reading drill through newspapers and magazines increases the vocabulary.

Cases III and IV: Significance of the difference between two means for correlated samples—large and small. The procedure followed for testing the significance of the difference between two means for correlated samples (when the data in one sample are correlated with the data in the other) is almost the same except for the difference in the process of computation of the standard error. Here, we make use of some particular formulae depending upon the design of experiment that an experimenter selects for his study. These designs, along with the respective formulae for the computation of standard error are summarized in the following sections.

The single group method. It consists of repetition of a test to a group. In actual process, a test of any type is administered to a group of subjects. It is called the initial test. Then the desired experimental treatment is given, followed by the re-administration of the same test to the same individuals of the group. The initial and final tests data thus constitute a correlated data because the same individuals are responding to the items both times, i.e. before and after the treatment.

In order to determine the significance of the difference between the means obtained from the initial and the final testing, we use the formula:

$$SE_D \text{ or } \sigma_D = \sqrt{\sigma^2_{M_1} + \sigma^2_{M_2} - 2r\sigma_{M_1}\sigma_{M_2}}$$

where

σ_{M_1} = Standard error of the initial test

σ_{M_2} = Standard error of the final test

r = Coefficient of correlation between scores on initial and final testing

Equivalent groups method. In experiments, when we have to compare the relative effect of one method or treatment over the other, we often make use of two groups (experimental and control). Then we give the desired treatment separately to the individuals of these groups and compute the pre-treatment and post-treatment scores by administering a test or a measure. Hence in such experimental design, instead of a single group, two separate groups are taken for the experimental study. For the desired results, these two groups need to be made equivalent. Let us explain this with the help of an example.

Suppose that a teacher wants to conduct a study in which the demonstration method is to be compared with the lecture method. For this purpose, he decides to divide the students of the class in two groups A and B, consisting of equal number of students. He plans to teach group A by demonstration method and group B by lecture method. While planning, he may quickly visualize that if the students in one group are more intelligent or have a better background of the subject than the other, the results of the research study will be distorted. In this case, it will be very difficult to distinguish whether the higher means of the scores of a group are the results of the teaching through an effective method or are due to the initial difference with respect to ability or intelligence. Such initial differences need to be overcome before administering the actual treatment to the groups. This can be done in the following ways.

Matching pair technique. In this technique, matching is done initially by pairs so that each individual in the first group has his equivalent or match in the second group in terms of some variables who are going to affect the results of the study like age, socio-economic status, intelligence, interest, aptitude, previous knowledge of the subject and so on.

Matching group technique. Here, instead of one to one correspondence or matching carried out in pairs on an individual level, the group as a whole is matched with the other group in terms of mean and standard deviation of some other variable/variables than the one under study.

Let us now consider the computation of standard error in both the cases (matching pair and matching group) of equivalent group samples.

In the case of a matching pair, the formula for calculating standard error of the difference between means is the same as used in the single group method, i.e.

$$\mathrm{SE}_D = \sigma_D = \sqrt{\sigma_{M_1}^2 + \sigma_{M_2}^2 - 2r\sigma_{M_1}\sigma_{M_2}}$$

In the group matched for mean and SD, this formula takes the following shape:

$$\mathrm{SE}_D = \sigma_D = \sqrt{\left(\sigma_{M_1}^2 + \sigma_{M_2}^2\right)\left(1 - r^2\right)}$$

where σ_{M_1} and σ_{M_2} are the standard errors of the means of the scores of X variable under study for the two groups which are matched or equated to mean and SD in terms of some other variable, Y. Here, r is the measure of coefficient of correlation between X and Y.

Let us illustrate the procedure of testing the significance of the difference between means of the correlated samples through some examples.

Example 10.5: A teacher of mathematics gave a test in multiplication to the 30 students of his class. Then he induced a state of anxiety among them and the achievement test was re-administered. The data obtained were as follows:

Initial test data		*Final test data*	
Mean	70	*Mean*	67
SD	6	*SD*	5.8

r between the initial and final test scores = 0.82. Find out the following on the basis of given data:

1. Is there a significant difference between the two sets of scores?
2. Test the hypothesis that the population mean on the final test is significantly lower than the population mean on the initial test.
3. Did the introduction of the state of anxiety affect the multiplication ability of the students adversely?

Solution. Here in the case of the correlated data of the two samples we may use the following formula for the computation of the standard error of the difference between means

$$SE_D = \sigma_D = \sqrt{\sigma_{M_1}^2 + \sigma_{M_2}^2 - 2r\sigma_{M_1}\sigma_{M_2}}$$

where

$$\sigma_{M_1} = \text{SE of the mean of the initial test}$$

$$= \frac{\sigma_1}{\sqrt{N_1}} = \frac{6}{\sqrt{30}} = \frac{6}{5.477} = 1.09$$

$$\sigma_{M_2} = \text{SE of the mean of the final test}$$

$$= \frac{\sigma_2}{\sqrt{N_2}} = \frac{5.8}{\sqrt{30}} = \frac{5.8}{5.477} = 1.06$$

$$\sigma_D = \sqrt{(1.09)^2 + (1.06)^2 - 2 \times 0.82 \times 1.09 \times 1.06}$$

$$= \sqrt{1.19 + 1.12 - 1.89} = \sqrt{0.42} = 0.648$$

$$z = \frac{M_1 - M_2}{\sigma_D} = \frac{70 - 67}{0.648} = \frac{3}{0.648} = 4.629$$

The computed value of z exceeds both 1.96 and 2.58, the critical values of z at 5% and 1% levels, respectively. Hence, it is to be taken as significant, resulting in the rejection of the null hypothesis. Consequently, it can be said that there exists a significant difference between the two sets of scores; population mean on the final test is significantly lower than the population mean on the initial test and introduction of the state of anxiety has affected adversely, the multiplication ability of the students.

Example 10.6: In the first trial of a practice period, 25 twelve-year olds have a mean score of 80 and an SD of 8 on a digit symbol learning test. On the tenth trial, the mean is 84 and the SD is 10. The r between scores on the first and 10th trails is 0.40. Our hypothesis is that practice leads to gain.

(a) Is the gain in score significant at the 0.05 level or the 0.01 level?
(b) What gain would be significant at the 0.01 level, other conditions remaining the same?

Solution. The given data in the present problem may be summarized as follows

Trials	*Mean*	*SD*	*N*
First trial	80	8	25
Tenth trial	84	10	25

r between the first and tenth trial = 0.40.

Our hypothesis is that, practice leads to gain. It shows a particular direction and therefore, we have to make use of a one-tailed test for the significance of the difference between correlated means. Then,

$$SE_D \quad \text{or} \quad \sigma_D = \sqrt{\sigma_{M_1}^2 + \sigma_{M_2}^2 - 2r\sigma_{M_1}\sigma_{M_2}}$$

where

$$\sigma_{M_1} = \text{SE of the first trial mean}$$

$$= \frac{\sigma_1}{\sqrt{N_1}} = \frac{8}{5} = 1.6$$

$$\sigma_{M_2} = \text{SE of the tenth trail mean}$$

$$= \frac{\sigma_2}{\sqrt{N_2}} = \frac{10}{5} = 2$$

Here,

$$\sigma_D = \sqrt{(1.6)^2 + (2)^2 - 2 \times .40 \times 1.6 \times 2}$$

$$= \sqrt{2.56 + 4 - 4 \times .64} = \sqrt{6.56 - 2.56}$$

$$= \sqrt{4} = 2$$

$$t \text{ ratio} = \frac{\text{Difference between means}}{\text{SE of the difference between means}} = \frac{D}{\sigma_D}$$

$$= \frac{4}{2} = 2$$

In the case of correlated data,

No. of degrees of freedom = No. of pairs – 1

$= N - 1 = 25 - 1 = 24$

For the one-tailed test, for the critical t values at the 0.05 level, we will read Table C under column $P = 0.10$, and at the 0.01 level, under column $P = 0.02$. Therefore,

Critical t value at 0.05 level = 1.71
Critical t value at 0.01 level = 2.49

1. Our computed t ratio 2.00 crosses the value 1.71. It shows that differences are significant at the 0.05 level, but does not reach 2.50. Hence it is not significant at the 0.01 level.
2. Let us find the gain, significant at the 0.01 level, critical t value read from the table at $P = 0.02$ for one-tailed test is 2.49.

This means for the gain significant at the 0.01 level the t value should be 2.49. Converting this t value into test score, we get $D/\sigma_D = t$, or

Gain in terms of scores = $t \times \sigma_D$ (Here, $\sigma_D = 2$)

Hence,

Gain = $2.49 \times 2 = 4.98$

may be considered significant at the 0.01 level.

Example 10.7: Two groups, each consisting of 20 students of a class were matched in pairs on the basis of IQ's. The use of film strip was the method used to teach the experimental group. The control group was exposed to a conventional "read and discuss" method. The researcher wanted to test the null hypothesis that there was no difference between the mean achievements of the two groups at the 0.05 level. The data obtained are as under:

Experimental group	*Control group*
$N_1 = 20$	$N_2 = 20$
$M_1 = 53.20$	$M_2 = 49.80$
$\sigma_1 = 7.4$	$\sigma_2 = 6.5$

Therefore, $r = 0.60$.

Solution. Here we have correlated data collected on two small samples. The researcher has established a null hypothesis $H_O : M_1 - M_2 = 0$. Therefore, he has to use a two-tailed test for the significance of the difference between means.

$$M_1 - M_2 = 53.20 - 49.80 = 3.40$$

$$\text{SE}_D \text{ or } \sigma_D = \sqrt{\sigma^2_{M_1} + \sigma^2_{M_2} - 2r\sigma_{M_1}\sigma_{M_2}}$$

where

$$\sigma_{M_1} = \frac{\sigma_1}{\sqrt{N_1}} = \frac{7.4}{\sqrt{20}} = \frac{7.4}{4.47} = 1.65$$

$$\sigma_{M_2} = \frac{\sigma_2}{\sqrt{N_2}} = \frac{6.5}{\sqrt{20}} = \frac{6.5}{4.47} = 1.45$$

Therefore,

$$\sigma_D = \sqrt{1.65 \times 1.65 + 1.45 \times 1.45 - 2 \times .60 \times 1.65 \times 1.45}$$

$$= \sqrt{2.72 + 2.10 - 2.87} = \sqrt{1.95} = 1.396$$

$$t \text{ ratio} = \frac{D}{\sigma_D} = \frac{M_1 - M_2}{\sigma_D} = \frac{3.40}{1.396} = 2.43$$

Number of degrees of freedom = No. of pairs − 1

= 20 − 1 = 19

For a two-tailed test, with 19 degrees of freedom we can read the critical t value at the 0.05 level, i.e. 2.09.

Our t value of 2.43 exceeds the critical t value of 2.09. Hence it is right to reject the null hypothesis.

Example 10.8: Two groups of high-school students are matched for M and SD on a group intelligence test. There are 58 subjects in group A and 72 in group B. The records of these two groups upon a battery of learning tests are as follows:

	Group A	Group B
M	48.52	53.61
σ	10.60	15.35
N	58	72

The correlation of the group intelligence test and the learning battery in the entire group from which A and B were drawn is 0.50. Test the significance of the difference between groups A and B at the 0.05 and 0.01 levels.

Solution. Here the groups are large ($N > 30$). These are matched in terms of M and σ. The data is, therefore, correlated. The difference between the two sample means is $53.61 - 48.52 = 5.09$

To determine the SE of the difference between means, the formula to be used is:

$$\sigma_D = \sqrt{\left(\sigma_{M_1}^2 + \sigma_{M_2}^2\right)\left(1 - r^2\right)}$$

where

$$\sigma_{M_1} = \frac{\sigma_1}{\sqrt{N_1}} = \frac{10.60}{\sqrt{58}}$$

$$\sigma_{M_2} = \frac{\sigma_2}{\sqrt{N_2}} = \frac{15.35}{\sqrt{72}}$$

Therefore,

$$\sigma_D = \sqrt{\left[\frac{(10.60)^2}{58} + \frac{(15.35)^2}{72}\right]\left[1 - 0.25\right]}$$

$$= \sqrt{\left[\frac{112.36}{58} + \frac{235.62}{72}\right](.75)}$$

$$= \sqrt{5.21 \times .75} = \sqrt{3.90} = 1.97$$

The samples are large. Thus, the sampling distribution of the difference between means may be taken as normal.
Therefore,

$$z = \frac{\text{Difference between means}}{\text{Standard error of the difference between means}}$$

$$= \frac{5.09}{1.97} = 2.58$$

For the significance at the 5% and 1% levels, the critical z values are 1.96 and 2.58, respectively. Our computed value of z is 2.58; hence it may be taken to be quite significant at the 0.05 level and almost significant at the 0.01 level.

An alternative method for small samples. In the case of small samples ($N > 30$), a method known as the "difference method", has been recommended by Ferguson in place of the one discussed earlier.

In this method, the value of t may be directly computed from the following formula without making use of the value of r between the scores made on the initial and the final testing:

$$t = \frac{\Sigma D^2}{\sqrt{\frac{N\Sigma D^2 - (\Sigma D^2)}{N-1}}}$$

where

D = Difference in score between initial and final testing (in the case of single group) or between pairs of matched subjects (in the case of equivalent groups)

Let us illustrate the use of this method with the help of example.

Example 10.9: Ten subjects were tested on an attitude scale. Then, they were made to read some literature in order to bring a change in their attitudes. The attitude scale was re-administered. The results of the initial and final testing are as under:

Initial	10,	9,	9,	8,	8,	7,	7,	5,	4,	4
Final	11,	7,	8,	9,	6,	6,	8,	4,	3,	4

Test the null hypothesis at the 5% level of significance.

Solution.

Initial	*Final*	D	D^2
10	11	–1	1
9	7	2	4
9	8	1	1
8	9	–1	1
8	6	2	4
7	6	1	1
7	8	–1	1
5	4	1	1
4	3	1	1
4	4	0	0
$N = 10$	$N = 10$	$\Sigma D = 5$	$\Sigma D^2 = 15$

$$t = \frac{\Sigma D}{\sqrt{\frac{N\Sigma D^2 - (\Sigma D^2)}{N-1}}} = \frac{5}{\sqrt{\frac{10\times15-5\times5}{9}}}$$

$$= \frac{5\times 3}{\sqrt{125}} = \frac{3}{\sqrt{5}} = \frac{3}{2.236} = 1.34$$

The No. of degrees of freedom is

$$df = N - 1 = 10 - 1 = 9$$

At the 5% level of significance, the critical value of t with 9 degrees of freedom = 2.26.

Our computed value of t i.e. 1.34, does not reach the critical table t value 2.26. Hence it is to be taken as insignificant and, consequently, the null hypothesis is not be rejected at the 5% level of significance.

Example 10.10: A researcher wanted to test the effect of drug in reducing anxiety. For this purpose he used two groups of individuals, experimental and control, matched in pairs. He made use of an anxiety scale for the assessment of anxiety among the subjects of the group. (The experimental group was given the drug while no such thing was given to the control group.) The results were pooled as under:

Experimental group scores	115, 114, 114, 110, 108, 107, 105, 100, 97, 95
Control group scores	120, 117, 112, 118, 102, 95, 107, 106, 93, 99

Test the null hypothesis at 0.05 level.

Solution.

Experimental group	*Control group*	*D*	D^2
115	120	–5	25
114	117	–3	9
114	112	2	4
110	118	–8	64
108	102	6	36
107	95	12	144
105	107	–2	4
100	106	–6	36
97	93	4	16
95	99	–4	16
$N = 10$	$N = 10$	$\Sigma D = -4$	$\Sigma D^2 = 354$

$$t = \frac{\Sigma D}{\sqrt{\dfrac{N\Sigma D^2 - (\Sigma D^2)}{N-1}}} = \frac{-4}{\sqrt{\dfrac{10 \times 354 - 4 \times 4}{9}}}$$

$$= \frac{-4 \times 3}{\sqrt{3524}} = \frac{-12}{59.4}$$

$$= 0.202$$

At the 5% level, for 10 – 1 = 9 degrees of freedom, our computed value of t does not reach the critical value 2.26, hence it is not significant. Consequently we cannot reject the null hypothesis at 5% level of significance.

SUMMARY

In carrying out various studies and experiments in the fields of education, psychology and sociology, we often need to test the significance of the difference between two sample means (independent or correlated) drawn from same or different populations.

The process of determining the significance of difference between two given sample means varies with respect to the largeness or smallness of the sample as well as the relatedness or unrelatedness (independence) of the samples. A sample having 30 or more cases is usually treated as a large sample while a sample containing less than 30 cases is considered a small sample. The samples are called uncorrelated or independent when they are drawn at random from totally different and unrelated groups or when uncorrelated tests are administered to the same sample. However, on a broader outlook, it may be summarized as follows:

1. Establishment of a null hypothesis.
2. Choosing a suitable level of significance, 5% or 1%.
3. Determining the standard error of the difference between means of two samples.
4. Determining standard score values in terms of z (for large samples) and in terms of t (for small samples).
5. Determining the critical value of z (for large samples) from the normal curve table and critical value of t (for small samples) from the t table for the computed value of degrees of freedom.
6. If the computed value of z or t in the given problem reaches the critical table value of z or t, then it is to be taken as significant, and consequently the null hypothesis stands

rejected. If this falls short of the critical value, the null hypothesis is not rejected.

7. The critical values of z or t are different in the case of two-tailed and one-tailed tests.
When we are interested only in knowing the magnitude of the difference between means, a two-tailed test is employed but in case the direction is also needed, then a one-tailed test is used. The critical values to be taken are summarized in the following:

Level of significance	*Two-tailed test*		*One-tailed test*	
	z-values	*t-values*	*z-values*	*t-values*
5% level	1.96	Read under the column P = .05	1.64	Read under the column P = .10
1% level	2.58	Read under the column P = 0.1	2.33	Read under the column P = .02

8. If the null hypothesis is rejected, we say that the difference found in the sample means is trustworthy and real but it is not rejected, we have to conclude that the difference between the means is not real; it may occur by chance or due to sampling fluctuations.

The process of computing standard error of the difference between the means shows in essence the difference on account of the size or nature of the samples. Different formula used in the various situations are as follows:

Case I: Large but independent (uncorrelated) samples

$$SE_D = \sqrt{\sigma_{M_1}^2 + \sigma_{M_2}^2} = \sqrt{\frac{\sigma_1^2}{N_1} + \frac{\sigma_2^2}{N_2}}$$

Case II: Small but independent (uncorrelated) samples

$$SE_D = \sigma\sqrt{\frac{1}{N_1} + \frac{1}{N_2}}$$

where σ or pooled SD is given by the formula

$$\sigma = \sqrt{\frac{\Sigma x_1^2 + \Sigma x_2^2}{(N_1 - 1) + (N_2 - 1)}}$$

Here, x_1 and x_2 are given by $X_1 - M_1$ and $X_2 - M_2$, respectively.

Case III: Correlated samples—large and small

1. For the two groups matched in pairs as well as in case if a single group is tested twice (before starting the experiment and after), here we use the formula

$$\sigma_D = \sqrt{\sigma_{M_1}^2 + \sigma_{M_2}^2 - 2r\sigma_{M_1}\sigma_{M_2}}$$

2. For the two groups matched in terms of the group as a whole (i.e. Mean and SD), the formula is

$$\sigma_D = \sqrt{\left(\sigma_{M_1}^2 + \sigma_{M_2}^2\right)\left(1 - r^2\right)}$$

A special method may be employed for small samples giving original raw scores, to determine t values directly without computing the standard error of the difference between means, as

$$t = \frac{\Sigma D}{\sqrt{\dfrac{N\Sigma D^2 - (\Sigma D)^2}{N-1}}}$$

where D stands for the difference in scores for the two samples.

EXERCISES

1. What do you understand by the term significance of the difference between means?
   Discuss its necessity in the fields of education and psychology.
2. Write short notes on the following:
   (a) Concept of standard error.
   (b) Null hypothesis.
   (c) Level of significance.
   (d) Two-tailed test and one-tailed test.
3. The critical values necessary for the rejection of a null hypothesis (at a given level of significance and for a given number of degrees of freedom) is higher for a one-tailed test than it is for a two-tailed test. Do you agree? Why?
4. Give the formulae (with full explanation) used in determining the Standard Error of the difference between the means in the following cases:
   (a) Two large but independent (uncorrelated) samples.
   (b) Two small but independent samples.
   (c) Two samples having correlated data on a single group.

(d) Samples having correlated data on two groups with matched pair.
(e) Samples having correlated data on two groups equated in terms of mean and SD.

5. Two group of pre-medical students belonging to two different colleges took a standardized medical aptitude test. The data collected are as follows:

	Group A	*Group B*
Mean	32	36
SD	6.2	7.4
N	145	82

Is there a significant difference between the two means?

6. One group of rats was given a vitamin supplement while the other group received a conventional diet. The rats were randomly divided into two groups. The experiment was performed under the assumption that vitamin supplement results in the increase in weight. The results obtained are:

Experimental Group	*Control Group*
$N_1 = 12$	$N_2 = 16$
$\sigma_1 = 15.5$	$\sigma_2 = 1.22$
$M_1 = 140$	$M_2 = 120$

Can you tell from the results whether the gain received in terms of weight is significant at 0.05 level.

7. The following data were collected from two separate groups of 144 men and 175 women, on an attitude scale.

	Mean	*SD*
Men	19.7	6.08
Women	21.0	4.89

(a) Test the significance of the difference between the mean of two groups at the .05 level of significance.
(b) In your own words, what does the result of the experiment say?

8. In a course of a psychological experiment on two large samples, the following data were collected:

Difference between means = 4.20

Standard error of the difference between means = 2.80

(a) Is the obtained difference between means is significant at the 0.05 level?

(b) What difference is necessary for being significant at the 0.01 level?

9. A vocabulary test was administered to a random sample of 8 students of section A and 7 students of section B of class IX of a school. The scores are:

Scores of Section A	16,	14,	12,	12,	10,	8,	6,	4
Scores of Section B	14,	8,	7,	6,	4,	4,	12	

Is the difference between the means of two groups significant at 0.05 level?

10. A group of subjects were given an attitude test on a controversial subject. Then they were shown a film favourable to the subject and the attitude test was then re-conducted. The scores were tabulated as under:

X_1	16,	18,	20,	24,	24,	22,	20,	18,	10,	8,	20
X_2	24,	20,	24,	28,	30,	20,	24,	22,	18,	18,	24

Test the null hypothesis at .05 and 0.1 levels.

11. The following data were obtained in the course of an experiment performed for testing the effect of a treatment on two groups of 50 subject each:

	Experimental group		*Control group*	
	Initial	*Final*	*Initial*	*Final*
M	74	97	73.8	82
σ	10.2	13.6	10.0	12.8
		$r = 0.75$		

Interpret the greater gain in the case of the experimental group.

12. The achievements of two groups (matched for mean and SD on an intelligence test) of 10 + 2 students, one from the academic and the other from the vocational channel were compared on a mechanical aptitude test. The data collected are:

	Academic group	*Vocational group*
No. of students	125	137
M	51.42	51.38
σ	6.24	7.14

Correlation between IQ scores and mechanical aptitude test scores = 0.30
Test the null hypothesis at 0.05 level.

13. Two groups A and B of class VII children, 72 in each group were paired child for child in terms of age and score on Form A of a group intelligence test. Three weeks later, both groups were given Form B of the same test. Before the second test, group A in the experimental group was praised for its performance on the first test and urged to try improve its score. Group B–the control group–was given the second test without any comment. The data were:

	Experimental group	*Control group*
Mean Score Form B	88.63	83.24
SD on Form B	23.36	21.62

r between scores of the experiment and control group = 0.65
Find out if the incentive (praise) causes the final scores of groups A and B to differ significantly.

14. A group of 20 students were given an achievement test under two conditions: (i) when tense (ii) when relaxed. Test the significance of the difference between means at 0.05 level on the basis of the following data.

Roll No.	*Score when tense*	*Score when relaxed*	*Roll No.*	*Score when tense*	*Score when relaxed*
1	18	20	11	10	10
2	16	22	12	8	12
3	18	24	13	20	22
4	12	10	14	12	14
5	20	25	15	16	12
6	17	19	16	16	20
7	18	20	17	18	22
8	20	21	18	20	24
9	22	23	19	18	23
10	20	20	20	21	17

11 Chi Square and Contingency Coefficient

In Chapters 9 and 10, we discussed the use of z and t tests for testing the significance of the mean and other statistics. The next two chapters suggest some other tests of significance with the help of chi square (χ^2) and F values.

In this chapter, to test the significance we will make use of a distribution known as the distribution of chi square (χ^2) which is quite different from the distribution—normal or t—already described. This distribution was first discovered by Helmert in 1875 and then rediscovered independently by Karl Pearson in 1900, who applied it as a test of 'goodness of fit'.

USE OF CHI SQUARE AS A TEST OF 'GOODNESS OF FIT'

As a test of 'goodness of fit', Karl Pearson tried to make use of the χ^2 distribution for devising a test for determining how well the experimentally obtained results fit in the results expected theoretically on some hypothesis. Let us make it clearer through some examples.

Hypothesis of Chance

In an experiment, we toss a number of coins (supposed to be unbiased) a certain number of times and record the results of the toss. Suppose we get 40 heads and 60 tails out of the 100 throws. These observed results, in terms of 40 and 60 observed frequencies, will be termed as experimental results. We also know that, theoretically, in the case of an unbiased coin, chances of getting a head or a tail are almost 50:50. Therefore, the expected results out of 100 throws, in terms of expected frequencies, must be as 50 heads and 50 tails. In such a situation, a null hypothesis will be established to know whether experimental results differ significantly from what the theoretical assumption calls as chance.

In all such experiments, the expected results are the outcome of chance factors. In the case of dice-throwing experiment, the chances will be 1 out of 6 for the values from 1 to 6 to appear at the top in the total throws of the experiment. Similarly, in a multiple choice test providing four possible responses to each item (having one correct response), the chance or probability of a right answer for a student, only on account of mere guessing, is 1/4 and of wrong answer is 3/4.

Hypothesis of Equal Probability

Many a time, the chance factor or the probability of the expected results is counted on the hypothesis of equal chances. Suppose we wish to get an opinion from a group of individuals concerning some new idea, e.g. should we go ahead with the newly planned educational policy or not? The data are collected on the categories, *yes, no* and *indifferent*. Then, the expected frequencies are determined on the basis of equal probability. If there are 60 individuals in our study, then the chances of getting yes, no and indifferent answers will be equal, i.e. 20 in each category.

Hypothesis of Normal Distribution

Here the expected results or frequencies are determined on the basis of the normal distribution of observed frequencies in the entire population. Suppose a researcher, through the administration of a Personality Adjustment Inventory, classifies a group of 200 individuals as very good, good, average, poor and very poor in terms of the scores made on the inventory. In these five categories, he records the observed frequencies as follows:

Very good	*Good*	*Average*	*Poor*	*Very poor*
55	45	35	35	30

If he hypothesizes that the adjustment in the large population is distributed in a normal way, then the expected number of individuals falling in each category must be determined on the basis of the population of the normal curve or distribution, as illustrates in Figure 11.1.

It is clear from the curve that the distribution in the categories, very poor, poor, average, good and very good is 3.5%, 23.84%, 45.14%, 23.84% and 3.5%, respectively. Further, it can be concluded that the expected frequencies in each of the above mentioned five categories out of the total of 200 would be 7, 48, 90, 48 and 7.

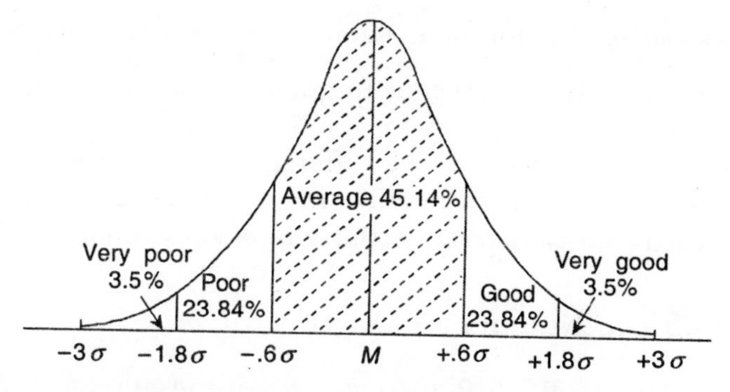

Figure 11.1 Normal distribution of adjustment scores into five categories.

In all such experiments relating to the hypothesis of chance, equal probability and normal distribution, the χ^2 test, based on χ^2 distribution, may be used as a test of significance much the same way as we make use of z and t tests based on normal and t distributions.

PROCEDURE OF CHI SQUARE TESTING

The procedure of utilizing χ^2 as a test of goodness of fit or significance, in general, may be summarized as follows.

Establishing Null Hypothesis

First, a null hypothesis is set up. In other words, it may be stated that there exists no actual difference between the observed frequencies (derived from experimental results) and expected frequencies (derived on the basis of some hypothesis of equal probability or chance factor or hypothesis of normal distribution).

In the case of testing goodness of fit, the hypothesis may be that the distribution of the given variable conforms to some widely known distribution such as the binomial or normal distribution.

Computation of the Value of χ^2

In the second step, the value of χ^2 is calculated through a formula meant for this purpose. The usual formula is as follows:

$$\chi^2 = \Sigma\left[\frac{(f_o - f_e)^2}{f_e}\right]$$

where

f_o = Observed frequency on some experiment

f_e = Expected frequency on some hypothesis

Application of this formula requires the following computation:

1. Computation of expected frequencies based on some hypothesis.
2. Finding the square of the differences between observed and expected frequencies and dividing it by the expected frequency in each case to determine the sum of these quotients.

Determining the Number of Degrees of Freedom

The data in chi square problems are usually available or may be arranged in the form of a contingency table showing observed and expected frequencies in some specific rows and columns. The formula for the computation of the number of degrees of freedom in a chi square problem usually runs as follows:

$$df = (r - 1)(c - 1)$$

where r = No. of rows in the contingency table

c = No. of columns in the contingency table

Determining the Critical Value of χ^2

As for the z and t tests of significance, there exists a table for the critical value of χ^2 required for significance at a predetermined significance level (5% or 1%) for the computed degrees of freedom. The desired critical value of χ^2, thus, may be read from Table F given in the Appendix of this text.

Comparing Critical Value of χ^2 with the Computed Value

In this step, the value of χ^2 computed in step 2 is compared to the critical value of χ^2 read from the table (as suggested in step 4) for the degrees of freedom (computed in step 3) at the pre-determined level of significance—0.05 or 0.01. If our computed value of χ^2 is greater than or equal to the critical value of χ^2, then we take it as significant and consequently, the null hypothesis is rejected. In other words, we may state that the difference between the observed and expected frequencies is significant and cannot be explained away as a matter of chance or by sampling fluctuation. But in case our computed value of χ^2 is less than the critical value of χ^2 then it is called non-significant and consequently, the null hypothesis is not rejected, i.e. we may agree that the difference between observed and expected frequencies is not real. It may occur by chance or due to sampling fluctuation. When a null hypothesis is not rejected, the theoretical distribution based on some hypothesis (equal probability or normal distribution) may be considered to be a good fit or substitute for the distribution based on experimentally obtained frequencies.

Let us illustrate the above process of using χ^2 as a test of goodness of fit or significance through some examples.

Case I: Expected frequencies based on the hypothesis of equal probability or chance

Example 11.1: A one rupee coin is tossed in the air 100 times and the recorded results of these 100 throws indicate 40 heads and 60 tails. Using the χ^2 test, find out whether this result is better than mere "chance".

Solution. Here the observed frequencies are 40 and 60 where the expected frequencies based on the hypothesis of 50:50 chance are 50 and 50. We state the null hypothesis thus:

There exists no real difference between the observed and expected frequencies.

The data along with computation work of χ^2 may be organized as in Table 11.1.

Table 11.1 Computation of χ^2 with the Data Given in Example 11.1

	f_o	f_e	$f_o - f_e$	$(f_o - f_e)^2$	$(f_o - f_e)^2/f_e$
Heads	40	50	–10	100	2
Tails	60	50	10	100	2
Total	100	100	$\chi^2 = \Sigma\left[\frac{(f_o - f_e)^2}{f_e}\right] = 4$		

Degrees of freedom $(df) = (r - 1)(c - 1) = (2 - 1)(2 - 1) = 1$

Let us refer Table F of the χ^2 distribution (given in the Appendix) with $df = 1$. We find that at the 5% level, the critical value of χ^2 is 3.841. Our computed value of χ^2 is 4 which is larger than 3.841, but less than 6.635, i.e. the critical value of χ^2 at the 1% level of significance. Hence, it may be taken as significant at 5% level but not at 1%. However, we may safely reject the null hypothesis at 5% level of significance and be fairly confident that our experimental results are different from those produced merely by chance alone.

Example 11.2: In an experiment a dice is tossed 180 times. It is observed that a five-spot face appears on the top 50 times. Are these results different from a mere "chance" appearance?

Solution. Here the observed frequencies are 50 for the appearance of five spots and 180–50 = 130 for non-five spots. The expected frequencies will be based upon the hypothesis of chance. Since the probability of tossing a five spot is 1 out of 6 (1/6), our expected frequencies will be 180/6 = 30 and 150 respectively for five spots and non-five spots, respectively.

The frequencies and computation work of χ^2 may be tabulated now as in Table 11.2.

Table 11.2 Computation of χ^2 with the Data Given in Example 11.2

	f_o	f_e	$f_o - f_e$	$(f_o - f_e)^2$	$(f_o - f_e)^2/f_e$
Five spots	50	30	20	400	400/30 = 13.333
Non-five spots	130	150	–20	400	400/150 = 2.666
Total	180	180			χ^2 = 15.999 or 16 (approx.)

Degrees of freedom = $(r - 1)(c - 1) = (2 - 1)(2 - 1) = 1$

The computed value of χ^2, 16 is quite significant both at the 5% and 1% levels as the critical values of χ^2 at these levels are 3.841 and 6.635, respectively, for 1 degree of freedom. Hence the null hypothesis is rejected. We can say quite confidently that the experimental results are not based on a mere chance factor.

Example 11.3: In 180 throws of the dice, the observed frequencies of the one, two, three, four, five and six-spot faces appearing on the top are 34, 27, 41, 25, 18 and 35. Test the hypothesis that the dice is not erratic.

Solution. The data for calculation of χ^2 may be arranged as in Table 11.3.

Table 11.3 Computation of χ^2 with the Data Given in Example 11.3

	f_o	f_e	$f_o - f_e$	$(f_o - f_e)^2$	$(f_o - f_e)^2/f_e$
One-spot face	34	30	4	16	16/30
Two-spot face	27	30	–3	9	9/30
Three-spot face	41	30	11	121	121/30
Four-spot face	25	30	–5	25	25/30
Five-spot face	18	30	–12	144	144/30
Six-spot face	35	30	5	25	25/30
Total	180	180			χ^2 = 340/30 = 11.333

Degrees of freedom = $(r - 1)(c - 1) = (6 - 1)(2 - 1) = 5$
For 5 degrees of freedom,

Critical value of χ^2 at 0.05 level = 11.07
Critical value of χ^2 at 0.01 level = 15.086

The computed value of χ^2, i.e. 11.333, is significant at the 0.05 level, but not significant at the 0.01 level. Consequently, we can reject the null hypothesis at the 0.05. Thus in this problem, we may assert with 5% level of confidence that the dice cannot be said to be unbiased and the difference between the observed and expected frequencies cannot be attributed to chance alone.

Example 11.4: A multiple choice test of 50 items provides five possible answers to each item. A student gets a score of 20 for his 20 correct answers. Find out whether or not his performance is better than mere guessing.

Solution. Null hypothesis may be stated as follows:

There exists no real difference between the scores actually obtained by the student and those expected on account of mere guessing.

Since there are five answers to each item, one of which is correct, the probability of a right answer by guessing is $1/5 \times 50 = 10$, and of a wrong answer is $4/5 \times 50 = 40$. The computation is given in Table 11.4.

Table 11.4 Computation of χ^2 with the Data Given in Example 11.4

	f_o	f_e	$f_o - f_e$	$(f_o - f_e)^2$	$(f_o - f_e)^2/f_e$
Right answer	20	10	10	100	100/10 = 10
Wrong answer	30	40	–10	100	100/40 = 2.5
Total	50	50			χ^2 = 12.5

Degrees of freedom (df) = $(r - 1)(c - 1) = (2 - 1)(2 - 1) = 1$
For $df = 1$

Critical value of χ^2 = 3.841 at 0.05 level of significance
Critical value of χ^2 = 6.635 at 0.01 level of significance

The computed value of χ^2 is much higher than both the critical values of χ^2 at .05 and .01 levels. Hence it is taken to be quite significant. Consequently, null hypothesis is rejected and we may conclude that the student could not have secured 20 marks by mere guessing.

Example 11.5: Sixty college principals, in a study, were asked to express their opinion in terms of yes, no or indifferent for the implementation of the new education policy from the current year. The obtained frequencies in each of these categories were 13, 27 and 20, respectively. Do these results indicate a significant trend of opinion?

Solution: *Null hypothesis*. There exists no real difference between the observed frequencies (opinion expressed by the principals) and the expected frequencies based on the hypothesis of equal probability or chance, i.e. in case all of them might have been asked to mark yes, no or indifferent without knowing what had been asked of them.

The data for computation of χ^2 may be dealt with as in Table 11.5:

Table 11.5 Computation of χ^2 with the Data Given in Example 11.5

Category of response	f_o	f_e	$f_o - f_e$	$(f_o - f_e)^2$	$(f_o - f_e)^2/f_e$
Yes	13	20	–7	49	49/20 = 2.45
No	27	20	7	49	49/20 = 2.45
Indifferent	20	20	0	0	0
Total	60	60			χ^2 = 4.90

Degrees of fredom $(df) = (r - 1)(c - 1) = (3 - 1)(2 - 1) = 2$

For $df = 2$,

Critical value of $\chi^2 = 5.991$ at 5% level of significance

The computed value of χ^2, i.e. 4.90, is less than the critical value, hence it cannot be taken as significant, and consequently, the null hypothesis cannot be rejected. We may, therefore, say that the opinion expressed by the principals cannot be said to differ significantly from those obtained by chance, i.e. random casual marking.

Example 11.6: A group of 100 young people was asked to comment on their attitude towards the success of love marriage by making quite successful, successful, cannot say anything, unsuccessful, quite unsuccessful. The number of responses falling under each of these categories were recorded as 12, 8, 25, 25 and 30 respectively. Do these results diverge significantly from the results expected merely by chance?

Solution. The expected frequencies in this case based on the hypothesis of equal probability or chance will be 20 in each category of response. The data for computing χ^2 is given in Table 11.6.

Table 11.6 Computation of χ^2 with the Data Given in Example 11.6

Category of response	f_o	f_e	$f_o - f_e$	$(f_o - f_e)^2$	$(f_o - f_e)^2/f_e$
Quite successful	12	20	−8	64	64/20 = 3.20
Successful	8	20	−12	144	144/20 = 7.20
Cannot say anything	25	20	5	25	25/20 = 1.25
Unsuccessful	25	20	5	25	25/20 = 1.25
Quite unsuccessful	30	20	10	100	100/20 = 5.00
Total	100	100			χ^2 = 17.9

Degrees of fredom $(df) = (r - 1)(c - 1) = (5 - 1)(2 - 1) = 4 \times 1 = 4$
For $df = 4$,

Critical value of χ^2 = 9.488 at 0.05 level of significance
Critical value of χ^2 = 13.277 at 0.01 level of significance

The computed value of χ^2 is much greater than the critical values of χ^2 at both the 0.05 and 0.01 levels. Hence, it is taken as quite significant. Therefore, the null hypothesis can be rejected with greater confidence, and we conclude that the obtained results diverge significantly from the results expected merely by chance.

Case II: Expected frequencies based on the hypothesis of normal distribution

Example 11.7: 384 school teachers were classified into six categories of adjustment ranging from a high level of adjustment to a low level of adjustment as under:

Categories	I	II	III	IV	V	VI	Total
No. of school teachers	48	61	82	91	57	45	384

Does this classification differ significantly from the one expected if adjustment is supposed to be distributed normally in our population of school teachers?

Solution. Here, the expected frequencies showing the number of teachers falling into the given six categories are to be determined on the basis of the normal distribution hypothesis. For this purpose, let us represent the position of the six sub-groups or categories diagrammatically on a normal curve as shown in Figure 11.2 by dividing the base line of the curve (taken to be 6σ) into six equal segments of σ each.

The proportion of the normal distribution from Table B of the normal curve and consequently, the expected frequencies to be found in each of these categories may be shown as in Table 11.7.

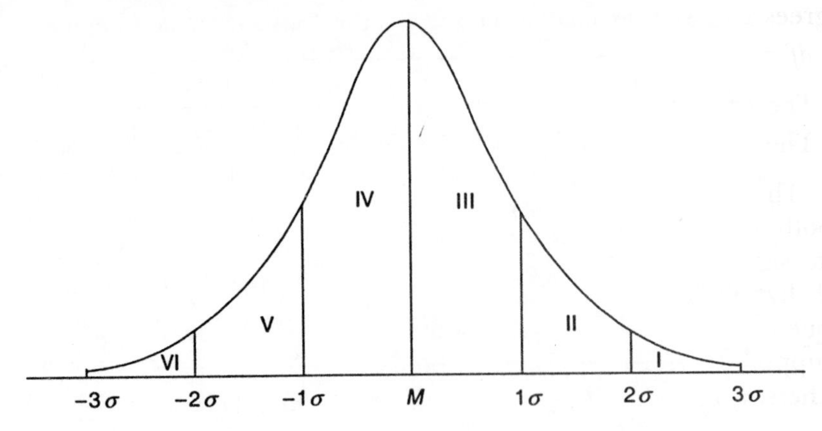

Figure 11.2 Normal curve showing normal distribution of adjustment into six categories.

Table 11.7 Computation of Expected Frequencies Based on Normal Distribution

Category	*Area of normal curve*	*Percentage of cases falling between the area (%)*	*No. of cases or frequencies out of 384*
I	$+3.00\sigma$ to $+2.00\sigma$	2.28	9
II	$+2.00\sigma$ to $+1.00\sigma$	13.59	52
III	$+1.00\sigma$ to M	34.13	131
IV	M to -1.00σ	34.13	131
V	-1.00σ to -2.00σ	13.59	52
VI	-2.00σ to -3.00σ	2.28	9

We will now test the null hypothesis of no difference existing between the observed and expected frequencies by computing the value of χ^2 as in Table 11.8.

Table 11.8 Computation of χ^2 with the Data Given in Example 11.7

Categories	f_o	f_e	$f_o - f_e$	$(f_o - f_e)^2$	$(f_o - f_e)^2/f_e$
I	48	9	39	1521	169.00
II	61	52	9	81	1.56
III	82	131	−49	2401	18.32
IV	91	131	−40	1600	12.21
V	57	52	5	25	0.48
VI	45	9	36	1296	144.00
Total	384	384			$\chi^2 = 345.57$

Degrees of freedom $= (r - 1)(c - 1) = (6 - 1)(2 - 1) = 5$
For $df = 5$,

The critical value of $\chi^2 = 11.070$ at 0.05 level of significance
The critical value of $\chi^2 = 15.086$ at 0.01 level of significance

The computed value of χ^2 is much greater than the critical values at both 5% and 1% levels of significance. Hence it may be regarded as quite significant at both the levels of significance. Consequently, the null hypothesis is rejected meaning, thereby, that the observed frequencies differ quite significantly from those expected if adjustment is supposed to be distributed normally in our population of school teachers.

USE OF CHI SQUARE AS A TEST OF INDEPENDENCE BETWEEN TWO VARIABLES

In addition to testing the agreement between observed frequencies and those expected from some hypothesis, e.g. equal probability or normal distribution, the χ^2 test may be usefully applied for testing the relationship between two variables (traits or attributes). It is done in the following two ways:

1. Testing a null hypothesis, stating that the two given variables are independent of each other.
2. Computing the value of the contingency coefficient, a measure of relationship existing between the two variables, i.e. sets of attributes can be computed.

Let us discuss these ways one by one, with the help of some examples.

Case I: Testing null hypothesis of independence (in any contingency table)

Example 11.8: 100 boys and 60 girls were asked to select one of the five elective subjects. The choices of the two sexes were tabulated separately.

Sex			*Subjects*			
	A	*B*	*C*	*D*	*E*	*Total*
Boys	25	30	10	25	10	100
Girls	10	15	5	15	15	60

Do you think that the choice of the subjects is dependent upon the sex of the students?

Solution.

Step 1. Establishing a null hypothesis—Null hypothesis. The choice of the subject is independent of sex, i.e. there exists no significant difference between the choices of the two sexes.

Step 2. Computation of the expected frequencies. For this purpose, we first present the given data in the contingency table form. The expected frequencies after being computed, are written within brackets just below the respective observed frequencies. The contingency table and the process of computation of expected frequencies is given in Table 11.9.

Table 11.9 Contingency Table with f_e for the Data Given in Example 11.8

	Categories					
Sex	*A*	*B*	*C*	*D*	*E*	*Total*
Boys	25 (21.9)	30 (28.1)	10 (9.4)	25 (25)	10 (15.6)	100
Girls	10 (13.1)	15 (16.9)	5 (5.6)	15 (15)	15 (9.4)	60
Total	35	45	15	40	25	160

Computation of expected frequencies

$$\frac{100 \times 35}{160} = 21.9 \qquad \frac{60 \times 35}{160} = 13.1$$

$$\frac{100 \times 45}{160} = 28.1 \qquad \frac{60 \times 45}{160} = 16.9$$

$$\frac{100 \times 15}{160} = 9.4 \qquad \frac{60 \times 15}{160} = 5.6$$

$$\frac{100 \times 40}{160} = 25 \qquad \frac{60 \times 40}{160} = 15$$

$$\frac{100 \times 25}{160} = 15.6 \qquad \frac{60 \times 25}{160} = 9.4$$

Step 3. Computation of the value of χ^2. The value of χ^2 may be computed with the help of the usual formula,

$$\chi^2 = \Sigma\left[\frac{(f_o - f_e)^2}{f_e}\right]$$

Table 11.10 Computation of χ^2 from Contingency Table 11.9

f_o	f_e	$f_o - f_e$	$(f_o - f_e)^2$	$(f_o - f_e)^2/f_e$
25	21.9	3.1	9.61	0.439
30	28.1	1.9	3.61	0.128
10	9.4	0.6	0.36	0.038
25	25.00	0	0	0.000
10	15.6	–5.6	31.36	2.010
10	13.1	–3.1	9.61	0.733
15	16.9	–1.9	3.61	0.214
5	5.6	–0.6	0.36	0.064
15	15.0	0	0	0.000
15	9.4	5.6	31.36	3.336
Total 160	160			χ^2 = 6.962

Step 4. Testing the null hypothesis

No. of degrees of freedom = $(r - 1)(c - 1) = (2 - 1)(5 - 1) = 4$

For 4 degrees of freedom, from Table F of the χ^2 distribution,

Critical value of χ^2 = 9.488 at 5% level of significance

Critical value of χ^2 = 13.277 at 1% level of significance

The computed value of χ^2 is much less than the critical values of χ^2 at 5% and 1% levels of significance. Hence it is to be taken as non-significant. Consequently, the null hypothesis cannot be rejected and we say that the choice of the subject is quite independent of sex.

Example 11.9: The opinions of 90 unmarried persons and 100 married persons were secured on an attitude scale. The data were collected as shown in the tabulated matter:

	Agree	*Disagree*	*No opinion*	*Total*
Unmarried	14	66	10	90
Married	27	66	7	100
Total	41	132	17	190

Do the data indicate a significant difference in opinion in terms of marital status of the individuals?

Solution. 1. *Null hypothesis of independence.* The opinions on an attitude scale are independent of the marital status. A look of Table 11.11 illustrates this.

Table 11.11 Contingency Table with f_e for the Data Given in Example 11.9

	Agree	*Disagree*	*No opinion*	*Total*
Unmarried	14	66	10	90
	(19.4)	(16.5)	(8)	
Married	27	66	7	100
	(21.6)	(69.5)	(9)	
Total	41	132	17	190

2. *Computation of expected frequencies for the respective observed frequencies*

$$\frac{90 \times 41}{190} = 19.4 \qquad \frac{100 \times 41}{190} = 21.6$$

$$\frac{90 \times 132}{190} = 62.5 \qquad \frac{100 \times 132}{190} = 69.5$$

$$\frac{90 \times 17}{190} = 8.05 \qquad \frac{100 \times 17}{190} = 9$$

$$df = (3 - 1)\ (2 - 1) = 2$$

3. *Computation of* χ^2 (Table 11.12)

Table 11.12 Computation of χ^2 from Contingency Table 11.11

f_o	f_e	$f_o - f_e$	$(f_o - f_e)^2$	$(f_o - f_e)^2/f_e$
14	19.4	–5.4	29.16	1.50
66	62.5	3.5	12.25	0.19
10	8	2.0	4.00	0.50
27	21.6	5.4	29.16	1.35
66	69.5	–3.5	12.25	0.18
7	9	–2.0	4.00	0.44
Total 190	190			$\chi^2 = 4.16$

4. *Testing the null hypothesis.* For $df = 2$, from Table F,

Critical value of $\chi^2 = 5.991$ at 0.05 level of significance
Critical value of $\chi^2 = 9.210$ at 0.01 level of significance

The computed value of χ^2, i.e. 4.16, is much lower than both the critical values, 5.991 and 9.210, and therefore, it is not significant.

Consequently, the null hypothesis cannot be rejected. Therefore, the given data do not provide an indication of significant difference in opinion in terms of the marital status of the individuals.

Case II: Testing null hypothesis of independence (in 2 × 2 contingency tables)
The data are arranged in a 2 × 2 contingency table as shown in Table 11.13.

Table 11.13 2 × 2 Contingency Table

A	B	$(A + B)$
C	D	$(C + D)$
$(A + C)$	$(B + D)$	$(A + B + C + D) = N$

Now, the value of χ^2 may be directly computed without calculating the expected frequencies by using the following formula:

$$\chi^2 = \frac{N(AD - BC)^2}{(A+B)(C+D)(A+C)(B+D)}$$

Let us illustrate the use of the given formula with the help of an example.

Example 11.10: The mothers of two hundred adolescents (some of them were graduates, and others, non-graduates) were asked whether they agreed or disagreed on a certain aspect of adolescent behaviour. The data collected are as follows:

	Agree	*Disagree*	*Total*
Graduate mothers	38	12	50
Non-graduate mothers	84	66	150
Total	122	78	200

Is the attitude of these mothers related to their being graduates or non-graduates?

Solution. 1. *Null hypothesis of independence.* Attitude of mothers is independent of the fact that they are graduates or non-graduates.

The data is arranged in the 2 × 2 fold contingency table, for the computation of expected frequencies as shown in Table 11.14

Table 11.14 Contingency Table for the Data Given in Example 11.10

	Agree	*Disagree*	*Total*
Graduate mothers	(*A*) 38	(*B*) 12	(*A* + *B*) 50
Non-graduate mothers	(*C*) 84	(*D*) 66	(*C* + *D*) 150
Total	(*A* + *C*) 122	(*B* + *D*) 78	*N* 200

Now, χ^2 may be computed using the following formula:

$$\chi^2 = \frac{N(AD - BC)^2}{(A+B)(C+D)(A+C)(B+D)}$$

Substituting the values from the contingency table, we get

$$\chi^2 = \frac{200(38 \times 66 - 84 \times 12)^2}{50 \times 150 \times 122 \times 78}$$

$$= \frac{200(2508 - 1008)^2}{50 \times 150 \times 122 \times 78} = 6.305$$

No. of degrees of freedom = $(r - 1)(c - 1) = (2 - 1)(2 - 1) = 1$
For $df = 1$, from Table F,

Critical value of χ^2 = 3.841 at 0.05 level of significance
Critical value of χ^2 = 6.635 at 0.01 level of significance

The computed value of χ^2, 6.305, is quite larger than 3.841, but it does not reach 6.635. Hence, it is taken as quite significant at the 0.05 level but not significant at the 0.01 level of significance. However, we can conclude that 95 times out of 100, the attitude of the mothers is quite independent of the fact that they are graduates or non-graduates.

CONTINGENCY COEFFICIENT

The contingency coefficient, denoted by *C*, provides a measure of correlation between two variables (attributes or traits), with each of these variables being classified into two or more categories. After computing the value of χ^2 from the given data, the value of contingency may be computed directly by the use of the following formula:

$$C = \sqrt{\frac{\chi^2}{N + \chi^2}}$$

Like r, ρ and other coefficients of correlation, C does not have limits (± 1). Its upper limit is dependent upon the number of categories. Like χ^2, it does not have negative values.

For a table made up of an equal number of columns and rows, $K \times K$, the upper limit of the contingency coefficient is given by the formula, $\sqrt{(K-1)/K}$. Thus, for a 2×2 table, it is 0.5, for a 3×3 table $\sqrt{2/3} = 0.82$ and for a 4×4 table $\sqrt{3/4} = 0.87, \ldots$ However, when the number of columns and rows differ in a table, like 2×3 or 3×4, to calculate the upper limit, the smaller number is taken as K.

How to Compute C

Let us illustrate the process of computing C with an example.

Example 11.11: Students belonging to three religious groups were asked to respond to a particular question related to their attitude by providing three alternatives: yes, no and undecided. The data collected are given below:

Religious groups	*Yes*	*No*	*Undecided*	*Total*
Hindu	10	25	15	50
Muslim	20	20	5	45
Christian	30	15	10	55
Total	60	60	30	150

Compute a contingency coefficient to test if there is a relationship between religious group membership and attitude.

Solution. (a) Contingency table and computation of expected frequencies (Table 11.15).

Table 11.15 Contingency Table with f_e for Data Given in Example 11.11

Religious groups	*Yes*	*No*	*Undecided*	*Total*
Hindu	10	25	15	50
	(20)	(20)	(10)	
Muslim	20	20	5	45
	(18)	(18)	(9)	
Christian	30	15	10	55
	(22)	(22)	(11)	
Total	60	60	30	150

$$\frac{50 \times 60}{150} = 20 \qquad \frac{45 \times 60}{150} = 18 \qquad \frac{55 \times 60}{150} = 22$$

$$\frac{50 \times 60}{150} = 20 \qquad \frac{45 \times 60}{150} = 18 \qquad \frac{55 \times 60}{150} = 22$$

$$\frac{50 \times 30}{150} = 10 \qquad \frac{45 \times 30}{150} = 9 \qquad \frac{55 \times 30}{150} = 11$$

(b) *Computation of* χ^2 (Table 11.16)

Table 11.16 Computation of χ^2 from Contingency Table 11.15

f_o	f_e	$f_o - f_e$	$(f_o - f_e)^2$	$(f_o - f_e)^2/f_e$
10	20	–10	100	5.00
25	20	5	25	1.25
15	10	5	25	2.50
20	18	2	4	0.22
20	18	2	4	0.22
5	9	–4	16	1.78
30	22	8	64	2.91
15	22	–7	49	2.23
10	11	–1	1	0.09

$$\chi^2 = \Sigma\left[\frac{(f_o - f_e)^2}{f_e}\right] = 16.20$$

(c) *Computation of C*

$$C = \sqrt{\frac{\chi^2}{N + \chi^2}} = \sqrt{\frac{16.2}{150 + 16.2}} = \sqrt{\frac{16.2}{166.2}} = 0.312$$

CORRECTION FOR SMALL FREQUENCIES IN A 2 × 2 TABLE

When we have a small sample of cases such that the least expected frequency in any cell of the 2 × 2 contingency table (with $df = 1$) is less than 5, computation in the usual way of χ^2 gives us an overestimate of the true value. As a result, we may reject some hypothesis which in fact, should not be rejected. This problem arising particularly in 2 × 2 tables with 1 degree of freedom can be avoided by using a correction called *Yates' correction*.

The procedure of applying *Yates' correction* is quite simple. The rule is to subtract 0.5 from the absolute value of the difference between observed and expected frequency, $|(f_o - f_e)|$. In other words, each observed frequency (f_o) which is larger than its expected frequency (f_e) is decreased by 0.5 and each observed frequency which is smaller than its expected frequency is increased by 0.5.

As a result, the following formulae for computing χ^2 changes are obtained:

Usual formula | *Corrected formula*

$$\chi^2 = \Sigma\left[\frac{(f_o - f_e)^2}{f_e}\right], \qquad \chi^2 = \Sigma\left[\frac{(|f_o - f_e| - 0.5)^2}{f_e}\right]$$

$$\chi^2 = \frac{N(AD-BC)^2}{(A+B)(C+D)(A+C)(B+D)}, \quad \chi^2 = \frac{N(|AD - BC| - N/2)^2}{(A+B)(C+D)(A+C)(B+D)}$$

Let us illustrate the use of *Yates' correction* in computing χ^2, with the help of a few examples.

Example 11.12: A student is asked to respond to 8 objective-type questions requiring responses in the yes or no form. He responds six times as 'Yes' and only two times as 'no'. Is this results different from what would have been obtained by merely guessing?

Solution. *Null hypothesis.* There is no significant difference between the observed frequencies of the response and the expected frequencies obtained on account of guessing or chance factor.

The data for the computation of χ^2 may be arranged as shown now:

	Yes	*No*	*Total*
Observed frequencies	6	2	8
Expected frequencies (calculated on the basis of equal probability)	4	4	8

The computation of χ^2 by applying *Yates' correction* is shown in Table 11.17.

Table 11.17 Computation of χ^2 with Yates' Correction

f_o	f_e	$\|f_o - f_e\|$	$\|f_o - f_e\| - 0.5$	$(\|f_o - f_e\| - 0.5)^2$	$\frac{(\|f_o - f_e\| - 0.5)^2}{f_e}$
6	4	2	1.5	2.25	2.25/4
2	4	2	1.5	2.25	2.25/4
					Total = 4.50/4

$$\chi^2 = \Sigma\left[\frac{(|f_o - f_e| - 0.5)^2}{f_e}\right] = \frac{4.50}{4} = 1.125$$

Degrees of freedom = (2 – 1) (2 – 1) = 1

For df = 1, from Table F,

Critical value of χ^2 = 3.841 at .05 level of significance

Critical value of χ^2 = 6.635 at .01 level of significance

The computed value of χ^2, 1.125, is much less than these critical values of χ^2. Hence it cannot be taken as significant. Consequently, the null hypothesis cannot be rejected, and it is presumed that the students might have used the guessing technique in making responses.

Example 11.13: 30 students (18 from public schools and 12 from government schools) participated in the debate "Love marriages are injurious to the well-being of the society". Some of them spoke in favour and some aganist the topic. The data are tabulated as follows:

	Favour	*Against*	*Total*
Public schools	12	6	18
Government schools	2	10	12
Total	14	16	30

Is the choice of speakers, for or against the topic independent of their belonging to a public or government school?

Solution. *Null hypothesis.* The choice of the speakers for or against the topic is independent of their belonging to a public or government school. Table 11.8 is the contingency table for the data.

Table 11.18 Contingency Table for the Data Given Example 11.13

	Favour	*Against*	*Total*
Public School	12 (A)	6 (B)	18 (A + B)
Govt. School	2 (C)	10 (D)	12 (C + D)
Total	14 (A + C)	16 (B + D)	30 (N)

Since the frequencies are small, we have to apply *Yates' correction*. Therefore, we make use of the following corrected formula for the computation of χ^2.

$$\chi^2 = \frac{N(|AD - BC| - N/2)^2}{(A+B)(C+D)(A+C)(B+D)}$$

$$= \frac{30(120-12-15)^2}{18\times12\times14\times16}$$

$$= \frac{30\times93\times93}{18\times12\times14\times16} = 5.36$$

For one degree of freedom, from the Table 11.18,

Critical value of χ^2 = 3.841 at .05 level of significance
Critical value of χ^2 = 6.635 at .01 level of significance

The computed value of χ^2, 5.36 is quite significant at 5% level. Hence it may be taken as significant at this level of significance. Consequently, the null hypothesis is rejected at 5% level of confidence. As a result, we can say confidently that 95 times out of 100, the choice of the speaker, for or against the proposal cannot be said to be independent of the fact that they belong to a particular type of school.

UNDERLYING ASSUMPTIONS, USES AND LIMITATIONS OF CHI SQUARE TEST

1. Chi square is used as a test of significance when we have data that are expressed in frequencies or in terms of percentages or proportions that can be reduced to frequencies.
2. Usually the test is used with discrete data. In case when any continuous data is reduced to categories, then also we can apply the chi square test.
3. Where tests of significance like z and t are based upon the assumption of normal distribution in the population studied and are referred to as parametric tests, χ^2 is altogether free from such assumption. We can use it with any type of distribution. That is why, it is usually called distribution free or a non-parametric test of significance.
4. In terms of its various uses, as we have already seen in this chapter, chi square is first used as a test of goodness of fit, to determine if the observed results on some experiment or study differ from the theoretically obtained results based on some hypothesis like equal probability or normal distribution and secondly, as a test of independence.
5. The χ^2 test demands that individual observations be independent of each other. The response that one individual gives to an item should have no influence on the response of any other individual in the study.
6. The sum of the expected frequencies must always be equal to the sum of the observed frequencies in a χ^2 test.

7. In the case of a 2 × 2 table (df = 1) with small cell frequencies (less than five), it needs the use of *Yates' correction*. But for more than 1 degree of freedom, the small cell frequencies may distort the results markedly. Therefore, we are left with no other alternative than combining the categories. This may cause approximation and decrease the required experimental sophistication.

SUMMARY

The Chi square test is used as a test of significance when we have data that are given or can be expressed in frequencies/categories. It does not require the assumption of a normal distribution like z or other parametric tests. It is a completely distribution free and non-parametric test.

The χ^2 test is used for two broad purposes. Firstly, it is used as a test of 'goodness of fit' and secondly, as a test of independence.

As a test of goodness of fit, χ^2 tries to determine how well the observed results on some experiment or study fit in the results expected theoretically on some hypothesis like hypothesis of chance, hypothesis of equal probability and hypothesis of normal distribution. In the case of a coin throwing experiment, the expected frequencies are 50 heads and 50 tails out of 100 throws. In the case of a dice throwing experiment, the chances are 1 out of 6 for the values from 1 to 6 to appear at the top, out of the total throws. In a multiple choice test having 4 possible responses, the chance for a correct response is 1/4 and for a wrong response, it is 3/4.

Hypothesis of equal probability demands the equal distribution of the total number of frequencies into the categories of responses.

In a normal distribution hypothesis, the expected results or frequencies are determined on the basis of the normal distribution of observed frequencies in the entire population.

After determining the expected frequencies on the basis of some given hypothesis, the task of using χ^2 as a test of goodness of fit or significance is usually carried out in the following steps:

1. Establishing null hypothesis (hypothesis of no difference).
2. Computation of the value of χ^2. The general formula used is

$$\chi^2 = \Sigma\left[\frac{(f_o - f_e)^2}{f_e}\right]$$

3. Determining the number of degrees of freedom by the formula:

$$df = (r - 1)(c - 1)$$

4. Determining the critical value of χ^2 at a pre-determined level of significance –0.05 or 0.01 for the computed degrees of freedom from the χ^2 distribution table (Table F of the Appendix).
5. Comparing critical value of χ^2 with its computed value. If computed χ^2 is equal to or greater than the critical value, then it is taken to be significant enough for the rejection of the null hypothesis.

As a test of independence, χ^2 is usually applied for testing the relationship between two variables in two ways. First, by testing the null hypothesis of independence, saying that the two given variables are independent of each other and second, by computing the value of contingency coefficient, a measurement of relationship existing between the two variables.

The method of testing the null hypothesis of independence is almost the same as employed in the case of the null hypothesis for testing the goodness of fit except with a slight difference in the computation of the values of expected frequencies. For this purpose, the given data are first presented in the form of a contingency table consisting of rows and columns. Then the cell frequencies are computed on the basis of proportion of the products of the totals written against the respective columns and rows with respect to the grand total of all the frequencies.

In the case of a 2 × 2 contingency table having A, B, C and D as cell frequencies, value of χ^2 may be computed directly without calculating expected frequencies with the help of the formula

$$\chi^2 = \frac{N(AD-BC)^2}{(A+B)(C+D)(A+C)(B+D)}$$

However, in the case of small samples where the least expected frequency in any cell of the 2 × 2 contingency table is less than five, a correction by the name of *Yates' cerrection* is applied for giving more reliable value of χ^2. For this, we subtract 0.5 from the absolute value of the difference between observed and expected frequency, $|(f_o - f_e)|$.

After determining the value of χ^2, the contingency coefficient (C) may be computed by the use of the formula

$$C = \sqrt{\frac{\chi^2}{N + \chi^2}}$$

EXERCISES

1. What is a chi square test? Discuss its application as a test of singnificance.
2. Discuss in brief the underlying assumptions, limitations and uses of chi square test.
3. What do you understand by the term "goodness of fit"? Discuss how chi square test can be applied to test the goodness of fit with a suitable example.
4. Discuss the use of χ^2 test as a test of independence with the help of an example.
5. What is contingency coefficient? How is it helpful in analyzing and interpreting statistical data? Discuss its application with the help of an example.
6. Out of 100 people who enter a cinema hall, 60 turn to the right and 40 to the left. Test the hypothesis that the people turn right or left, randomly.
7. A dice is tossed 144 times and the five-spot face appears on the top 36 times. Test the hypothesis that the dice is unbiased.
8. A student responds to a 70-item true-false test by guessing the responses to every item. He obtains a score of 45. Does this differ significantly from what would be expected by chance?
9. In a study of colour preference, 48 girl students of a college were asked to select the colour they liked best, out of the three basic colours—red, blue and yellow. The data collected is as follows:

Red	*Blue*	*Yellow*
24	12	12

On the basis of the above data, test the hypothesis that the observed choices do not differ from a random selection.

10. A group of 30 college students were asked to respond on a five point scale to the statement "Seeing Hindi films is a waste of time". The distribution of responses is shown below.

Agree strongly	*Agree slightly*	*Indifferent*	*Disagree slightly*	*Disagree strongly*
5	8	8	6	3

Do these responses diverge significantly from the distribution to be expected by chance or in the case of casual responses made without thinking about the statement.

11. 42 lecturers were rated into three groups, very effective; satisfactory and poor, in terms of their professional competency by their principal as shown below:

Very effective	*Satisfactory*	*Poor*
16	20	6

Does the distribution of ratings differ significantly from that to be expected if professional competency is normally distributed in our population of lecturers?

12. To the question "should women have competition with men in getting jobs", the replies received from a sample of two hundred subjects of both sexes were as follows:

	Yes	*No*	*Total*
Males	34	46	80
Females	72	48	120

Were these responses independent or belong to a particular sex?

13. The responses of these groups of students on an item of Likert's attitude scale were recorded and are as follows:

	Strongly disagree	*Disagree*	*Undecided*	*Agree*	*Strongly agree*	*Total*
Medical College	12	18	4	8	12	54
Engineering College	48	22	10	8	10	98
Law College	10	4	12	10	12	48
Total	70	44	26	26	34	200

At the 1 per cent level of significance do the data indicate that opinions expressed are independent of the kind of college attended by the respondents.

14. Below are given the responses of three groups on an interest inventory. Compute C, the contingency coefficient, to find out if there is a relationship between marital status and interest held. Test the significance of the responses at 1 percent level of confidence.

	Yes	*Undecided*	*No*	*Total*
Single	20	10	10	40
Married	60	10	30	100
Divorced	10	20	30	60
Total	90	40	70	200

15. In a study, a few office clerks belonging to two different socio-economic groups were asked to express their opinion in three categories—yes, no, cannot say anything on the subject "do you prefer radio news to reading a newspaper?" Obtained responses were as follows.

	Yes	*No*	*Can't say anything*	*Total*
Middle class	25	12	5	42
Lower class	20	10	8	38
Total	45	22	13	80

Are socio-economic classes and the opinion expressed independent of each other at the 1 per cent level?

16. In a test of true-false nature, a student made a correct response 3 times and an incorrect 9 times. Can it be said that he was merely guessing?

17. In a study, an equal number of teacher-educators were asked to express their preference for lecture method and discussion method. The data recorded were as follows:

Teacher educators	*Lecture method preferred*	*Discussion method preferred*	*Total*
Male	10	5	15
Female	12	3	15
Total	22	8	30

Is preference for a certain type of method independent of the sex of a teacher educator at the 1 per cent level of significance?

18. A physician wanted to study the effect of the two types of vitamin ingredients in terms of the increase in the weight of small children. He took 15 children of 5 years of age and divided them into two homogenous groups and then administered the treatments. The results were as below:

	Weight increase	*No increase*	*Total*
Treatment A	5	2	7
Treatment B	3	5	8
Total	8	7	15

Test the hypothesis "increase in weight is independent of the treatment applied" at 5% level.

19. In a survey to determine the preference of the employees of an establishment for a particular type of soft drink, the results were recorded as below:

	Coca-cola	*Pepsi*	*Fanta*
Officers (Class I and II employees)	25	30	52
Other staff (Class III and IV)	46	22	28

Was there any relationship between the preference for a particular type of soft drink and the class or status of the employee?

12

Further Methods of Correlations

In Chapter 7, we tried to compute Pearson '*r*'. When both the variables involved in the data were continuous, the relationship between them was linear and the distributions pertaining to these variables were fairly symmetrical within themselves.

However, in case, if the above conditions are not fulfilled, we have to resort to other special measures or methods for computing correlation between the variables. In this chapter, we will throw light on some of these special measures or methods such as *biserial correlation*, *point biserial correlation*, *tetrachoric biserial correlation*, and *phi correlation*. We now discuss these one by one.

THE BISERIAL CORRELATION

In educational or psychological studies, we often come across situations where both the variables correlated are continuously measurable, while one of them is artificially reduced to dichotomy. In such a situation, when we try to compute correlation between a continuous variable and a variable reduced to artificial dichotomy, we always compute the coefficient of biserial correlation. At this point, the question may arise as to what do we mean by a dichotomy as also by an artificial and a natural dichotomy?

The term *dichotomous* means cut into two parts or divided into two categories. This reduction into two categories may be the consequence of the nature of the data obtained. For example, in a study to find out whether or not a student passes or fails a certain standard, we place the crucial point dividing pass and fail students anywhere we please. Hence, measurement in the variable is reduced to two categories (pass and fail). This reduction into two categories, however, is not natural as we can have the crucial or dividing point according to our convenience.

Such a reduction of the variable into two artificial categories (artificial dichotomy) may be seen in the following classifications:

1. Socially adjusted and socially maladjusted
2. Athletic and non-athletic
3. Radical and conservative
4. Poor and not poor
5. Social minded and mechanical minded
6. Drop-outs and stay-ins
7. Successful and unsuccessful
8. Moral and immoral.

If we try to analyze the nature of distributions involving these dichotomized variables (i.e. adjustment in the topmost classification), we can come to the conclusion that artificial dichotomy is based on a clear assumption that the variable underlying the dichotomy should be continuous and normal.

In the two-fold division of socially adjusted and socially maladjusted, the division is quite artificial. If sufficient data were available, we could have found the trait 'adjustment', normally distributed among the studied population and it could have been distributed equally, instead of being discrete or limited (restricted to two-fold division).

In conclusion, we may term a dichotomy (division of a variable into two categories) an artificial dichotomy, when we do not have any clear-cut crucial point or criteria for such a division. We fix the dividing point according to our own convenience. In case sufficient data were available, the continuity as well as the normality of the distribution involving this variable can be easily established. Hence the basic assumption in using biserial correlation as an estimate of the relationship between a continuous variable and a dichotomous variable is that the variable underlying the dichotomy is continuous and normal. This implies that it should be an artificial dichotomous variable rather than a natural dichotomous variable.

Distinction between Artificial and Natural Dichotomy

In contrast to artificial dichotomy, the variable can be reduced to two categories—natural or genuine dichotomy. Here we do not apply an artificial crucial point for the division as we do in artificial dichotomy. The examples of such a division of the related variables into natural or genuine categories are:

1. Scored as 1 and scored as 0
2. Right and wrong
3. Male and female

4. Owning a home and not owning a home
5. Living in Delhi and not living in Delhi
6. Being alcoholic and non-alcolohic
7. Living and dead
8. Delinquent and non-delinquent
9. Colour blind and having normal vision
10. Being a farmer and not being a farmer
11. Having likes and dislikes
12. Being a Ph.D. and not being a Ph.D.

In these categories, the division of the relevant variable into two categories is quite clear. In such cases, even if sufficient data were available, we could not have more than two categories. The answers or responses scored as one and zero or right and wrong, cannot have more than two categories. Similarly, we cannot have more than two divisions in the case of being a Ph.D. and not being a Ph.D.

Thus, before deciding the type of measure of correlation betweer a continuous variable and a variable reduced to dichotomy, we mus try to find out what type of dichotomy-artificial or natural is involved in the categorization of the second variable. If it is artificial, then we should try to compute the coefficient of biserial correlation (r_{bis}). But if there is a genuine or a natural dichotomy, then we should try to compute coefficient of point biserial ($r_{p,\text{bis}}$) instead of r_{bis}.

Computation of Biserial Coefficient of Correlation

FORMULA. The general formula for biserial coefficient of correlation (r_{bis}) is

$$r_{\text{bis}} = \frac{M_p - M_q}{\sigma_t} \times \frac{pq}{y}$$

where

p = Proportion of cases in one of the categories (group) of dichotomous variable
q = Proportion of cases in the lower group = $1 - p$
M_p = Mean (M) of the values of higher group
M_q = Mean (M) of the values of the lower group
σ_t = Standard deviation (SD) of the entire group
y = Height of the ordinate of the normal curve separating the portion p and q

Let us illustrate the use of this formula with an example.

Example 12.1: The following table shows the distribution of scores on an achievement test earned by two groups of students those who passed and those who failed in a test of Arithmetic. Compute the coefficient of biserial correlation.

Scores on a test of achievement	*Result in Arithmetic test*	
	Passed	*Failed*
185–194	7	0
175–184	16	0
165–174	10	6
155–164	35	15
145–154	24	40
135–144	15	26
125–134	10	13
115–124	3	5
105–114	0	5
	120	110

Solution. The formula for calculating r_{bis} is

$$r_{\text{bis}} = \frac{M_p - M_q}{\sigma_t} \times \frac{pq}{y}$$

Based on this, we can assign values to the above variables by using the following steps:

Step 1. Here,

p = Proportion of cases in the higher group

$$= \frac{n_1}{N} = \frac{\text{Those who passed}}{\text{Total No. of students}} = \frac{120}{120 + 110}$$

$$= \frac{120}{130} = .52$$

Step 2. $q = 1 - p = 1 - .52 = .48$

Step 3. y = Height of the normal curve ordinate separating the portions p and q

= .3984 (as read from the Table G given in th Appendix)

Step 4. For the calculation of M_p (Mean of the scores of the passed group), M_q (Mean of the scores of the failed group), and σ_t (Standard deviation of scores of total group), we shall now compute as in Table 12.1.

Table 12.1 Worksheet for Calculating M_p, M_q and σ_t

Achievement test scores	Arithmetic Test: Pass students (higher group)	Arithmetic Test: Failures (lower group)	Total	Higher group x'	Higher group fx'	Lower group y'	Lower group fy'	Entire group z'	Entire group fz'	Entire group fz'^2
185–194	7	0	7	4	28	4	0	4	28	112
175–184	16	0	16	3	48	3	0	3	48	144
165–174	10	6	16	2	20	2	12	2	32	64
155–164	35	15	50	1	35	1	15	1	50	50
145–154	24	40	64	0	0	0	0	0	0	0
135–144	15	26	41	–1	–15	–1	–26	–1	–41	41
125–134	10	13	23	–2	–20	–2	–26	–2	–46	92
115–124	3	5	8	–3	–9	–3	–15	–3	–24	72
105–114	0	5	5	–4	0	–4	–20	–4	–20	80
	$n_1 = 120$	$n_2 = 110$	$N = 230$		$\Sigma fx' = 87$		$\Sigma fy' = -60$		$\Sigma fz' = 27$	$\Sigma fz'^2 = 655$

$$M_p = A + \frac{\Sigma fx'}{N} \times i$$

where

$$A = \text{Assumed mean} = \frac{145 + 154}{2} = 149.5$$

$$x' = \frac{X - A}{i} = \frac{\text{Mid-value of } X \text{ scores} - \text{Assumed mean}}{\text{Class interval}}$$

Here,

N = Total No. of passed students = 120

i = Class interval = 10

Hence

$$M_p = 149.5 + \frac{87}{120} \times 10$$

$$= 149.5 + \frac{87}{12} = 149.5 + 7.25 = 156.75$$

$$M_q = A + \frac{\Sigma fy'}{N} \times i$$

$$= 149.5 + \frac{(-60)}{110} \times 10 = 149.5 - \frac{60}{11}$$

$$= 149.5 - 5.45 = 144.05$$

$$M_p - M_q = 156.75 - 144.05 = 12.70$$

$$\sigma_t = i\sqrt{\frac{fz'^2}{N} - \left(\frac{fz'}{N}\right)^2}$$

$$= 10\sqrt{\frac{655}{230} - \left(\frac{27}{230}\right)^2}$$

$$= 10\sqrt{\frac{655}{230} - \frac{27 \times 27}{230 \times 230}}$$

$$= \frac{10}{230}\sqrt{655 \times 230 - 27 \times 27}$$

$$= \frac{1}{23}\sqrt{149{,}921} = \frac{387.2}{23} = 16.83$$

Step 5. Substitute the value of p, q, y, M_p, M_q and σ_t in the following formula:

$$r_{\text{bis}} = \frac{M_p - M_q}{\sigma_t} \times \frac{pq}{y}$$

$$= \frac{12.7 \times .52 \times .48}{16.83 \times .3984}$$

$$= \frac{127 \times 52 \times 480}{1683 \times 398} = 0.47$$

[**Ans.** Coefficient of biserial correlation, $r_{\text{bis}} = 0.47$.]

Alternative Formula for r_{bis}

The coefficient of biserial correlation, r_{bis}, can also be computed with the help of the following formula:

$$r_{\text{bis}} = \frac{M_p - M_t}{\sigma_t} \times \frac{p}{y}$$

In this formula, we have to compute M_t (mean of the entire group) in place of M_q.

Characteristics of Biserial Correlation

The biserial correlation coefficient, r_{bis}, is computed when one variable is continuous and the other variable is artificially reduced to two categories (dichotomy).

Assumptions. The biserial correlation coefficient, r_{bis} gives an estimate of the product moment r for the given data when the following assumptions are fulfilled:

1. Continuity in the dichotomized trait
2. Normality of the distribution underlying the dichotomy
3. A large N
4. A split near the median

Limitations

1. The biserial r cannot be used in a regression equation.
2. Does not have any standard error of estimate.
3. Is not limited unlike r to a range of ±1.00.
4. Creates problems in matching comparison with other coefficients of correlation.

THE POINT BISERIAL CORRELATION

As already discussed, we resort to the computation of point biserial correlation coefficient ($r_{p,bis}$) for estimating the relationship between two variables when one variable is in a continuous state and the other is in the state of a natural or genuine dichotomy.

We have already thrown light on the nature of genuine or natural dichotomy, by distinguishing it clearly from the artificial dichotomy. Hence, if we are sure that the dichotomized variable does not belong to the category of artificial dichotomy, then we should try to compute point biserial correlation coefficient ($r_{p,\,bis}$).

Computation of Point Biserial Correlation Coefficient ($r_{p,\,bis}$)

FORMULA. The general formula for $r_{p,bis}$ is

$$r_{p,bis} = \frac{M_p - M_q}{\sigma_t}\sqrt{pq}$$

and an alternative for this is

$$r_{p,bis} = \frac{M_p - M_t}{\sigma_t}\sqrt{p/q}$$

where

p = Proportion of cases in one of the categories (higher group) of dichotomous variable

q = Proportion of cases in the lower group = $1 - p$
M_p = Mean of the higher group, the first category of the dichotomous variable
M_q = Mean of the values of lower group
M_t = Mean of the entire group
σ_t = Standard deviation (SD) of the entire group

Example 12.2: The data given in the following table shows the distribution of scores of 100 students on a certain test (X) and on another test (Y) which was simply scored as right or wrong, 1 and 0. Compute the necessary coefficient of correlation.

Scores on Test X	*Those who responded rightly*	*Those who responded wrongly*
70–74	3	0
65–69	6	1
60–64	6	2
55–59	5	4
50–54	6	2
45–49	7	6
40–44	6	8
35–39	3	6
30–34	3	9
25–29	1	4
20–24	0	12
	46	54

Solution. Here we have to compute the correlation between two sets of variables, one of which is in a continuous measure and the other in a genuine dichotomy. Hence it needs the computation of coefficient of point biserial correlation ($r_{p,\text{bis}}$). Therefore, the formula for $r_{p,\text{bis}}$ is

$$r_{p,\,\text{bis}} = \frac{M_p - M_t}{\sigma_t}\sqrt{p/q}$$

For finding the related values of the formula, let us proceed as follows:

Step 1.

p = Proportion of cases in the first group

$$= \frac{46}{100} = 0.46$$

Step 2. $q = 1 - p = 1 - 0.46 = 0.54$

Step 3. Calculation of M_p, M_t and σ_t

The computation process is illustrated in Table 12.2

Table 12.2 Worksheet for Computation of M_p and σ_t

Scores on X	*Those who responded rightly*	*Those who responded wrongly*	*Total*	*x′*	*fx′*	*z′*	*fz′*	*fz′²*
70–74	3	0	3	5	15	5	15	75
65–69	6	1	7	4	24	4	28	112
60–64	6	2	8	3	18	3	24	72
55–59	5	4	9	2	10	2	18	36
50–54	6	2	8	1	6	1	8	8
45–49	7	6	13	0	0	0	0	0
40–44	6	8	14	–1	–6	–1	–14	14
35–39	3	6	9	–2	–6	–2	–18	36
30–34	3	9	12	–3	–9	–3	–36	108
25–29	1	4	5	–4	–4	–4	–20	80
20–24	0	12	12	–5	0	–5	–60	300
	$n_1 = 46$	$n_2 = 54$	$N = 100$		$\Sigma fx' = 48$		$\Sigma fz' = -55$	$\Sigma fz'^2 = 841$

$$M_p = A + \frac{\Sigma fx'}{n_1} \times i = 47 + \frac{48}{46} \times 5 = 47 + 5.2 = 52.2$$

(Here, A = Assumed mean $= \dfrac{45 + 49}{2} = 47$, $i = 5$ and $n_1 = 46$)

$$M_t = A + \frac{\Sigma fz'}{N} \times \text{i} = 47 + \frac{-55}{100} \times 5 = 47 - 2.75 = 44.2$$

$$\sigma_t = i\sqrt{\frac{\Sigma fz'^2}{N} - \left(\frac{\Sigma fz'}{N}\right)^2} = 5\sqrt{\frac{841}{100} - \left(\frac{-55}{100}\right)^2} = 5\sqrt{\frac{841}{100} - \frac{55 \times 55}{100 \times 100}}$$

$$= \frac{5}{100}\sqrt{84{,}100 - 3025} = \frac{1}{20}\sqrt{81{,}075} = \frac{284.73}{20} = 14.236$$

$$r_{p,\text{bis}} = \frac{M_p - M_t}{\sigma_t}\sqrt{p/q} = \frac{52.2 - 44.2}{14.236}\sqrt{0.46/0.54}$$

$$= \frac{8}{14.236}\sqrt{0.8518518} = 0.562\sqrt{0.923} = 0.52$$

[**Ans.** Point biserial correlation coefficient $r_{p,\text{bis}} = 0.52$.]

Which One of the Correlation r_{bis} or $r_{p,bis}$ is Better and Why?

The biserial correlation coefficient, r_{bis} has an advantage over $r_{p,bis}$ in that tables are available from which we can quickly read the values of r_{bis} (with sufficient accuracy). All we need to know are the values of p and q (percentages of passing a given item in relation to the higher and the lower groups). However, as a whole $r_{p,bis}$ is always regarded as a better and a much more dependable statistics than r_{bis} on account of the following features:

- The point biserial correlation makes no assumptions regarding the form of distribution in the dichotomized variable where biserial correlation makes too many assumptions such as continuity, normality, and large N split near the median .
- It may be used in regression equation.
- In comparison to r_{bis}, it can be easily and conveniently computed.
- The point biserial r is a product moment r and can be checked against r. This is usually not possible with r_{bis}.
- Like Pearson r, the range of $r_{p,bis}$ is equal to ± 1, but this is not true for r_{bis}. Due to its range, $r_{p,bis}$ can be easily compared with other measures of correlation.
- The standard error of $r_{p,bis}$ can be exactly determined and its significance can be easily tested against the null hypothesis.
- Although $r_{p,bis}$ and r_{bis} both are useful in item analysis yet r_{bis} is generally not as valid or a defensible measure as $r_{p,bis}$.
- It is always safe to compute $r_{p,bis}$ when we are not sure whether the dichotomy is natural or artificial. However, the use of r_{bis} is always restricted to the artificial dichotomy of the dichotomized variable.

THE TETRACHORIC CORRELATION

Sometimes we find situations where both, the variables are dichotomous (reduced to two categories) and none of them can be expressed in scores. In such situations, we cannot use biserial or point biserial as a measure of correlation between these variables. We can only use Tetrachoric correlation or compute the ϕ (phi) coefficient.

We make use of tetrachoric correlation when these variables have artificial dichotomy. However, the basic assumption of these variables can be stated as follows: *Both variables are continuous, normally distributed and linearly related to each other, if it were possible to obtain scores or exact measures for them.*

In practice, these variables are not expressed in scores, though they are artificially separated into the following categories:

1. To study the relationship between intelligence and emotional maturity, the first variable, "intelligence," may be dichotomized as *above average* and *below average* and the other variable "emotional maturity", as *emotionally mature* and *emotionally immature*.
2. If we want to study the relationship between "adjustment" and "success" in a job, we can dichotomize the variables as *adjusted–maladjusted* and *success–failure*.
3. If we want to seek correlation between "poverty" and "delinquency", we can dichotomize the variables as *poor–not poor*, and *delinquent–non-delinquent*.

Computation of Tetrachoric Correlation

Let us illustrate the computation of tetrachoric correlation with the help of an example.

Example 12.3: In order to seek correlation between adjustment and job success, the data were obtained in a 2 × 2 table as shown in the following representation: Compute the tetrachoric correlation.

	X-variable		
	Success	Failure	
Adjusted	25	35	60
Maladjusted	20	40	60
	45	75	120

In such problems, the contents of entries in a 2 × 2 table are denoted by A, B, C and D, and the formula for computation of tetrachoric correlation (r_t) is as follows:

(i) When $AD > BC$,

$$r_t = \cos\left(\frac{180° \times \sqrt{BC}}{\sqrt{AD} + \sqrt{BC}}\right)$$

Where A, B, C, and D are frequencies in 2 × 2 table. Here the value of r_t is always positive.

(ii) When $BC > AD$,

$$r_t = \cos\left(\frac{180° \times \sqrt{AD}}{\sqrt{AD} + \sqrt{BC}}\right)$$

Here, the value of r_t is always negative.

(iii) When $BC = AD$,

$$r_t = \cos \frac{180° \times \sqrt{AD}}{2\sqrt{AD}} = \cos 90° = 0$$

Here, the value of r_t is always 0.

Worksheet for Computation of Tetrachoric Correlation (r_t)

Y-variable	X-variable: *Success*	*Failure*	*Total*
Adjusted	25 (*A*)	35 (*B*)	60 (*A* + *B*)
Maladjusted	20 (*C*)	40 (*D*)	60 (*C* + *D*)
Total	45 (*A* + *C*)	75 (*B* + *D*)	120 (*A* + *B* + *C* + *D*)

Step 1. Compute *AD* and *BC*:

$$AD = A \times D = 25 \times 40 = 1000$$

$$BC = B \times C = 35 \times 20 = 700$$

Here $AD > BC$. Thus we use the following formula:

Step 2.

$$r_t = \cos\left(\frac{180° \times \sqrt{BC}}{\sqrt{AD} + \sqrt{BC}}\right)$$

Substituting the respective values of *AD* and *BC* in the given formula, we get

$$r_t = \cos\left(\frac{180° \times \sqrt{700}}{\sqrt{1000} + \sqrt{700}}\right)$$

$$r_t = \cos\left(\frac{180° \times 26.4575}{31.6228 + 26.4575}\right)$$

$$= \cos\left(\frac{180° \times 26.4575}{58.0803}\right)$$

$$= \cos\left(\frac{4762.35}{58.08}\right) = \cos 82°$$

Step 3. Convert cos 82° into r_t. (It can be done directly with the help of Table H given in the Appendix.) Then,

$$r_t = 0.139$$

[**Ans.** Tetrachoric correlation = 0.139.]

Limitations of the general formula $r_t = \cos\left(\frac{180° \times \sqrt{BC}}{\sqrt{AD} + \sqrt{BC}}\right)$

$$= \cos \frac{180°}{\sqrt{AD/BC} + 1}$$

The foregoing formula shows good results in computation of r_t only when (i) N is large and (ii) the splits into dichotomized variables are not far removed from the median.

THE PHI (ϕ) COEFFICIENT

In studies where we have to compute correlation between two such variables which are genuinely dichotomous, it is the ϕ coefficient that is computed. Generally, its computation may involve the following situations:

1. When the classification of the variables into two categories is entirely and truly discrete, we are not allowed to have more than two categories, i.e. living vs. dead, employed vs. not employed, blue vs. brown eyes and so on.
2. When we have test items which are scored as Pass-Fail, True-False, or opinion and attitude responses, which are available in the form of yes-no, like-dislike, agree-disagree etc., no other intermediate type of responses is allowed.
3. With such dichotomized variables which may be continuous and may even be normally distributed, but are treated in practical operations as if they were genuine dichotomies, e.g. test items that are scored as either right or wrong, 1 and 0 and the like.

Computation of Phi (ϕ) Coefficient

FORMULA. The formula for computation of ϕ coefficient is

$$\phi = \frac{AD - BC}{\sqrt{(A + B)(C + D)(B + D)(A + C)}}$$

where A, B, C, D represent the frequencies in the cells of the following 2×2 table:

Y-variable	X-variable: Yes	No	Total
Yes	A	B	$A + B$
No	C	D	$C + D$
Total	$A + C$	$B + D$	$A + B + C + D$

Let us illustrate the use of forgoing formula with the help of an example.

Example 12.4: There were two items X and Y in a test which were responded by a sample of 200, given in the 2×2 table. Compute the phi coefficient of correlation between these two items.

Solution.

Item Y	Item X: Yes	No	Total
Yes	55 (A)	45 (B)	100 ($A + B$)
No	35 (C)	65 (D)	100 ($C + D$)
Total	90 ($A + C$)	110 ($B + D$)	200 ($A + B + C + D$)

FORMULA.

$$\phi \text{ coefficient} = \frac{AD - BC}{\sqrt{(A+B)(C+D)(B+D)(A+C)}}$$

Substituting the respective values in the formula, we obtain

$$\phi = \frac{55 \times 65 - 45 \times 35}{\sqrt{100 \times 100 \times 110 \times 90}}$$

$$= \frac{3575 - 1575}{\sqrt{99000000}}$$

$$\phi = \frac{2000}{1000\sqrt{99}} = \frac{2}{\sqrt{99}} = \frac{2}{9.95} = .201$$

[**Ans.** ϕ coefficient = 0.201.]

Features and Characteristics of ϕ Coefficient

- The phi coefficient is used for measuring the correlation between two variables when both are expressed in the form of genuine or natural dichotomies.
- The phi coefficient has the same relation with tetrachoric correlation (r_t) as point biserial ($r_{p,\text{ bis}}$) has with the biserial coefficient (r_{bis}).
- It can be checked against pearson 'r' obtained from the same table.
- It is most useful in item analysis when we want to know the item to item correlation.
- It bears a relationship with χ^2 to be expressed as $\chi^2 = N\phi^2$.
- The values of phi coefficient range between –1 and +1, but these are influenced by marginal totals.
- It makes no assumptions regarding the form of distribution in dichotomized variables like r_t which needs the assumptions of large N and continuity and normality of the distributions.
- For providing a better measure like r_t, it does not require a split near median and large N rather, it proves to be a better measure when the split is away from the median.
- Standard error of ϕ can be easily computed and ϕ can be easily tested against the null hypothesis by means of its relationship to χ^2.
- When there is any doubt regarding the exact nature of the dichotomized variables, it is always safe to compute ϕ. Also, its computation is much easier and regarded as a better and a more dependable statistics than r_t.

SUMMARY

1. Biserial correlation is computed between two variables when one of them is in continuous measure and the other is reduced to artificial dichotomy (forced division into two categories), e.g. pass-fail, adjusted-maladjusted, and poor-rich. The formulae for computing biserial correlation are

$$\text{(i) } r_{\text{bis}} = \frac{M_p - M_q}{\sigma_t} \times \frac{pq}{y}, \quad \text{(ii) } r_{\text{bis}} = \frac{M_p - M_t}{\sigma_t} \times \frac{p}{y}$$

2. Point biserial correlation is used as a measure of relationship between two variables when one variable falls in a continuous scale and the other is in the state of natural or genuine dichotomy, e.g. right-wrong, living-dead, and scored, for instance, as 1 and 0. The formulae for computing point biserial correlation coefficient are

$$\text{(i) } r_{p,\text{bis}} = \frac{M_p - M_q}{\sigma_t}\sqrt{pq}\,, \quad \text{(ii) } r_{p,\text{bis}} = \frac{M_p - M_t}{\sigma_t}\sqrt{p/q}$$

3. In comparison to biserial correlation, point biserial correlation is regarded as a better and a more dependable statistics due to its easy computation, no-requirement of special assumption regarding distributions of variables, exact determination of its standard error, and testing of significance against null hypothesis, usefulness in regression equation, and its verifiability against Pearson '*r*', including the range limits of ±1.
4. Tetrachoric correlation is used as a measure of relationship between two variables when both are reduced to artificial dichotomy (two forced categories) as neither of them is available in terms of continuous measure like scores. For example, when we have data for the adjustment variable as *adjusted-maladjusted* and job success as *success-failure*, then, to find the correlation between "adjustment" and "job success", we have to compute tetrachoric correlation coefficient (r_t). The formula for tetrachoric correlation is

$$r_t = \cos\left(\frac{180° \times \sqrt{BC}}{\sqrt{AD} + \sqrt{BC}}\right) \quad \text{or} \quad \cos\left(\frac{180°}{\sqrt{AD/BC} + 1}\right)$$

where in the 2 × 2 table A, B, C, D represent the cells frequencies.

5. The phi coefficient is that system of correlation which is computed between two variables, where neither of them is available in a continuous measure and both of them are expressed in the form of natural or genuine dichotomies, i.e. items scored as 1–0, right-wrong, yes-no, and so on. The formula for computation of phi coefficient is

$$\phi = \frac{AD - BC}{\sqrt{(A + B)(C + D)(B + D)(A + C)}}$$

where A, B, C, D represent the cell frequencies of the 2 × 2 table.

6. The ϕ coefficient is a proper and a dependable statistics in comparison to r_t. This is because of its ease in computation, less dependence on special assumptions on the nature of distribution of variables, and non-dependence on the use of any table for finding the value of cos measurement, its resemblance with pearson '*r*', determination of SE, and its

testing against null hypothesis by using its relationship with χ^2, reliable use in item analysis and so on.
In fact, it bears the same ratio to r_t as $r_{p,\,bis}$ bears to r_{bis}.

EXERCISES

1. What is biserial correlation? How is it computed?
2. What is point biserial correlation? How is it different from biserial correlation? How is it computed?
3. Discuss, with the help of examples, the various situations when you have to compute r_{bis}, $r_{p,\,bis}$, r_t and ϕ as a measure of relationship between two variables.
4. What is tetrachoric correlation? When is it computed? Discuss its computation process.
5. What is phi coefficient? Why is it regarded as a better and more dependable statistics than tetrachoric correlation? Discuss its computational process.
6. Compute the coefficient of biserial correlation from the given data to know the extent to which success on job is related to adjustment.

Scores on adjustment scale	*Success on job*	*Failure on job*
95–99	1	0
90–94	6	0
85–89	18	1
80–84	22	1
75–79	31	3
70–74	20	5
65–69	18	9
60–64	12	13
55–59	6	10
50–54	4	8
45–49	1	5
40–44	0	3
35–39	1	0
30–34	0	1
25–29	0	1
	140	60

7. (a) Find the coefficient of biserial correlation from the following data:

Performance scores	*Normal and above intelligence*	*Below normal intelligence*
130–139	5	0
120–129	7	0
110–119	21	3
100–109	26	7
90–99	30	16
80–89	27	21
70–79	10	11
60–69	3	4
50–59	1	6
40–49	0	2
	130	70

(b) A group of students, with and without training, obtained the following scores on a performance test. Find out the biserial correlation between training and performance:

Performance test scores	*Trained*	*Untrained*
90–99	6	0
80–89	19	3
70–79	31	5
60–69	58	17
50–59	40	30
40–49	18	14
30–39	9	7
20–29	5	4
	186	80

8. (a) Compute the point biserial correlation coefficient from the data given in Problem 6.

(b) A group of individuals were asked to answer 'yes' or 'no' for a particular item. Compute the point biserial correlation coefficient between the item and total score from the following data:

Total scores on the opinion scale	Yes	No
95–99	0	1
90–94	1	1
85–89	0	6
80–84	2	11
75–79	4	6
70–74	6	9
65–69	8	3
60–64	3	2
55–59	2	1
50–54	6	0
45–49	2	0
40–44	3	0
35–39	1	0
30–34	1	0
	39	40

9. (a) Compute tetrachoric correlation from the given data to find the relationship between emotional maturity and the state of married life.

	Happy married life	*Unhappy married life*
Emotionally mature	65	35
Emotionally immature	25	75
	90	110

(b) 125 students were first tested on a test of achievement motivation and then on a test of anxiety, and the results were tabulated as follows: Find the tetrachoric correlation between the level of achievement motivation and anxiety.

	High anxiety level	*Low anxiety level*
High achievement motivation	30	40
Low achievement motivation	35	20
	65	60

10. (a) 100 individuals in a survey sample responded to items Nos. 15 and 20 of an interest invertary (in "yes" or "no") as given in the following table. Compute the ϕ coefficient with the help of cell frequencies.

Item No. 15

Item No. 20	*No*	*Yes*
Yes	27	20
No	24	29
	51	49

(b) The number of candidates passing and failing in two items of a test are given in the following tabular representation.

Item No. 1

Item No. 2	*Pass*	*Fail*
Pass	80	55
Fail	20	70
	100	125

Compute phi coefficient between these two items.

13

Partial and Multiple Correlation

NEED AND IMPORTANCE OF PARTIAL CORRELATION

While conducting studies in the field of education and psychology, we often find that the relationship between two variables is greatly influenced by a third variable or an additional variable. In such a situation, it becomes quite difficult to have a reliable and an independent estimate of correlation between these two variables unless there is some possibility of nullifying the effects of a third variable (or a number of other variables) on the variables in question. It is the partial correlation which helps in such a situation for nullifying the undesired influence of a third or any additional variable on the relationship of the two variables.

Let us illustrate such a possibility with the help of an example. Suppose in a study, we want to know the effect of participation in co-curricular activities upon the academic achievement. For this, we take the sample of students studying in various schools. We collect two types of scores regarding their performance in co-curricular activities and academic achievement and then try to find a measure of correlation between these two variables. A close analysis of the factors affecting the academic achievement or participation in co-curricular activities may reveal that both these variables are certainly influenced by so many other factors or variables like intelligence, socio-economic status, environmental differences, age, health and physique and other similar factors.

However, in our study, we are only concerned with the evaluation of the correlation between participation in co-curricular activities and academic achievement. Our aim is to have an independent and a reliable measure of correlation between these two variables. It can only happen when we first adopt some measures to nullify the effect of the intervening variables like intelligence, socio-economic status, age, and health, on both the variables being correlated. In other words, there is an urgent need for exercising control over all other variables and factors except the two whose relationship we have to measure.

There are two ways of controlling or ruling out the influence of undesirable or intervening variables on the two variables being correlated. One calls for experimental technique in which we can select students of the same intelligence, socio-economic status, age, health and physique, and thus apply the matching pair technique. However, to select and make use of such a sample is quite impracticable. Here we may have to reduce drastically the size of our sample. Otherwise, matching them for so many factors will be a cumbersome task; also, it will neither be feasible nor appropriate.

Another, and the most practicable and convenient way, is to exercise statistical control. In this, we hold the undesirable or the intervening variables constant through the partial correlation method. Here, we can make use of the whole data without sacrificing any information as needed in the experimental method, for making equal and matching pairs.

Partial correlation can thus be described as a special correlation technique, which is helpful in estimating independent and reliable relationship between any two variables by eliminating and ruling out any undesirable influence or interference of a third or an additional variable on the variables being correlated.

Assumption. The partial correlation technique is based on the following important assumption:

> *Control the main variables (two or three) and they will automatically control so many other variables since other variables are related to these controlled variables.*

Working on this assumption in the following example, we can attempt at eliminating a few intervening variables like intelligence and socio-economic status to study the correlation between academic achievement and participation in co-curricular activities. The other intervening variables such as age, health and physique, environmental condition, education and health of the parents, living habits and temperament will be automatically controlled.

Computation of Partial Correlation

We now give some formulae for the computation of partial correlation.

1. **Formulae for the Computation of First Order Partial Correlation:**

$$r_{12.3} = \frac{r_{12} - r_{13} - r_{23}}{\sqrt{1-r_{13}^2}\sqrt{1-r_{23}^2}}$$

$$r_{13.2} = \frac{r_{13} - r_{12}\, r_{23}}{\sqrt{1-r_{12}^2}\sqrt{1-r_{23}^2}}$$

$$r_{23.1} = \frac{r_{23} - r_{12}\, r_{13}}{\sqrt{1-r_{12}^2}\sqrt{1-r_{13}^2}}$$

First order partial correlations are those in which the relationship between two variables is estimated while making the third variable constant or partialled out.

2. **Formula for the Computation of Second Order Partial Correlation:**

$$r_{12.34} = \frac{r_{12.3} - r_{14.3}\, r_{24.3}}{\sqrt{1-r_{14.3}^2}\sqrt{1-r_{24.3}^2}}$$

3. **Formula for the Computation of Third Order Partial Correlation:**

$$r_{12.345} = \frac{r_{12.34} - r_{15.34}\, r_{25.34}}{\sqrt{1-r_{15.34}^2}\sqrt{1-r_{25.34}^2}}$$

The second or the third order partial correlations are those correlations in which the relationship between two variables is estimated while making two or three other variables constant or partialled out.

Let us now clarify the concept and working of these formulae with the help of an example. Let

1 = Achievement scores
2 = Participation in co-curricular activities scores
3 = IQ scores
4 = Socio-economic status scores
5 = Age score

Hence in the first order partial correlation, $r_{12.3}$ means the correlation between 1 and 2 (achievement and participation in co-curricular activities) while making the third variable "intelligence" as constant or partialled out.

In the second order partial correlation, $r_{12.34}$ means correlation between 1 and 2 (achievement and participation) while making the third and fourth ("intelligence" and "socio-economic status") as constant or partialled out.

In the third order partial correlation, $r_{12.345}$ means the correlation between 1 and 2 while making the third, fourth and fifth variables (i.e. "intelligence", "socio-economic status" and "age") constant or partialled out.

In this way, the number to the right of the decimal point (here in first order 3, second order 34, third order 345) represents variables whose influence is ruled out and the number to the left (here 12) represents those two variables whose relationship needs to be estimated.

It is also clear from the given formulae that, for computation of second order correlations, all the necessary first order correlations have to be computed, and for the third order correlations, the second order correlations must be known.

Let us now illustrate the process of computation of partial correlation with the help of examples.

Example 13.1: From a certain number of schools in Delhi, a sample of 500 students studying in classes IX and X was taken. These students were evaluated in terms of their academic achievement and participation in co-curricular activities. Their IQ's were also tested. The correlation among these three variables was obtained and recorded as follows:

$$r_{12} = 0.18, \qquad r_{23} = 0.70, \qquad r_{13} = 0.60$$

Find out the independent correlation between the main (first two) variables—academic achievement and participation—in co-curricular activities.

Solution. The independent and reliable correlation between academic achievement and participation in co-curricular activities—the main two variables—can be found by computing partial correlation between these two variables, i.e. by computing $r_{12.3}$ (keeping constant the third variable)

$$r_{12.3} = \frac{r_{12} - r_{13}\, r_{23}}{\sqrt{1 - r_{13}^2}\sqrt{1 - r_{23}^2}}$$

Substituting the given value of correlation in the foregoing formula, we obtain

$$r_{12.3} = \frac{0.80 - 0.60 \times 0.70}{\sqrt{1 - 0.60 \times 0.60}\sqrt{1 - 0.70 \times 0.70}}$$

$$= \frac{0.80 - 0.42}{\sqrt{1 - 0.36}\sqrt{1 - 0.49}}$$

$$= \frac{0.38}{\sqrt{0.64}\sqrt{0.51}} = \frac{0.38}{0.8 \times 0.714}$$

$$= \frac{0.38}{0.5712} = \frac{3800}{5712} = \frac{1900}{2856} = 0.67$$

[**Ans.** Partial correlation = 0.67.]

Example 13.2: While pursuing further with the experiment in the sample cited in Example 13.1, the researcher also collected data regarding socio-economic status (fourth variable) of all the 500 students and then recorded the computed correlations as follows:

$$r_{12} = .80, \quad r_{23} = .70, \quad r_{13} = .60, \quad r_{14} = .50$$
$$r_{24} = .40 \text{ and } r_{34} = .30$$

Compute the independent correlation between academic achievement and participation in co-curricular activities of the main variables.

Solution. Here, the researcher has to exercise control or partial out the two intervening variables, viz. variable 3 (i.e. intelligence), and variable 4 (i.e. socio-economic status). Hence the problem requires the computation of second order partial correlation.
The formula required for such a correlation is

$$r_{12.34} = \frac{r_{12.3} - r_{14.3}\, r_{24.3}}{\sqrt{1 - r_{14.3}^2}\,\sqrt{1 - r_{24.3}^2}}$$

Since we have already computed the value of $r_{12.3}$ in Example 13.1 as $r_{12.3} = 0.67$, now we have to compute only the values of $r_{14.3}$ and $r_{24.3}$.
Thus,

$$r_{14.3} = \frac{r_{14} - r_{13}\, r_{34}}{\sqrt{1 - r_{13}^2}\,\sqrt{1 - r_{34}^2}}$$

$$= \frac{.50 - (.60 \times .30)}{\sqrt{1 - .60 \times .60}\,\sqrt{1 - .30 \times .30}}$$

$$= \frac{.50 - .18}{\sqrt{1 - .36}\,\sqrt{1 - .09}} = \frac{.32}{\sqrt{.64 \times .91}}$$

$$= \frac{3200}{\sqrt{64 \times 91}} - \frac{50}{91} = 0.42$$

$$r_{24.3} = \frac{r_{24} - r_{23}\, r_{34}}{\sqrt{1 - r_{23}^2}\,\sqrt{1 - r_{34}^2}}$$

$$= \frac{.40 - .70 \times .30}{\sqrt{1 - .70 \times .70}\,\sqrt{1 - .30 \times .30}}$$

$$= \frac{.40 - .21}{\sqrt{1 - .49}\,\sqrt{1 - .09}} = \frac{.19}{\sqrt{.51}\,\sqrt{.91}}$$

$$= \frac{.19}{.714 \times .953} = \frac{190{,}000}{714 \times 953} = 0.28$$

$$r_{12.34} = \frac{.67 - (.55 \times .28)}{\sqrt{1 - (.55 \times .55)}\sqrt{1 - (.28 \times .28)}}$$

$$= \frac{.5160}{\sqrt{1 - .3205}\sqrt{1 - .0784}}$$

$$= \frac{.5160}{\sqrt{.6975}\sqrt{.9216}} = \frac{.5160}{.835 \times .96}$$

$$= \frac{.5160}{.8016} = \frac{5160}{8016} = .64$$

[**Ans**. Partial correlation = 0.64.]

Application of Partial Correlation

Partial correlation can be used as a special statistical technique for eliminating the effects of one or more variables on the two main variables, for which we want to compute an independent and a reliable measure of correlation. Besides its major advantage lies in the fact that it enables us to set up a multiple regression equation (see Chapter 14) of two or more variables, by means of which we can predict another variable or criterion.

Significance of Partial Correlation Coefficient

The significance of the first and the second order partial correlation '*r*' can be tested easily by using the '*t*' distribution

$$t = r\sqrt{\frac{N - 2 - K}{1 - r^2}}$$

where

K = Order of partial r
r = Value of partial correlation
N = Total frequencies in the sample study

Therefore,

$$\text{Degree of freedom} = N - 2 - K$$

NEED AND IMPORTANCE OF MULTIPLE CORRELATION

In many studies related to education and psychology, we find that a variable is dependent on a number of other variables called *independent variables*. For example, if we take the case of one's academic achievement, it may be found associated with or dependent on variables like intelligence, socio-economic status, education of the parents, the methods of teaching, the quality of teachers, aptitude, interest, environmental set-up, number of hours spent on studies and so on. All these independent variables affect the achievement scores obtained by the students. If we want to study the combined effect or influence of these variables on a single dependent variable, then we have to compute a special statistic called *coefficient of multiple correlation*.

The coefficient of multiple correlation signifies a statistic used for denoting the strength of relationship between one variable, called *dependent variable,* and two or more variables, called *independent variables.* In simple terms, therefore, by multiple correlation, we mean the relationship between one variable and a combination of two or more variables.

Let us make the meaning of the term clearer by taking the simple case of one dependent variable and two independent variables, known for exercising their influence on the dependent variable. Once again, let this dependent variable be "academic success" (to be obtained from achievement scores in an examination). We can have two independent variables which are well known for their impact on academic success, namely, general intelligence (to be known through a battery of intelligence tests) and socio-economic status (known through a scale). We can name the dependent variable as X_1, and the two independent variables as X_2 and X_3. In order to compute multiple correlation here, we try to find out the measure of correlation between X_1 and the combined effects of X_2 and X_3. In such a case, we designate the required multiple correlation coefficient as $R_{1.23}$, meaning thereby that we are computing a correlation between the dependent variable 1, and the combination of the two independent variables 2 and 3.

Computation of Multiple Correlation

Formula for Computation of Multiple Correlation Coefficient:

$$R_{1.23} = \sqrt{\frac{r_{12}^2 + r_{13}^2 - 2r_{12}\,r_{13}\,r_{23}}{1 - r_{23}^2}}$$

where, $R_{1.23}$ denotes the coefficient of multiple correlation between the dependent variable X_1 and the combination of two independent variables X_2 and X_3, in

r_{12} = Correlation between X_1 and X_2
r_{13} = Correlation between X_1 and X_3
r_{23} = Correlation between X_2 and X_3

Let us now illustrate the use of this formula.

Example 13.3: In a study, a researcher wanted to know the impact of a person's intelligence and his socio-economic status on his academic success. For computing the coefficient of multiple correlation, he collected the required data and computed the following inter-correlations:

$$r_{12} = 0.60, \qquad r_{13} = 0.40, \qquad r_{23} = 0.50$$

where 1, 2, 3 represent the variables "academic success", "intelligence" and "socio-economic status", respectively. In this case, find out the required multiple correlation coefficient.

Solution. The multiple correlation coefficient

$$R_{1.23} = \sqrt{\frac{r_{12}^2 + r_{13}^2 - 2r_{12} \cdot r_{13} \cdot r_{23}}{1 - r_{23}^2}}$$

Substituting the respective values of r_{12}, r_{13} and r_{23} in the above formula, we get

$$R_{1.23} = \sqrt{\frac{0.60^2 + 0.40^2 - 2 \times 0.60 \times 0.40 \times 0.50}{1 - (0.50)^2}}$$

$$= \sqrt{\frac{0.36 + 0.16 - 0.24}{1 - 0.25}} = \sqrt{\frac{0.28}{0.75}} = \sqrt{0.3733}$$

[**Ans.** Multiple correlation coefficient = 0.61.]

Other Methods of Computing Coefficient of Multiple Correlation

Multiple correlation coefficient can also be computed by other means like below.

First, it can be done with the help of partial correlation. Thus,

$$R_{1.23} = \sqrt{1 - \left(1 - r_{12}^2\right)\left(1 - r_{13.2}^2\right)}$$

In this formula, to understand the relationship between variable 1 and the combined effect of variables 2 and 3, we compute the multiple correlation coefficient. The formula requires the values of r_{12} (correlation between 1 and 2) and the partial correlation $r_{13.2}$, which can be computed by using the formula

$$r_{13.2} = \frac{r_{13} - r_{12} r_{23}}{\sqrt{1 - r_{12}^2}\sqrt{1 - r_{23}^2}}$$

However, in case if there are four variables instead of three, then we can compute the multiple correlation coefficient as

$$R_{1.234} = \sqrt{1-(1-r_{12}^2)(1-r_{13.2}^2)(1-r_{14.23}^2)}$$

where

r_{12} = Correlation between 1 and 2
$r_{13.2}$ = First order partial correlation
$r_{14.23}$ = Second order partial correlation

The value of $r_{14.23}$ can be computed by the following formula:

$$r_{14.23} = \frac{r_{14.2} - r_{13.2}\, r_{34.2}}{\sqrt{1-r_{13.2}^2}\sqrt{1-r_{34.2}^2}}$$

Secondly, multiple correlation coefficient can also be computed with the help of standard partial regression coefficient called betas, which are used in multiple regression equation (see Chapter 14). Now,

$$R_{1.23} = \sqrt{\beta_{12.3}\, r_{12} + \beta_{13.2}\, r_{13}}$$

where

$$\beta_{12.3} = \frac{r_{12} - r_{13}\, r_{23}}{1-r_{23}^2}$$

$$\beta_{13.2} = \frac{r_{13} - r_{12}\, r_{23}}{1-r_{23}^2}$$

Note: These two methods are used only when we have the required partial correlations or the values of β_1, β_2, ... In most of the cases, it is quite economical to make use of the general formula

$$R_{12.3} = \sqrt{\frac{r_{12}^2 + r_{13}^2 - 2r_{12} \cdot r_{13} \cdot r_{23}}{1-r_{23}^2}}$$

Let us make use of this formula to find solutions to some more problems.

Example 13.4: A researcher was interested in studying the relationship between success in a job and the training received. He collected data regarding these and treated them as the two main variables and added a third variable, "interest" (measured by interest inventory). The correlations among these three variables were

$$r_{12} = .41, \qquad r_{13} = .50, \qquad r_{23} = .16.$$

This data enabled him to compute the multiple correlation coefficient and thus to find out the relationship between success in the job and the combined effect of the two independent variables—"training" and "interest". Find the value of the correlation coefficient in his study.

Solution. The multiple correlation coefficient is given by

$$R_{1.23} = \sqrt{\frac{r_{12}^2 + r_{13}^2 - 2r_{12}\,r_{13}r_{23}}{1 - r_{23}^2}}$$

$$= \sqrt{\frac{0.41^2 + 0.50^2 - 2 \times 0.41 \times 0.50 \times 0.16}{1 - (0.16)^2}}$$

$$= \sqrt{\frac{0.1681 + 0.2500 - 0.0656}{1 - 0.0256}}$$

$$= \sqrt{\frac{0.4181 - 0.0656}{0.9744}} = \sqrt{\frac{0.3525}{0.9744}} = \sqrt{0.3618}$$

$$= 0.601$$

[**Ans**. Multiple correlation coefficient = 0.601.]

Example 13.5: One thousand candidates appeared for an entrance test. The test had some sub-tests, namely, general intelligence test, professional awareness test, general knowledge test and aptitude test. A researcher got interested in knowing the impact or the strength of the association of any two sub-tests on the total entrance test scores (X_1). Initially, he took two sub-tests scores—intelligence test scores (X_2) and professional awareness scores (X_3)—and derived the necessary correlations. Compute the multiple correlation coefficient for measuring the strength of relationship between X_1 and ($X_2 + X_3$), if $r_{12} = .80$, $r_{13} = .70$ and $r_{23} = .60$.

Solution. The multiple correlation coefficient

$$R_{1.23} = \sqrt{\frac{r_{12}^2 + r_{13}^2 - 2r_{12}\,r_{13}\,r_{23}}{1 - r_{23}^2}}$$

$$= \sqrt{\frac{0.80^2 + 0.70^2 - 2 \times 0.80 \times 0.70 \times 0.60}{1 - 0.60^2}}$$

$$= \sqrt{\frac{0.640 + 0.490 - 0.672}{1 - 0.36}} = \sqrt{\frac{0.458}{0.64}}$$

$$= \sqrt{\frac{458}{640}} = \sqrt{0.7156} = 0.845$$

[**Ans.** Multiple correlation coefficient = 0.845.]

Characteristics of Multiple Correlation

- Multiple correlation is the correlation that helps one to measure the strength of association of a dependent variable with two or more independent variables.
- It is related to the correlations of independent variables as well as to the correlations of these variables with the dependent variable.
- It helps us estimate the combined effect or influence of the independent variables on the dependent variable.
- It helps in the selection and rejection of the sub-tests for a particular test or tests.
- For proper computation of multiple correlation it is desirable that the number of cases and, especially, the number of variables, be large.
- The multiple correlation coefficient R is always positive, less than 1.00, and is greater than the zero order correlation coefficients $r_{12}, r_{13}, \ldots$.

Significance of Multiple Correlation Coefficient *R*

The significance of multiple correlation R can be easily tested with the help of its standard error. The standard error of multiple R can be computed by using the following formula:

$$SE_R = \frac{1 - R^2}{\sqrt{N - m}}$$

where

m = Number of variables being correlated
N = Size of the sample
$N - m$ = Degree of freedom

SUMMARY

1. Partial correlation, as a special type of correlation technique, is used to exercise statistical control for partialling out, or holding constant, undesirable or intervening variables in order to make possible the measurement of association between any two variables under study.
2. The formulae used for the computation of partial correlation coefficients are as follows:
   For first order partial correlation,

$$r_{12.3} = \frac{r_{12} - r_{13}\, r_{23}}{\sqrt{1 - r_{13}^2}\sqrt{1 - r_{23}^2}}$$

where $r_{12.3}$ means that the partial correlation coefficient which helps in estimating the correlation between variables 1 and 2 by partialling out variable 3 and r_{12}, r_{13} and r_{23} are correlations between the variables 1 and 2, 1 and 3, and 2 and 3, respectively.

For second order partial correlation,

$$r_{12.34} = \frac{r_{12.3} - r_{14.3}\, r_{24.3}}{\sqrt{1 - r_{14.3}^2}\,\sqrt{1 - r_{24.3}^2}}$$

where $r_{12.34}$ represents the partial correlation coefficient which helps in estimating the correlation between variables 1 and 2 by partialling out variables 3 and 4, while $r_{12.3}$, $r_{14.3}$ and $r_{24.3}$ are the first order partial correlation coefficients.

3. Partial correlation helps us in setting up a multiple regression equation of two or more variables to be employed for prediction purposes. The significance of partial correlation can be tested by using '*t*' distribution. The values of '*t*' can be computed by the formula

$$t = r\sqrt{\frac{N-2-K}{1-r^2}}$$

where

$N - 2 - K$ = Degree of freedom

K = Order of partial '*r*'

4. Multiple correlation, as a special correlational technique, is used to measure the strength of relationship between a dependent variable and a combination of two or more independent variables. For dependent variable 1 and independent variables 2 and 3, it is denoted by the $R_{1.23}$ and computed by the formula

$$R_{1.23} = \sqrt{\frac{r_{12}^2 + r_{13}^2 - 2r_{12}\, r_{13}\, r_{23}}{1 - r_{23}^2}}$$

where r_{12}, r_{13}, r_{23} are the correlations between variables 1 and 2, 1 and 3, and 2 and 3.

5. Multiple correlation coefficient can also be computed by using the formula

$$R_{1.23} = \sqrt{1 - \left(1 - r_{12}^2\right)\left(1 - r_{13.2}^2\right)}$$

Here, r_{12} represents the correlation between variables 1 and 2 and $r_{13.2}$ the first order partial correlation between variables 1 and 3 (while keeping variable 2 as constant).

6. The multiple correlation coefficient R is always positive and less than 1.0. It helps estimate the combined effect of two or more independent variables on a single dependent variable. Because of this contribution, it has its wide utility in the selection and rejection of the tests used in a battery.
7. The significance of multiple R can be tested by making use of its standard Error (SE) that can be computed by the use of the formula

$$SE_R = \frac{1-R^2}{\sqrt{N-m}}$$

where

$N - m$ = Degree of freedom
N = Size of the sample, and
m = Number of variables being correlated

EXERCISES

1. What do you mean by partial correlation? Describe its characteristics and applications. Discuss the situations where it is used in educational and psychological studies by citing specific examples.
2. What is multiple correlation? Describe its characteristics and applications. Discuss where you would like to use it in the educational and psychological investigations by citing specific examples.
3. An investigator, during one of his studies, collected some data and arrived at the following conclusions:
   (a) The correlation between height and weight = 0.80
   (b) The correlation between weight and age = 0.50
   (c) The correlation between height and age = 0.60

   Compute the net correlation between height and weight by partialling out the third variable, viz age.
4. (a) Compute the partial correlation coefficients ($r_{23.1}$) from the data given in Example 3 for computing correlation between weight and age by partialling out the third variable, viz. height.

   (b) Compute $r_{13.2}$ the net correlation between height and age, by partialling out the third variable, namely, weight.
5. During test construction, an investigator obtained the following results:
   (a) Correlation between total test score and a sub-test = 0.72

(b) Correlation between total test score and another sub-test = 0.36

(c) Correlation between both the sub-tests = 0.54

Compute the multiple correlation between the total test (X_1) and the combination of the sub-tests X_2 and X_3.

6. In an experimental study, a researcher obtained the following results:

(a) The correlation between learning (X) and motivation (Y) = .67

(b) The correlation between learning (X) and hours per week devoted to study (Z) = 0.75

(c) The correlation between motivation (Y) and hours per week devoted to study (Z) = 0.63

Find out the multiple correlation between X (the dependent variable) and the combination of Y and Z (the independent variables).

14

Regression and Prediction

REGRESSION

Concept of Regression Lines and Regression Equations

The coefficient of correlation tells us the way in which two variables are related to each other. How the change in one is influenced by a change in the other may be explained in terms of direction and magnitude of these measures. However, a coefficient of correlation between two variables cannot prove to be a good estimate for predicting the change in one variable in some systematic way, with the change in the other variable. For example, we cannot predict the IQ scores of a student with the help of academic achievement scores unless this correlation is perfect. In most of the data related to education and psychology, the correlations are hardly found to be perfect. Therefore, for reliable prediction, we generally use the concept of regression lines and regression equations. Let us see what it means and how it can help in this task.

In a scatter diagram of the scores of two variables, if we try to compute the means for each of the columns, we may find that they all lie on a straight line. Similarly, the means for each of the rows may also be found to fall nearly in a straight line. Each of these straight lines is known as the line of regression. One of these regression lines is linked with the regression of Y variable on X variable and is represented by the equation

$$Y - M_y = r\frac{\sigma_y}{\sigma_x}(X - M_x)$$

This equation helps predict the score value of Y variable in correspondence with any value of the X variable.

The other regression line is linked with the regression of X variable on Y variable and is represented by the equation

$$X - M_x = r\frac{\sigma_x}{\sigma_y}(Y - M_y)$$

This equation helps to predict the score value of the X variable in correspondence with any value of the Y variable.

In these equations, X and Y alternately represent a given score and a score to be predicted. M_x and M_y represent means for the X and Y variables, σ_x and σ_y represent the values of standard deviations for the distributions of X and Y scores, and r represents Pearson's r for the variables X and Y.

In this way, there are two regression equations, one for the prediction of scores on Y variable and the other for the prediction of scores on X variable.

Procedure for the Use of Regression Lines

Let us now understand the use of regression lines with the help of some examples.

Case I: Computation of regression equations when all the desired statistics are given

Example 14.1: Given the following data

Marks in History (X)	*Marks in English (Y)*
$M_x = 75.00$	$M_y = 70.00$
$\sigma_x = 6.00$	$\sigma_y = 8.00$

$$r = 0.72$$

determine the regression equations and predict

1. the marks in English of a student whose marks in History are 65, and
2. the marks in History of a student whose marks in English are 50.

Solution. The equation for the prediction of Y is:

$$Y - M_y = r\frac{\sigma_y}{\sigma_x}(X - M_x)$$

Substituting all the known values

$$Y - 70 = 0.72 \times \frac{8}{6}(X - 75)$$

$$= 0.96X - 72$$

$$Y = 0.96X - 2$$

when

$$X = 65, \quad Y = 0.96 \times 65 - 2 = 62.4 - 2 = 60.4$$

The equation for the prediction of X is

$$X - M_x = r\frac{\sigma_x}{\sigma_y}(Y - M_y)$$

Substituting the values in this equation, we get

$$X - 75 = 0.72 \times \frac{6}{8}(Y - 70)$$

$$X = 75 + 0.54(Y - 70)$$

$$X = 75 + 0.54Y - 37.8$$

$$X = 0.54Y + 37.2$$

When $Y = 50$, we have

$$X = 0.54 \times 50 + 37.2 = 27.00 + 37.2 = 64.2$$

Case II: Computation of regression equations from the scatter diagram data

Example 14.2: Compute the two regression equations for the prediction of both the variables of the scatter diagram data given in Table 7.5.

Solution. The equation for the prediction of Y is

$$Y - M_y = r\frac{\sigma_y}{\sigma_x}(X - M_x)$$

and the equation for the prediction of X is

$$X - M_x = r\frac{\sigma_x}{\sigma_y}(Y - M_y)$$

The value of r, as computed earlier from the given scatter diagram, is 0.54. Now we have to compute the values of M_x, M_y, σ_x and σ_y.

1. M_x = Mean for the distribution of X Scores

$$= A + \frac{\Sigma fx'}{N} \times i_x$$

where

i_x = Class interval for X distribution

$$= 18.50 + \frac{10}{85} \times 2$$

$$= 18.50 + 0.24 = 18.74$$

2. M_y = Mean for the distribution of Y scores

$$= A + \frac{\Sigma fy'}{N} \times i_y$$

(where i_y = class interval for Y distribution)

$$= 27 + \frac{9}{85} \times 3 = 27 + \frac{27}{85}$$

$$= 27 + .32 = 27.32$$

3.
$$\sigma_x = i_x \sqrt{\frac{\Sigma fx'^2}{N} - \left(\frac{\Sigma fx'}{N}\right)^2} = 2\sqrt{\frac{174}{85} - \frac{100}{85 \times 85}}$$

$$= \frac{2}{85}\sqrt{174 \times 85 - 100} = \frac{2}{85}\sqrt{14{,}690}$$

$$= \frac{2}{85} \times 121.2 = 2.85$$

4.
$$\sigma_y = i_y \sqrt{\frac{\Sigma fy'^2}{N} - \left(\frac{\Sigma fy'}{N}\right)^2} = 3\sqrt{\frac{119}{85} - \frac{81}{85 \times 85}}$$

$$= \frac{3}{85}\sqrt{10{,}115 - 81} = \frac{3}{85}\sqrt{10{,}034}$$

$$= \frac{3 \times 100.16}{85} = 3.53$$

$$r\frac{\sigma_y}{\sigma_x} = 0.54 \times \frac{3.53}{2.85} = \frac{1.90}{2.85} = 0.66$$

$$r\frac{\sigma_x}{\sigma_y} = 0.54 \times \frac{2.85}{3.53} = \frac{1.54}{3.53} = 0.44$$

Therefore, the regression equations is

$$Y - 27.32 = 0.66(X - 18.74)$$

or $$Y - 27.32 = 0.66X - 12.37$$

or $$Y = 0.66X + 27.32 - 12.37$$

or $$Y = 0.66X + 14.95$$

and $$X - 18.74 = 0.44(Y - 27.32)$$

or $$X = 18.74 + 0.44Y - 12.02$$

or $$X = 0.44Y + 6.72$$

Case III: Computation of regression equations directly from raw data

Example 14.3: Given the following data, find the two regression equations.

$X = 2, \quad 3, \quad 6, \quad 4, \quad 5, \quad 4$

$Y = 1, \quad 3, \quad 4, \quad 2, \quad 5, \quad 3$

Solution. The regression equations are:

$$Y - M_y = r\,\frac{\sigma_y}{\sigma_x}(X - M_x)$$

$$X - M_x = r\,\frac{\sigma_x}{\sigma_y}(Y - M_y)$$

In these equations, $r\sqrt{\sigma_y/\sigma_x}$ and $r\sqrt{\sigma_x/\sigma_y}$ (called regression co-efficients) are calculated by using the following formulae:

$$r\frac{\sigma_y}{\sigma_x} = \frac{N\Sigma XY - \Sigma X \cdot \Sigma Y}{N\Sigma X^2 - (\Sigma X)^2}$$

$$r\frac{\sigma_x}{\sigma_y} = \frac{N\Sigma XY - \Sigma X \cdot \Sigma Y}{N\Sigma Y^2 - (\Sigma Y)^2}$$

Individuals	X	Y	XY	X^2	Y^2
A	2	1	2	4	1
B	3	3	9	9	9
C	6	4	24	36	16
D	4	2	8	16	4
E	5	5	25	25	25
F	4	3	12	16	9
$N = 6$	$\Sigma X = 24$	$\Sigma Y = 18$	$\Sigma XY = 80$	$\Sigma X^2 = 106$	$\Sigma Y^2 = 64$

Here,

$$M_x = \frac{\Sigma X}{N} = \frac{24}{6} = 4$$

$$M_y = \frac{\Sigma Y}{N} = \frac{18}{6} = 3$$

$$r\frac{\sigma_y}{\sigma_x} = \frac{6 \times 80 - 24 \times 18}{6 \times 106 - 24 \times 24} = \frac{480 - 432}{636 - 576}$$

$$= \frac{48}{60} = \frac{4}{5} = 0.8$$

$$r\frac{\sigma_x}{\sigma_y} = \frac{6 \times 80 - 24 \times 18}{6 \times 64 - 18 \times 18} = \frac{480 - 432}{384 - 324}$$

$$= \frac{48}{60} = \frac{4}{5} = 0.8$$

Now, the equation for the prediction of Y is

$$Y - 3 = 0.8(X - 4)$$

or
$$Y = 3 + 0.8X - 3.2$$

or
$$Y = 0.8X - 0.2$$

The equation for the prediction of X is

$$X - 4 = 0.8\,(Y - 3)$$

or
$$X = 4 + 0.8Y - 2.4$$

or
$$X = 0.8Y + 1.6$$

Error in the Prediction

The regression equations, as already discussed, help in the task of prediction. If we have scores on the variables X and Y (the dependent and independent), then we can set two regression equations, one for predicting the values of Y variable for the given values of X variable, and the other for predicting the values of X variable for the given values of Y variable.

We cannot predict things to happen exactly in the same way as they happen in practice. There remains always some gap between what is predicted and what actually happens. This variation or difference between the predicted values or scores and the observed values or scores is termed as the *error in prediction*.

This error in prediction (when we use regression equations for predictive purpose) can be computed in the form of SE of the estimate by using the following formulae:

(i) The SE of the estimate for predicting Y from X is

$$\sigma_{yx} = \sigma_y \sqrt{1 - r_{xy}^2}$$

where

σ_y = Standard deviation of the scores for y distribution
r_{xy} = Coefficient of correlation between the variables X and Y

(ii) The SE of the estimate for predicting X from Y is

$$\sigma_{xy} = \sigma_x \sqrt{1 - r_{xy}^2}$$

Here,

σ_x = Standard deviation of the scores for X-distribution

To interpret the SE of the estimate, we can set the confidence intervals at 95% or 99% level. Here, at 95% we have

(i) Y' (predicted scores on the basis of regression equation) $\pm 1.96\sigma_{yx}$

(ii) X' (predicted scores) $\pm 1.96\,\sigma_{xy}$

and at 99% we have

(i) $Y' \pm 2.58\sigma_{yx}$

(ii) $X' \pm 2.58\sigma_{xy}$

Role of Coefficient of Alienation in Prediction

We have used two formulae to compute the standard error of estimate for predicting Y from X and X from Y (while making use of two regression equations).
These formulae are

(i) $\sigma_{yx} = \sigma_y\sqrt{1-r_{xy}^2}$

(ii) $\sigma_{xy} = \sigma_x\sqrt{1-r_{xy}^2}$

The first formula enables us to tell how the regression equation is able to predict the scores in Y variable when we know the scores in X, and the second variable enables us to predict X scores with the help of the knowledge of Y scores. Here,

$\sqrt{1-r_{xy}^2}$ or, simply, $\sqrt{1-r^2}$ is called the coefficient of alienation. It is usually denoted by the letter $K\left(K=\sqrt{1-r^2}\right)$.

The coefficient of alienation, K actually measures the absence of relationship between two variables X and Y in the same way as 'r' measures the presence of this relationship. if we take

$$K = 1, \quad \text{i.e} \quad \sqrt{1-r^2} = 1$$

or

$$1 - r^2 = 1,$$

then r becomes zero, if we take $K = 0$, then r becomes ± 1.

Thus, we can easily conclude that the lesser the value of K, the larger the extent of relationship between X and Y. Also, more reliable prediction of the Y variable from the respective value of X is then possible.

MULTIPLE REGRESSION AND PREDICTION

So far, in this chapter we have only discussed regression prediction based on two variables—dependent and independent. In fact, here we have made use of linear correlation for deriving two regression equations, one for predicting Y from X scores, and the other for predicting X from Y scores. However, in practical situations in the studies made in education and psychology, quite often we find that the dependent variable is jointly influenced by more than two variables, e.g. academic performance is jointly influenced by variables like intelligence, hours devoted per week for studies, quality of teachers, and facilities available in the school, parental education and socio-economic status. In such a situation, we have to compute a multiple correlation coefficient (R) rather than a mere linear correlation coefficient (r). Accordingly, the line of regression is also to be set up in accordance with the concept of multiple R. Here, the resulting regression equation is called the *multiple regression equation*.

Let us now discuss the setting up of multiple regression equation and its use in predicting the values of the dependent variable on the basis of the values of two or more independent variables.

Setting up of a Multiple Regression Equation

Suppose there is a dependent variable X_1 (say academic achievement) which is controlled by or dependent upon two variables designated as X_2 and X_3 (say, intelligence and number of hours studied per week). The multiple regression equation helps us predict the values of X_1 (i.e., it gives X_1 as the predicted value) by knowing the values of X_2 and X_3. The equation used for this is as follows:

$$\bar{X}_1 = b_{12.3}X_2 + b_{13.2}X_3 \text{ (in deviation form)}$$

where

$$\bar{X}_1 = (\bar{X}_1 - M_1), \quad X_2 = (X_2 - M_2), \quad X_3 = (X_3 - M_3)$$

Hence the equation becomes

$$(\bar{X}_1 - M_1) = b_{12.3}(X_2 - M_2) + b_{13.2}(X_3 - M_3)$$

or

$$\bar{X}_1 = b_{12.3}X_2 + b_{13.2}X_3 + M_1 - b_{12.3}M_2 - b_{13.2}M_3$$

$$= b_{12.3}X_2 + b_{13.2}X_3 + K \text{ (in the score form)}$$

when K is a constant and is equal to $M_1 - b_{12.3}M_2 - b_{13.2}M_3$. In this equation,

$\bar{X}_1$ = Predicted value of dependent variable
$b_{12.3}$ = Multiplying constant or weight for the X_2
$b_{13.2}$ = Multiplying constant or weight for the X_3 value.

Both $b_{12.3}$ and $b_{13.2}$ are generally named as partial regression coefficients. The partial regression coefficient:

$b_{12.3}$ tells us how many units $\bar{X}_1$ increases for every unit increase in X_2 while X_3 is held constant; and $b_{13.2}$ tells us how many units $\bar{X}_1$ increases for every unit increase in X_3 while X_2 is held constant.

Computation of b coefficients or partial regression coefficients ($b_{12.3}$ and $b_{13.2}$)

$$b_{12.3} = \left(\frac{\sigma_1}{\sigma_2}\right)\beta_{12.3}$$

$$b_{13.2} = \left(\frac{\sigma_1}{\sigma_3}\right)\beta_{13.2}$$

Here, σ_1, σ_2 and σ_3 are the standard deviations for the distributions related to variable X_1, X_2 and X_3 and $\beta_{12.3}$ and $\beta_{13.2}$ are called β coefficients (beta coefficients). These β coefficients are also called standard partial regression coefficients and are computed by using the following formulae:

$$\beta_{12.3} = \frac{r_{12} - r_{13}\, r_{23}}{1 - r_{23}^2}$$

$$\beta_{13.2} = \frac{r_{13} - r_{12}\, r_{23}}{1 - r_{23}^2}$$

Steps to Formulate a Regression Equation

The steps for framing a multiple regression equation for predicting the dependent variable value X_1 with the help of the given values of independent variables X_2 and X_3 can be summarized as follows:

Step1. Write the multiple regression equation as

$$\bar{X}_1 = b_{12.3}X_2 + b_{13.2}X_3 + K$$

where

$$K = M_1 - b_{12.3}M_2 - b_{13.2}M_2 - b_{13.2}M_3$$

Step 2. Write the formula for the calculation of partial regression coefficients

$$b_{12.3} = \left(\frac{\sigma_1}{\sigma_2}\right)\beta_{12.3}$$

$$b_{13.2} = \left(\frac{\sigma_1}{\sigma_3}\right)\beta_{13.2}$$

Step 3. Compute the values of standard partial regression coefficients $\beta_{12.3}$ and $\beta_{13.2}$:

$$\beta_{12.3} = \frac{r_{12} - r_{13}r_{23}}{1 - r_{23}^2}$$

$$\beta_{13.2} = \frac{r_{13} - r_{12}r_{23}}{1 - r_{23}^2}$$

Step 4. Put the values of $\beta_{12.3}$ and $\beta_{13.2}$ in the formulae for computing the values of $b_{12.3}$ and $b_{13.2}$, along with the values of σ_1, σ_2 and σ_3.

Step 5. Compute the value of K by putting the values of M_1, M_2, M_3 (means of distribution X_1, X_2 and X_3) and the computed values of $b_{12.3}$ and $b_{13.2}$ in the equation

$$K = M_1 - b_{12.3}M_2 - b_{13.2}M_3$$

Step 6. Put the values of $b_{12.3}$, X_2 (the given value of independent variable X_2), $b_{13.2}$, X_3 (the given value of independent variable X_3) and the value of constant K in multiple regression equation as given in step1.

Now, the task of formulating regression equations can be illustrated with the help of a few examples.

Example 14.4: Given the following data for a group of students:

X_1 = Scores on achievement test

X_2 = Scores on intelligence test

X_3 = Scores calculated showing study hours per week

$M_1 = 101.71$, $M_2 = 10.06$, $M_3 = 3.35$

$\sigma_1 = 13.65$, $\sigma_2 = 3.06$, $\sigma_3 = 2.02$

$r_{12} = 0.41$, $r_{13} = 0.50$, $r_{23} = 0.16$

(a) Make out a multiple regression equation involving the dependent variable X_1, and independent variables X_2 and X_3.

(b) If a student scores 12 in the intelligence test X_2, and 4 in X_3 (study hours per week), what will be his estimated score in X_1 (achievement test)?

Solution.

Step 1. Write the multiple regression equation

$$\bar{X}_1 = b_{12.3}X_2 + b_{13.2}X_3 + K$$

where $$K = M_1 - b_{12.3}M_2 - b_{13.2}M_3$$

Step 2. Obtain the partial regression coefficients

$$\text{(i) } b_{12.3} = \frac{\sigma_1}{\sigma_2} \quad \beta_{12.3} = \frac{13.65}{3.06} \beta_{12.3}$$

$$\text{(ii) } b_{13.2} = \frac{\sigma_1}{\sigma_3} \quad \beta_{13.2} = \frac{13.65}{2.02} \beta_{13.2}$$

Step 3. Find the values of the standard partial regression coefficients:

$$\beta_{12.3} = \frac{r_{12} - r_{13}\, r_{23}}{1 - r_{23}^2} = \frac{0.41 - 0.50 \times 0.16}{1 - (0.16)^2} = \frac{0.41 - 0.08}{1 - 0.0256}$$

$$= \frac{0.3300}{0.9744} = 0.338$$

$$\beta_{13.2} = \frac{r_{13} - r_{12}\, r_{23}}{1 - r_{23}^2} = \frac{0.50 \times 0.41 \times 0.16}{1 - (0.16)^2} = \frac{0.50 - 0.0656}{1 - 0.0256}$$

$$= \frac{0.4344}{0.9744} = 0.446$$

Step 4. Substituting the values of $\beta_{12.3}$ and $\beta_{13.2}$ in the relations in step 2, we obtain

$$b_{12.3} = \frac{13.65}{3.06} \beta_{12.3} = \frac{13.65}{3.06} \times 0.338 = 1.507$$

$$b_{13.2} = \frac{13.65}{2.02} \times 0.446 = 3.014$$

Step 5. Compute the values of constant K:

$$K = M_1 - b_{12.3}M_2 - b_{13.2}M_3$$

$$= 101.71 - 1.507(10.06) - 3.014(3.35)$$

$$= 101.710 - 15.160 - 10.097$$

$$= 101.710 - 25.257 = 76.453$$

Step 6. The multiple regression equation, as laid down in step 1, is

$$\bar{X}_1 = b_{12.3}X_2 + b_{13.2}X_3 + K$$

Putting the values of $b_{12.3}$, $b_{13.2}$ and K in the above equation, we get

$$\bar{X}_1 = 1.507(X_2) + 3.014(X_3) + K$$
$$= 1.507(X_2) + 3.014(X_3) + 76.453$$

The required multiple regression equation is

$$\bar{X}_1 = 1.507X_2 + 3.014X_3 + 76.453$$

Here,

$$X_2 = 12, \quad X_3 = 4$$

Hence the predicted value of X_1 variable is

$$\bar{X}_1 = 1.507\ (12) + 3.014\ (4) + 76.453$$
$$= 18.084 + 12.056 + 76.453$$
$$= 106.593 = 107 \text{ (nearest whole number)}$$

Example 14.5: Given the following data for a group of students:

X_1 = Scores on an intelligence test
X_2 = Scores on a memory sub-test
X_3 = Scores on a reasoning sub-test

$M_1 = 78.00$,	$M_2 = 87.20$,	$M_3 = 32.80$
$\sigma_1 = 10.21$,	$\sigma_2 = 6.02$,	$\sigma_3 = 10.35$
$r_{12} = 0.67$,	$r_{13} = 0.75$,	$r_{23} = 0.63$

(a) Establish a multiple regression equation involving the dependent variable X_1 and two independent variables X_2 and X_3.

(b) If a student obtains a score of 80 on memory sub-test and a score of 40 on reasoning sub-test, what can be his expected score in total intelligence test?

Solution.

Step 1. Write the multiple regression equation

$$\bar{X}_1 = b_{12.3}X_2 + b_{13.2}X_3 + K$$

where

$$K = M_1 - b_{12.3}M_2 - b_{13.2}M_3$$

Step 2. Compute partial regression coefficients:

(i) $$b_{12.3} = \frac{\sigma_1}{\sigma_2}\beta_{12.3} = \frac{10.21}{6.02}\beta_{12.3}$$

(ii) $$b_{13.2} = \frac{\sigma_1}{\sigma_3}\beta_{13.2} = \frac{10.21}{10.35}\beta_{13.2}$$

Step 3. Calculate the standard partial regression coefficients:

$$\beta_{12.3} = \frac{r_{12} - r_{13}\,r_{23}}{1 - r_{23}^2} = \frac{0.67 - (0.75 \times 0.63)}{1 - (0.63)^2}$$

$$= \frac{0.1975}{0.6031} = 0.327$$

$$\beta_{13.2} = \frac{r_{13} - r_{12}\,r_{23}}{1 - r_{23}^2} = \frac{0.75 - (0.67 \times 0.63)}{1 - (0.63)^2}$$

$$= \frac{0.3279}{0.6031} = 0.543$$

Step 4. Put the values of $\beta_{12.3}$ and $\beta_{13.2}$ in the relations given in Step 2 and obtain

$$b_{12.3} = \frac{10.21}{6.02} \times 0.327$$

$$= 1.7 \times 0.327 = 0.5559 = 0.556 \text{ approximately}$$

$$b_{13.2} = \frac{10.21}{10.35} \times 0.543$$

$$= 0.986 \times 0.543 = 0.5353 = 0.535 \text{ approximately}$$

Step 5. Compute the values of constant K

$$K = M_1 - b_{12.3}M_2 - b_{13.2}M_3$$

$$= 78.00 - (0.556 \times 87.2) - (0.535 \times 32.8)$$

$$= 78.00 - 48.483 - 17.548$$

$$= 78.00 - 66.031 = 11.969 = 12 \text{ approximately}$$

Step 6. The multiple regression equation, as laid down in Step 1, is

$$\bar{X}_1 = b_{12.3}X_2 + b_{13.2}X_3 + K$$

$$= .556X_2 + .535X_3 + 12$$

Step 7. The predicted value of X_1 variable is

$$\bar{X}_1 = .556 \times 80 + .535 \times 40 + 12$$

$$= 44.480 + 21.40 + 12$$

$$= 77.88 = 78 \text{ (approximate)}$$

Standard Error of Estimate

With the help of multiple regression equation, we try to predict or estimate the value of X_1 (the dependent variable), when the values of the independent variables X_2 and X_3 ... are given. The difference between the actual value of X_1 and the predicted or estimated value $\bar{X}_1$ is known by the *Standard error* (SE) of the estimate and can be computed by the following formula:

$$\sigma \text{ (estimated } X_1) \quad \text{or} \quad \sigma_{1.23} = \sigma_1 \sqrt{1-R_{1.23}^2}$$

Here, σ_1 is the standard deviation of X_1, which is the dependent variable, and $R_{1.23}$ is multiple correlation coefficient (correlation between X_1 and $X_2 + X_3$). This can be computed by using formula

$$R_{1.23} = \sqrt{\frac{r_{12}^2 + r_{13}^2 - 2r_{12}\, r_{13}\, r_{23}}{1 - r_{23}^2}}$$

As discussed in Chapter 13, it can also be computed with the help of β's (Beta coefficients) which are computed during the course of establishment of multiple regression equation.

The formula for computing multiple regression coefficient with the help of beta is

$$R_{1.23} = \sqrt{\beta_{12.3}\, r_{12} + \beta_{13.2}\, r_{13}}$$

or

$$R_{1.23}^2 = \sqrt{\beta_{12.3}\, r_{12} + \beta_{13.2}\, r_{13}}$$

The SE of the estimate can be computed by using the following formula:

$$\sigma \text{ (estimated } X_1) \quad \text{or} \quad \sigma_{1.23} = \sigma_1 \sqrt{1 - R_{1.23}^2}$$

The above formula can be illustrated with the help of examples.

Example 14.6: In the Example 14.4, X_1 represents the scores on achievement test (dependent variable) and X_2 and X_3 indicates scores on intelligence and study hours (independent variables). The other related values needed are:

(i) σ_1, SD of the scores $X_1 = 13.65$

(ii) $r_{12} = 0.41, \quad r_{13} = 0.50$

(iii) $\beta_{12.3} = 0.338, \quad \beta_{13.2} = 0.446$

Let us now compute the value of $R_{1.23}^2$:

$$R_{1.23}^2 = \beta_{12.3}\, r_{12} + \beta_{13.2}\, r_{13}$$

$$= .338 \times .41 + .446 \times .50$$

$$= .13858 + .22300 = .36158$$

Then,

σ (estimated X_1), or

$$\sigma_{1.23} = \sigma_1 \sqrt{1 - R^2_{1.23}}$$

$$= 13.65\sqrt{1 - .36158}$$

$$= 13.65\sqrt{.63842}$$

$$= 13.65 \times .799 = 10.9$$

Example 14.7: The related given and computed data in Example 14.5 are as follows:

(i) $\sigma_1 = 10.21$

(ii) $r_{12} = 0.67, \quad r_{13} = 0.75$

(iii) $\beta_{12.3} = 0.327, \; \beta_{13.2} = 0.543$

Let us first compute the value of $R^2_{1.23}$:

$$R^2_{1.23} = \beta_{12.3}\, r_{12} + \beta_{13.2}\, r_{13} = (0.327 \times 0.67) + (0.543 \times 0.75)$$

$$= 0.219 + 0.407 = 0.626$$

Then, σ (estimated X_1), or

$$\sigma_{1.23} = \sigma_1 \sqrt{1 - R^2_{1.23}}$$

$$= 10.21\sqrt{1 - 0.632}$$

$$= 10.21\sqrt{0.368} = 10.21 \times .606$$

$$= 6.187$$

SUMMARY

1. The coefficient of correlation helps us in finding the degree and direction of association between two variables. However, the concepts of regression lines and regression equations help us predict the value of one variable when the values of a correlated variable or variables are known to us.
2. In simple regression based on r, there are two regression equations:

   (i) $Y - M_y = r\dfrac{\sigma_y}{\sigma_x}(X - M_x)$

   (This equation helps us predict the score value of Y variable corresponding to any value of the X variable.)

(ii) $X - M_x = r\frac{\sigma_x}{\sigma_y}(Y - M_y)$

In the above equations, M_x and M_y represent the means of X and Y distribution and σ_x and σ_y are the standard deviations of these distributions.

3. Multiple regression is based on multiple correlation R. It is used to predict the values of the dependent variable when the values of two or more independent variables (being associated with dependent variable) are known to us. A general multiple regression equation has the following formula:

$$\bar{X}_1 = b_{12.3} X_2 + b_{13.2} X_3 + K$$

where

$$K = M_1 - b_{12.3} M_2 - b_{13.2} M_3$$

Here, $b_{12.3}$ and $b_{13.2}$ are partial regression coefficients. These values are computed as

$$b_{12.3} = \frac{\sigma_1}{\sigma_2}\beta_{12.3}$$

$$b_{13.2} = \frac{\sigma_1}{\sigma_3}\beta_{13.2}$$

where

$$\beta_{12.3} = \frac{r_{12} - r_{13}\, r_{23}}{1 - r_{23}^2}$$

$$\beta_{13.2} = \frac{r_{13} - r_{12}\, r_{23}}{1 - r_{23}^2}$$

and M_1, M_2, M_3, σ_1, σ_2, σ_3 are the means and standard deviation of the distribution X_1, X_2 and X_3. Now, from this equation, we can predict the value of X_1, the dependent variable, when we are given the values of X_2 and X_3 (the independent variables).

4. There remain gaps and differences between the predicted values or scores and the observed values or scores. This deviation of $\bar{X}_1$ (the predicted score) from X_1 (the actual score) is called *error in prediction*. This error can be computed in the form of SE of the estimate by using the following formulae:

   (i) The SE of the estimate for predicting Y from X is

$$\sigma_{yx} = \sigma_y\sqrt{1 - r_{xy}^2}$$

(ii) The SE of the estimate for predicting X and Y is

$$\sigma_{xy} = \sigma_x \sqrt{1 - r_{xy}^2}$$

(iii) The SE of the estimate for predicting dependent variable X_1 from the given values of independent variables X_2 and X_3 is

$$\sigma \text{ (estimated } X_1) \quad \text{or} \quad \sigma_{1.23} = \sigma_1 \sqrt{1 - R_{1.23}^2}$$

where σ_1 is the SD of the X_1 and $R_{1.23}$ is the multiple correlation coefficient.

EXERCISES

1. What are the regression lines in a scatter diagram? How would you use them for the prediction of variables? Explain with the help of an example.
2. Given the following data for two tests:

History (X)	*Civics* (Y)
Mean = 25	Mean = 30
SD = 1.7	SD = 1.6

Coefficient of correlation $r_{xy} = 0.95$

(a) Determine both the regression equations.

(b) Predict the probable score in Civics of a student whose score in History is 40.

(c) Predict the probable score in History of a student whose score in Civics is 50.

3. From the scatter diagram in Figure 7.8,

(a) Calculate both the regression equations.

(b) Predict the probable score on X when $Y = 100$.

4. A group of five students obtained the following scores on two achievement tests X and Y:

Students	*A*	*B*	*C*	*D*	*E*
Scores in *X* test	10	11	12	9	8
Scores in *Y* test	12	18	20	10	10

(a) Determine both the regression equations.

(b) If a student scores 15 in test X, predict his probable score in test Y.

(c) If a student scores 5 in test Y, predict his probable score in test X.

5. What is a multiple regression equation? How is it used for predicting the value of a dependent variable? Illustrate with the help of an example.

6. A researcher collected the following data during the course of his study.

Dependent variable X_1	*Independent variable* X_2	*Independent variable* X_3
$M_1 = 78$	$M_2 = 73$	$M_3 = 55$
$\sigma_1 = 16$	$\sigma_2 = 12$	$\sigma_3 = 10$
$r_{12} = .70$	$r_{13} = .80$	$r_{23} = .50$

(a) Set up the multiple regression equation for predicting the value of dependent variable for the given values of both the independent variables.

(b) If $X_2 = 60$ and $X_3 = 40$, predict the value of X_1

7. A researcher on psychology wanted to study the relationship of physical efficiency and hours per week devoted to practice with the performance in athletics. He obtained the following results during the course of his study:

Performance in athletics (X_1)	*Physical efficiency test* (X_2)	*Hours practised per week* (X_3)
$M_1 = 73.8$	$M_2 = 19.7$	$M_3 = 49.5$
$\sigma_1 = 9.1$	$\sigma_2 = 5.2$	$\sigma_3 = 17.0$
$r_{12} = .465$	$r_{13} = .583$	$r_{23} = .562$

(a) Set up the multiple regression equation for predicting performance in athletics on the basis of scores on physical efficiency test and hours per week practice.

(b) If $X_2 = 20$ and $X_3 = 42$, predict the value of X_1.

15

Scores Transformation

NEED AND IMPORTANCE

From educational and psychological tests, quite often we obtain numerical scores for assessing the ability and capacity of students. These scores are termed as *raw scores*. The mere knowledge of these raw scores obtained from different tests is quite insufficient to make comparisons—inter-individual (comparing a person's score with these scores of others) or intraindividual (within the individual). Let us illustrate this with an example.

For a vocational course entrance test, a group of students were given some intelligence subtests and aptitude tests. The findings for two students were as given in Table 15.1

Table 15.1 Raw Scores Obtained by Two Students in Entrance Test

Name of student	*Verbal ability*	*Numerical ability*	*Perceptual ability*	*Mechanical aptitude*	*Artistic aptitude*
Ramesh	28	26	30	17	35
Rakesh	17	32	16	30	40

1. Let us analyze first the intraindividual comparison. From the raw scores given above, it is not possible to have intra-individual comparisons. Ramesh who obtained 35 in artistic aptitude and 17 in mechanical cannot be called better in artistic aptitude unless we have some way of finding at the comparative scores. The mechanical aptitude test scores can be compared with the scores in artistic aptitude test only if we transfer these raw scores into some standard scores having a relative meaning. Similar is the case with the raw scores obtained in different sub-tests of mental ability. We cannot say Ramesh is better in verbal ability than in numerical ability. The scales of measurement must be comparable. Here, the scores on these two aptitude tests make different sets of distribution. Unless we convert these distributions into a common distribution (in most cases it may be normal

distribution), we cannot have a common or a comparable scale for making relative comparisons.

2. Similarly, we cannot have inter-individual comparisons with the help of the data given in raw scores. For instance, let us take the case of mental abilities. Who is better between Ramesh and Rakesh, with regard to the performance in various sub-tests? Can we add the scores obtained in various sub-tests and then make comparison on the basis of the total obtained? Obviously, the answer is No, unless we convert the raw scores into some common or standard scores. The units of a common scale can only be added. Here, raw scores obtained in various sub-tests can only be added in case these are first converted into scores of relative value, i.e. measures on some common scale. Similarly, we cannot say Ramesh is better in perceptual ability than in mechanical or numerical unless we have a common scale for the measurement of these abilities.

In this way, scores obtained by an individual in different tests and sub-tests or by individuals for assessing a particular trait or an ability with the help of different types of tests or sub-tests can only be compared, if these raw scores are transformed into scores of relative meanings or a scale of common measure.

Thus, for making inter-individual or intraindividual comparisons, the raw scores obtained in some educational and psychological tests are to be transformed into some standard scores or scores of relative meanings. The most general and frequently used derived or transformed scores in education and psychology are the following:

1. Standard scores
2. *T* scores
3. *C* Scores and Stanine scores.

These are now discussed in detail.

Standard Scores

In a distribution, deviations of the scores from its mean expressed in σ (Sigma, i.e. standard deviation of the distribution) units are called *standard scores*. These are also referred to as σ scores or z scores. A standard score or z score of any raw score tells us where and how far above or below the mean that particular score lies in the distribution. Since most of the distributions of the scores obtained from educational and psychological tests are normal or near normal, it is quite customary to assume normality for any set of raw scores that we need to transform into standard or z scores.

We have already discussed the properties of normal curve and normal distribution in Chapter 8. In order to explain the concept of standard scores, let us recall them.

If we plot the raw scores of a test on the *X*-axis and their frequencies on the *Y*-axis, we will get a bell-shaped curve, i.e. normal curve. This curve has two identical divisions, with the Mean of the distribution as its centre or starting point. The distances from the mean, the starting point for both the directions (negative or positive), are measured in σ (the standard deviation of the distribution) units. Then the distances from the mean can be equally subdivided, ranging from -3σ (or more) to $+3\sigma$ (or more), as shown in the Figure 15.1.

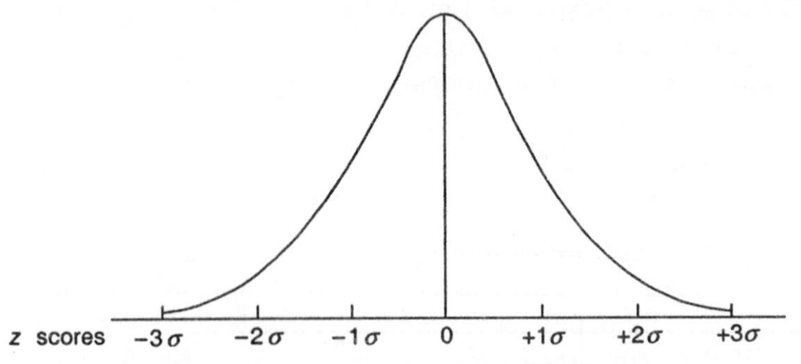

Figure 15.1 Standard scores expressed in σ units with their mean as zero.

Since standard scores are deviations of the scores from the mean and are expressed in SD units, it is imperative that the mean of the standard scores essentially be zero and their SD be equal to one. This is the reason why the mean (zero) serves as the starting point (the origin) and SD with its value 1 becomes the unit of measurement. Here, any score is interpreted in terms of its negative or positive distances (in σ units) from the mean. Such a position where the standard scores in σ units are above or below the mean provides an accurate picture of the relative position of the scores in a given distribution. Further, it can help us make their true comparison for which the raw scores need to be converted into standard scores.

Procedure for converting raw scores into standard or *z* scores. For converting raw scores belonging to a distribution into a *z* score, the steps to be taken are as follows:

1. First, compute the mean (*M*) and standard deviation (σ) of the distribution.
2. Then substitute the value of *M* and σ in the following formula for computing *z* (the standard score)

$$z = \frac{X - M}{\sigma}$$

Here, *X* stands for raw score.

Note: The process of conversion of raw scores into z scores has already been explained in Chapter 8. Application of this conversion for comparing the scores on different tests has also been explained through examples. To recall these, we can take up two examples, illustrating the role of standard scores in the task of inter-individual and intra-individual comparisons.

Example 15.1: There are two sections, A and B in class IX of a school. To test their achievement in Maths, two different question papers are prepared. Ramesh, a student of section A got 80 marks, while Suresh, a student of section B, got 60. Can you say which of these two students stands better in terms of achievement in Maths? Mean and SD of the distribution of scores for sections A and B are as follows:

Section A	*Section B*
Mean = 70	Mean = 50
SD = 20	SD = 10

Solution. Here, we cannot conclude that Ramesh with 80 marks is a better student in Maths, as compared to Suresh who has earned only 60 marks. The paper set for section A might have been quite easy; or, it could have contained objective type questions or so many other variations in contrast to those in section B. As a result, the marks obtained by these two students do not belong to the same scale of measurement. Their raw scores, then, need to be transformed into standard scores or z scores for comparison.

The formula for transformation is as follows:

$$z = \frac{X - M}{\sigma}$$

where

X = Raw score obtained in a test

M = Mean of the distribution of raw score in the test meant for section A

σ = SD of the distribution of scores for this test

$$\text{Therefore, } z \text{ score of Ramesh} = \frac{80 - 70}{20} = \frac{10}{20} = 0.5$$

Similarly,

$$z \text{ score of Suresh} = \frac{60 - 50}{10} = \frac{10}{10} = 1.0$$

Thus we can conclude that Suresh is placed better (with 1σ score) in terms of his achievement compared to Ramesh (with 0.5σ score).

Example 15.2: In the sub-tests of an entrance test, Naresh scored 56 in spelling test, 72 in reasoning test, and 38 in arithmetic test. The mean and the SD of these sub-tests were as follows:

	Spelling test	*Reasoning test*	*Arithmetic test*
M	50	66	30
σ	8	12	10

Assuming the distribution of these sub-tests as normal, find out in which sub-test Naresh performed better than the other two.

Solution. We cannot take original scores for comparing Naresh's scores on the three sub-tests. Apparently, it can mislead us to conclude that Naresh scored better in reasoning test than in spelling and arithmetic tests. The comparison can only be made by converting these raw scores into standard scores (the same scale of measurement).

The formula for transforming raw scores into standard scores (z score) is:

$$z = \frac{X - M}{\sigma}$$

where

X = Raw scores

M = Mean of distribution

σ = SD of distribution

Therefore, the z scores of Naresh in three tests are:

(i) Spelling test:

$$\frac{X - M}{\sigma} = \frac{56 - 50}{8} = \frac{6}{8} = 0.75\sigma$$

(ii) Reasoning test:

$$\frac{X - M}{\sigma} = \frac{72 - 66}{12} = \frac{6}{12} = 0.50\sigma$$

(iii) Arithmetic test:

$$\frac{X - M}{\sigma} = \frac{38 - 30}{10} = \frac{8}{10} = 0.80\sigma$$

The comparison of z scores may safely lead us to conclude that Naresh performed better (with 0.8σ) in arithmetic test than the other two sub-tests (with 0.50σ and 0.75σ).

Merits and limitations of standard scores

Merits:

1. Standard scores have essentially the same meaning for all tests.
2. Transformation of raw scores into z scores does not change the shape or characteristics of the distribution.

3. Standard scores can be safely used for inter-individual and intraindividual comparisons.

Limitations. Standard scores are said to suffer from the following limitations:

1. In these scores, plus and minus signs are used. These can be overlooked or misunderstood.
2. Decimal points used may create difficulty.

T Scores

In the scale of measurement involving standard (σ or z) scores, the starting point is the mean of the distribution, i.e. zero, and the unit of measurement is 1σ (standard deviation of the distribution). Travelling from zero on this scale to both sides may involve minus and plus signs, and the use of unit of measurement, 1σ, may carry decimal points. To overcome such limitations of σ scores, a more useful scale named T scale may be used. This scale was derived and first used by William A. McCall and named as T scale in honour of Thorndike and Terman. In this scale, McCall made use of another type of score, slightly different from the standard or z scores. These T scores may be defined as normalized standard scores converted into a distribution with a mean of 50 and σ of 10.

Thus, in sharp contrast to the scale of measurement used for standard or z scores, in the scale of measurement for T scores, the starting point (0) is placed 5 SD below the mean, and the finishing point (100), 5 SD above the mean. The scale is thus divided into 100 units. In other words, T scale ranges from 0 to 100, with a mean of 50. Its unit of measurement is T which is 0.1 of σ, and σ here has a value of 10.

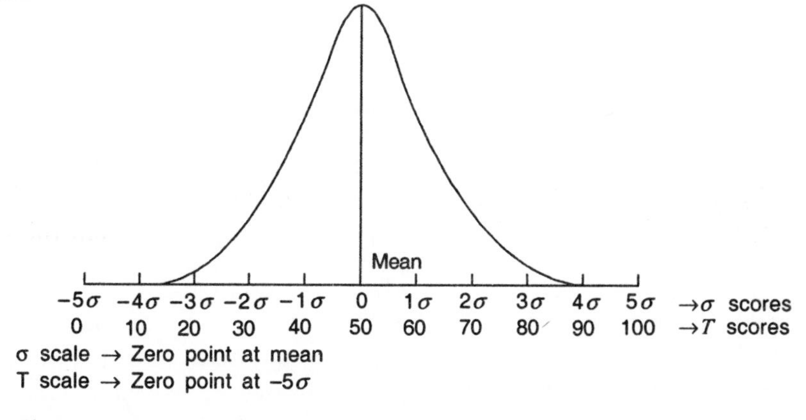

Figure 15.2 T scale (with *T* points and standard deviation).

How to Construct a T Scale

We can construct a T scale having *T* scores from the set of raw scores obtained by a large number of examines in a particular examination. Let us illustrate the construction process with the help of an example.

Example 15.3: In a university entrance test, a group of 200 students got the following scores distributed from a total score of 70 marks:

65–69	*60–64*	*55–59*	*50–54*	*45–49*	*40–44*	*35–39*	*30–34*	*25–29*	*20–24*	*15–19*
7	4	8	20	42	57	38	19	6	3	2
										N = 200

Solution. The conversion of raw scores into T scale scores can be done as follows:

Table 15.2 Conversion of Raw Scores into T Scale

Test scores	*Mid-point*	*f*	*Cumula-tive f*	*Cumula-tive f to mid-point*	*Cumula-tive f to mid-point* %	*Normal SD unit z*	*T score (z × 10 + 50)*	*T score from Appendix Table G*
(1)	(2)	(3)	(4)	(5)	(6)	(7)	(8)	(9)
65–69	67	1	200	199.5	99.75	2.81	78.1	78.1
60–64	62	4	199	197.0	98.50	2.17	71.7	71.7
55–59	57	8	195	191.0	95.50	1.70	67.0	67.0
50–54	52	20	187	177.0	88.50	1.20	62.0	62.0
45–49	47	42	167	146.0	73.00	0.61	56.1	56.1
40–44	42	57	125	96.5	48.25	–0.04	49.6	49.6
35–39	37	38	68	49.0	24.50	–0.69	43.1	43.1
30–34	32	19	30	20.5	10.25	–1.27	37.3	37.3
25–29	27	6	11	8.0	4.0	–1.75	32.5	32.5
20–24	22	3	5	3.5	1.75	–2.11	28.9	28.9
15–19	17	2	2	1.0	0.50	–2.57	24.3	24.3

Necessary explanation for the computation steps

Step 1. Enter the given class intervals (test scores) and frequencies in columns 1 and 3, and mid-points of the class intervals in column 2.

Step 2. Compute cumulative frequencies and enter these in column 4.

Step 3. In column 5, cumulative frequencies to the mid-points are entered. These are the cumulative frequencies at the bottom of a particular class interval plus, half the frequencies within that class interval. Let us make it a little more clear in the following manner:

(a) The class interval (65–69) has 199 as the cumulative frequency at the bottom. Its own frequency is 1. Half of its own frequency 1 is 0.5. By adding 0.5 to 199, we arrive at 199.5 as cumulative frequency to the mid-point corresponding to the class interval (65–69).

(b) Similarly, for the mid-point of class interval (60–64), we can compute its cumulative frequency as 195 + 4/2 = 197, and for the mid-point of the class interval (55–59) as 187 + 8/2 = 191.

(c) In the same way, we can compute cumulative frequencies of the mid-points of other class intervals. For computing cumulative frequency of the mid-point related to the lowest class interval (15–19), we can proceed as follows: In the bottom of the class interval, we have zero cumulative frequencies. Hence, cumulative frequency of the mid-point of the class interval will be 0 + 1/2 of the frequency of the class interval

$$(15\text{–}19) = 0 + 1/2 \times 2 = 1.$$

Step 4. In column 6, cumulative percentage frequencies to the mid-points of each class interval are entered. These are, in fact, the percentile ranks corresponding to the mid-points of the class intervals. These are computed as follows:

(a) For the mid-point 67 of the class interval (65–69), cumulative

$$\text{percent frequency} = \frac{199.5 \times 100}{200} = 99.75$$

(b) For the mid-point 62 of the class interval (60–64), cumulative

$$\text{percent frequency} = \frac{197 \times 100}{200} = 98.50$$

(c) For the mid-point 57 of the class interval (55–59), cumulative

$$\text{percent frequency} = \frac{191 \times 100}{200} = 95.50$$

In a similar way, the cumulative percentage frequencies for the other mid-points can be computed.

Step 5. Column 7 carries the values of the σ or z scores corresponding to the mid-points of the original score intervals. These can be computed with the help of Table B given in the Appendix (titled Area of the Normal Curve and Critical Value of z) and the cumulative values of cumulative percentage frequencies already entered in column 6. Let us illustrate this computing process.

(a) The top entry in column 6 is 99.75. Subtracting 50 from 99.75, we get 49.75. Multiply it by 10,000 and we get 4975. The corresponding value of z for this area, 4975 can then be read as 2.81 from Table B of the Appendix.

(b) Similarly, for the cumulative percent frequency of 98.50, first we have to subtract 50 from it and then multiply the result by 10,000. We get 4850 which gives z value as 2.17.

(c) For the cumulative percent of frequency of the mid-points like 48.25, 24.50 and 10.25, we can have negative values like $48.25 - 50 = -1.75$. Multiplying this by 10,000 we get 0175 as area of the normal curve, which again gives the z value as -0.04.

Step 6. In column 8, we have T scores. These can be computed by the formula $T = z \times 10 + 50$. For example, we can multiply the top value 2.81 of z by 10 and add 50 to it $(2.81 \times 10 + 50)$ to give us 78.1 as the value of T scores.

Step 7. Column 9 shows the values of T scores that can be directly worked out from the values of the cumulative percentage frequencies of the mid-points given in column 6. The T values read directly from Table G given in the Appendix. They are almost identical to the values of T scores computed from z scores, and hence, there is no need for computing z scores for the cumulative percentage frequencies of the mid-points of the class interval. These can be directly worked out from Table G.

Conversion of the Raw Scores into *T* Scores

There is no need to construct T scale for the conversion of raw scores into T scores for any given frequency distribution. Simply we must compute the mean and the SD of that distribution. This will help us compute the value of σ or z and once we know the value of z, we can compute its equivalent T score with the help of the formula $T = 10z + 50$. Let us illustrate the process with the help of an example.

Example 15.4: In an examination, two students, Sunita and Preeti, obtained the following scores (Table 15.3) in three different papers. Find out which one of them performed better.

Table 15.3 Recorded Scores of the Two Students in Three Papers along with their Mean and Standard Deviation

	Scores of Sunita	*Scores of Preeti*	*M*	*SD*
Physics	70	62	65	10
Mathematics	80	75	70	5
Chemistry	42	55	45	6

Solution. A look at the above examination record may reveal that Sunita and Preeti did equally well by scoring a total of 192 marks. However, it is quite erroneous conclusion since we cannot add the scores obtained in three different subjects in this way. The frequency distribution of the marks obtained by the examinees are different. (The mean and the SD of these distribution are different.) The total scores indicating the overall performance can only be obtained if these are first transformed into some similar scales of measurement or standard scores and then, added to their total scores.
The process may thus be carried out in two steps:

Step 1. Computation of T scores obtained by Sunita and Preeti in different subjects.

(a) *Physics*

$$T \text{ scores of Sunita} = 10z + 50 = 10\frac{X - M}{\sigma} + 50$$

$$= 10\frac{70 - 65}{10} + 50 = 55$$

$$T \text{ scores of Preeti} = 10z + 50 = 10\frac{X - M}{\sigma} + 50$$

$$= 10\frac{62 - 65}{10} + 50 = 47$$

(b) *Mathematics*

$$T \text{ scores of Sunita} = 10z + 50 = 10\frac{X - M}{\sigma} + 50$$

$$= 10\frac{80 - 70}{5} + 50 = 70$$

$$T \text{ scores of Preeti} = 10z + 50 = \frac{X - M}{\sigma} + 50$$

$$= 10\frac{75 - 70}{5} + 50 = 60$$

(c) *Chemistry*

$$T \text{ scores of Suntia} = 10z + 50 = 10\frac{X - M}{\sigma} + 50$$

$$= 10\frac{42 - 45}{6} + 50 = -5 + 50 = 45$$

$$T \text{ scores of Preeti} = 10z + 50 = 10\frac{X - M}{\sigma} + 50$$

$$= 10\frac{55 - 45}{6} + 50 = \frac{10 \times 10}{6} + 50$$

$$= 16.66 + 50 = 66.66$$

Step 2. Add the T scores of the three subjects of both the students.

Total T scores of Sunita = 55 + 70 + 45 = 170

Total T scores of Preeti = 47 + 60 + 66.66 = 173.66

Conclusion. The overall performance of Preeti is better than that of Sunita.

C-Scores and Stanine Scores

C-Scores and C-Scale. For tansforming raw scores into *C*-scores, the C-scale is so arranged as to have its mean as 5.0 (exactly at the middle) with 0 and 10 as the lowest and the highest point on the scale. This scale ranges from 0 to 10 having 11 units. In this scale, we have 11 score categories or groups for a given distribution of original raw scores. Each of these categories or groups is assigned an integer value ranging from 1 to 10.

For this purpose, the normality of distribution is strictly assumed for the given distribution having raw scores, whose transformation has to be in terms of *C*-scores.

For constructing a C-scale, the base line of the normal curve is divided into 11 equal parts in terms of SD units and thus as a result, the percentages of area under the normal curve is obtained as in Table 15.4.

Table 15.4 The C-Scale System

C-*Scale*	*Standard scores or σ scores limits*	*Percentage of the area falling in this limit*	*Percentage of the area (rounded)*	*Cumulative percentage*
10	2.25 to 3σ	0.9	1	100
9	1.75σ to 2.25σ	2.8	3	99
8	1.25σ to 1.75σ	6.6	7	96
7	0.75σ to 1.25σ	12.1	12	89
6	0.25σ to 0.75σ	17.4	17	77
5	-0.25σ to 0.25σ	19.8	20	60
4	-0.75σ to -0.25σ	17.4	17	40
3	-1.25σ to -0.75σ	12.1	12	23
2	-1.75σ to -1.25σ	6.6	7	11
1	-2.25σ to -1.75σ	2.8	3	4
0	-2.25σ to -3σ	0.9	1	1

The diagrammatic representation of C-scale having 11 equal sub-divisions is given in Figure 15.3.

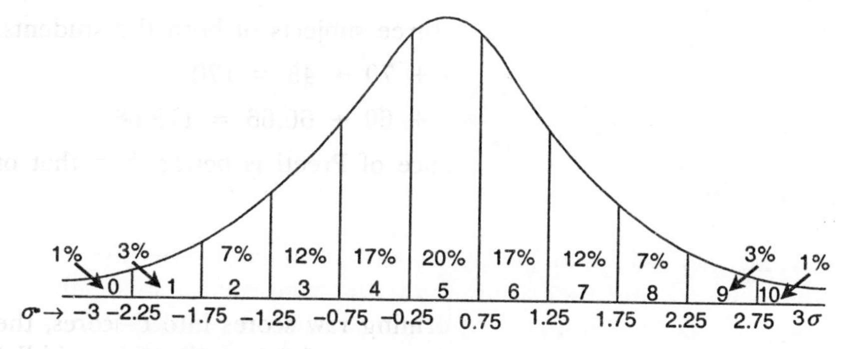

Figure 15.3 C-scale having 11 equal sub-divisions.

Based on the division of the entire distribution into 11 categories, we can transform the raw scores data into *C*-scores by adopting the following procedure:

Step 1. Arrange the set of scores in an ascending order, i.e. from the lowest to the highest.

Step 2. For the lowest 1%, assign a score of 0 and for the next lowest 3%, assign a score of 1 and, similarly, for the next lowest 7%, assign a score of 2. Continue this process till the top 1% get a score of 10, as shown in the Figure.

These transformed scores ranging from 0 to 10 are the *C*-score values of the related raw scores in a given distribution. These transformed scores are normal and form a C-scale.

Merits and demerits of C-scale. The C-scaling and transformation of raw scores into 11 specific categories or groups may prove quite valuable in terms of grading or classifying the individuals, scores in a test. It may prove quite beneficial in ability grouping. However, the use of 0 as a *C*-scores may prove quite unwise and unpracticable. Grading someone as 0 or telling him that he has obtained '0' score will be quite demoralising to him and hence, the 0 unit needs to be dropped from the scale. This would leave us with 10 units. If we want to have 5 as a mean, then we should have 11 units (ranging from 1 to 11) or if we want to have 9, then we should have a condensed scale (ranging from 1 to 9).

Stanine scale. The need to bring in reforms in C-scale gave birth to this new scale, and was named *Stanine scale*. In this condensed scale, we have 9 categories instead of 11, used in C-scale. For such condensation, the ten categories on both the upper and the lower ends of the C-scale are combined and thus we have 4% of the distribution in categories 1 and 10. The categories 0 and 10 of C-scale are thus replaced with 9 divisions, numbered from 1 to 9. This 9 point scale is named as Stanine (contraction of standard nine) scale. The mean of a Stanine scale is 5 and its SD, 1.46. Stanine scale was first used during Word War II by the United States Army Air Force Aviation Psychology Program for converting their test scores into standard nine categories. In such a procedure, they tried a coarse grouping of obtained scores into nine categories by assigning the integers 1 to 9 from the lowest to the highest.

As a general rule, for grouping, the normality of the distribution may be assumed, and the baseline of the normal curve may be divided into 9 equal divisions in terms of SD units. The percentage of the area covered by each category ranging from 1 to 9 on the Stanine scale can now be seen in Table 15.5.

Table 15.5 The Stanine Scale System

Stanine scale	*Standard scores or σ scores limits*	*Percentage of the area falling in this limit*	*Percentage of the area (rounded)*	*Cumulative percentage*
9	1.75σ to 3σ	3.88	4	100
8	1.25σ to 1.75σ	6.6	7	96
7	0.75σ to 1.25σ	12.1	12	89
6	0.25σ to 0.75σ	17.4	17	77
5	-0.25σ to 0.25σ	19.8	20	60
4	-0.75σ to -0.25σ	17.4	17	40
3	-1.25σ to -0.75σ	12.1	12	23
2	-1.75σ to -1.25σ	6.6	7	11
1	-3σ to -1.75σ	3.88	4	4

The diagrammatic presentation of Stanine scale, showing percentages of cases belonging to each unit of 9-point scale and corresponding σ scores limits on the base line of the curve, may be illustrated as in Figure 15.4.

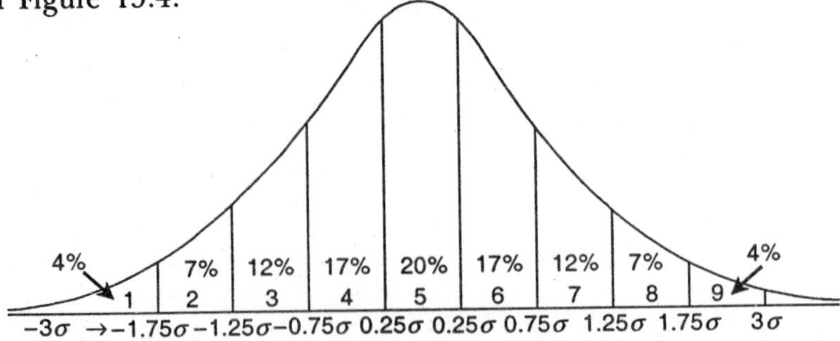

Figure 15.4 Illustration of relationship of Stanines with the σ scores and area percent.

The procedure for converting raw scores into Stanine scores can be summarized as follows:

Step 1. Arrange the set of raw scores in the ascending order, i.e. from the lowest to the highest.

Step 2. For the lowest 4%, assign a score of 1 and for the next lowest 7% , assign a score of 2. Similarly, for the next in the ascending order. Continue this process until you assign a Stanine score of 9 for the top 4%.

SUMMARY

1. It becomes essential in many cases to transform raw scores obtained in some educational or psychological tests into some standard scores or scores of relative meanings for carrying out inter-individual or intraindividual comparisons. Standard scores, *T* scores, *C*-scores and Stanine scores are the names of some such commonly tranformed or derived scores used in Education and Psychology.
2. Standard scores are also named σ scores or *z* scores. A standard σ or *z* score of any raw score tells us where and how far above or below the mean this particular score lies in the distribution. Actually, the deviations of the scores from the mean expressed in σ or SD units, are referred to as standard (σ or *z*) scores. The following formula is used to convert raw scores into *z* scores:

$$z = \frac{X - M}{\sigma}$$

   Here, *X* stands for raw scores; *M* and σ for the mean and SD of the distribution.
   In a scale consisting of σ scores, the starting point is zero (mean) and the unit is one σ unit.
3. To overcome the limitations of *z* scores involving minus sign and decimal points, *T* score transformation carries a valuable significance. *T* scores may be simply defined as normalized standard scores converted into a distribution with a mean of 50 and σ of 10. For converting a raw score into a *T* score, the following formula is used:

$$T = 10z + 50 \quad \text{or} \quad 10\frac{X - M}{\sigma} + 50$$

   where *X*, *M* and σ have their usual meanings.

4. In C-scale transformation of raw scores, the distribution is grouped into 11 equal categories and each category is assigned the integer 0 to 10, from the lowest to the highest. For this categorization, the distribution is taken as normal, and the base line of the normal curve divided into 11 equal units. The percentages of the cases falling in the interval units thus form the basis of categorization. These cases are 1, 3, 7, 12, 17, 20, 17, 12, 7, 3, 1 from both the ends. In this way, the top or bottom 1% cases of the distribution scores may be assigned the *C*-score of 10 and 0 on a C-scale and the middle 20%, *C*-score of 5. Similarly, the *C*-score values may be assigned to other categories.
5. The Stanine scale represents a simple and a condensed form of C-scale transformation of raw scores. Here we have 9 categories instead of 11, ranging from 1 to 9. The base line of the normal curve is here divided into 9 units and the % of cases falling under these subdivisions are assigned the integer value of 1 to 9 from the lowest to the highest. The mean of this scale is 5 and the Standard deviation is 1.96.

EXERCISES

1. Why does it become essential to convert raw scores of the tests into some standard scores for inter-individual or intra-individual comparison? Illustrate with examples.

2. What are σ and z scores? How can you transform raw scores into such standard scores? Illustrate with example.

3. What are *T* scores? Where and when are they used? How can you transform raw scores belonging to a distribution to *T* scores? Explain and illustrate with a hypothetical example.

4. What is a T scale? Explain the process of T scale construction by a hypothetical frequency distribution.

5. What are *C* and Stanine scores? How can you construct C and Stanine scales? What is their importance?

6. Rani, Anita and Sweeti obtained the following scores in the sub-tests of an achievement test. (The mean and the SD of these sub-tests are also given.)

Students	*Scores on different sub-tests*		
	Spelling	Vocabulary	Grammar
Rani	50	120	40
Anita	72	90	37
Sweeti	48	110	46
Mean	60	100	22
SD	10	20	6

On the basis of above data find out (i) which one of them demonstrated on the whole, better performance and also (ii) compare their own individual performances in three sub-tests.

7. Compute T scores for the data given in problem 6 and find out which of the three students performed better.

8. Convert the raw scores of the following distribution into T scores

Scores

	45–49	*40–44*	*35–39*	*30–34*	*25–29*	*20–24*	*15–19*	*10–14*	*5–9*
f	1	4	7	8	10	8	6	4	2

9. Prepare a Stanine scores transformation for the frequency distribution given in problem 8.

10. In an examination two students Ajay and Vijay obtained the following scores in three papers. Find out which one of them has an overall better performance.

Students	*Maths*	*English*	*Physics*
Ajay	70	31	60
Vijay	65	43	53
Mean	60	55	50
SD	10	12	5

16

Non-Parametric Tests

PARAMETRIC AND NON-PARAMETRIC TESTS

We have already learned that representative values such as mean, median, and standard deviation, when calculated directly from the population, are termed *parameters*. However, it is quite a tedious task to approach each and every element or attribute of the entire population and compute the required parameters. The best way is to select an appropriate sample, compute statistics such as mean and median for the elements of this sample and then use these computed statistics for drawing inferences and estimation about the parameters. How far these inferences and estimation are trustworthy or significant can then be tested with the help of some appropriate tests, called *tests of significance*.

In Chapters 9 and 10, we studied about such tests of significance, for example, z and t tests. Another such test, called F test, will be discussed in Chapter 17. All these tests, namely t, z and F, are termed *parametric tests*. We also studied and used another type of test, viz., χ^2, and contingency coefficient in Chapter 11, and techniques like rank order correlation ρ in Chapter 7. Many such tests, e.g. Sign test, Median test, the Mann-Whitney U test, Run test and KS test fall under another category, called *non-parametric tests*. In this way, we make use of two different types of tests, namely parametric and non-parametric tests, for drawing inferences and estimation about the trustworthiness or significance of sample statistics.

WHEN TO USE PARAMETRIC AND NON-PARAMETRIC TESTS

Parametric tests like 't and F' tests may be used for analysing the data which satisfy the following conditions (Seigel 1956):

1. The population from which the samples have been drawn should be normally distributed. This is known by the term *assumption of normality*.

2. The variables involved must have been measured in interval or ratio scale.
3. The observations must be independent. The inclusion or exclusion of any case in the sample should not unduly affect the results of the study.
4. These populations must have the same variance or, in special cases, must have a known ratio of variance. This we call *homosedasticity*.

However, in many cases where these conditions are not met, it is always advisable to make use of the non-parametric tests for comparing samples and to make inferences or to test the significance or trustworthiness of the computed statistics. In other words, the use of non-parametric tests is recommended in the following situations:

1. *Where N is quite small.* If the size of the sample is as small as $N = 5$ or $N = 6$, the only alternative is to make use of non-parametric tests.
2. *When assumptions like normality of the distribution of scores in the population are doubtful.* In other words, where the distribution is free, i.e. the variates under question need not be distributed in a certain specific way in the population. It is the characteristic of the non-parametric tests which enables them to be called distribution-free tests.
3. *When the measurement of the data is available either in the form of ordinal or nominal scales.* That is, when it can be expressed in the form of ranks or in the shape of + signs or – signs and classifications like "good-bad"

In practice, although non-parametric tests are typically simpler and easier to be carried out, their use should be restricted to those situations in which the required conditions for using parametric tests are not met. It is simply for the reason that non-parametric tests are less powerful (less able to detect a true difference when it exists) than parametric tests in the same situations.

However, the use of non-parametric tests in the task of statistical inferences cannot be underestimated. It will be made clear now as we analyze the nature and use of some of the important non-parametric tests.

McNemar Test for the Significance of Change

The McNemar test represents a very simple non-parametric test which is applied in the following situations:

1. When we are interested in knowing the effects of a particular treatment on a selected group of subjects by organizing the collected data into a 'before' and 'after' method in which each subject has its own control.
2. When the subjects in the study are randomnly drawn from a population.
3. When data are available either in nominal or ordinal levels of measurement.
4. When assumptions such as normality, continuity, equality, and of variances required in parametric tests regarding the distribution are not met.

Let us try to illustrate the procedure with the help of an example.

Example 16.1: A randomnly selected group of 60 parents were asked to give their opinion on whether they like their children's participation in co-curricular activities or not. Their responses were recorded. Then they were shown a movie highlighting the role of co-curricular activities in personality development. They were again asked to give their responses in the form "like/dislike", and these responses were also recorded. The data so collected were recorded in the form of a 2 × 2 contingency table (Table 16.1). Can you conclude from this data, whether or not a significant change took place in the attitude of parents towards co-curricular activities, after seeing the movie.

Table 16.1 Data Arranged in 2 × 2 Table

		After seeing movie	
		Like	Dislike
Before seeing movie	Dislike	20	24
	Like	14	2

Solution.

Step 1. Setting up of the Hypothesis (H_0) and the level of significance

H_0: There is no significant change in the attitudes of parents about co-curricular activities after their exposure to the movie.

Level of significance: 0.05

Step 2. Taking decision about the use of statistical test. The use of McNemar test will be suitable for the testing of H_0 at the set level of significance since the sample has been randomnly drawn, the method is 'before' and 'after', the subjects serve as their own controls, and the data is available in the form of nominal measurement. The procedure of its use may be explained through further steps.

Step 3. Arrangement of the data into 2 × 2 table and explanation about cell frequencies

Before seeing movie		After seeing movie	
		Like	Dislike
	Dislike	20 (A)	24 (B)
	Like	14 (C)	2 (D)

(a) Cell A of this 2 × 2 table shows the number of parents who disliked the participation of their children in co-curricular activities before seeing the movie, but began to like it after seeing the movie (change in attitude).

(b) Cell B depicts the number of parents who dislike the participation before and after seeing the movie, demonstrating no change in their attitude (no change in attitude).

(c) Cell C shows the number of parents who liked the participation before seeing the movie and liked it even after seeing the movie (no change in attitude).

(d) Cell D illustrates the number of parents who liked the participation before seeing the movie, but disliked it after seeing the movie (change in attitude).

Step 4. Deciding the test to be used. If the expected frequencies in cells A and D are small, i.e. less than 5, then the use of Binomial test is recommended in place of McNemar test. But if it is equal to or more than 5, then the McNemar test can be safely employed. For determining the expected frequencies in cells A and D, use of the following formula is recommended:

$$E = \frac{1}{2}(A + D)$$

In our present example A = 20 and D = 2
Hence

$$E = \frac{1}{2}(20 + 2) = 11$$

It is quite greater than 5, hence use of McNemar test is absolutely recommended.

Note. In case the value of E would have been less than 5, we had to make use of Binomial test and for this we have to consult the table J of the appendix with N = A + D (the sum of the two cell frequencies, the significances of the difference of which we want to measure) and x = the cell frequency smaller than A and D to give the value of p for deciding the rejection or acceptance of H_0.

Step 5. Computation or the value of χ^2. From the above analysis, it becomes clear that the cells A and D show change in their attitudes. Since in the use of McNemar test we are only interested in determining the significance of change in attitude, we would only consider the frequencies in the cells A and D to compute the value of χ^2, by using the following formula (with consideration of necessary correction for continuity)

$$\chi^2 = \frac{(|A - D| - 1)^2}{A + D}$$

Here we have $A = 20$, and $D = 2$

Hence

$$\chi^2 = \frac{(20 - 2 - 1)^2}{20 + 2} = \frac{17^2}{22} = \frac{289}{22} = 13.14$$

Step 6. Interpretation While consulting the table F of the appendix, with $df = 1$ we find that a value of 3.84 of χ^2 is taken as significant at 0.05 level of significance. Our computed value of χ^2 is 13.14. It is much larger than the value required for being significant. Hence it is to be taken as quite significant for rejecting H_0 at 0.05 level, leading us to conclude that there is a significant change in the attitude of the parents towards co-curricular activities as a consequence of seeing movie.

Sign Test

Among the non-parametric tests, the Sign test is known for its simplicity. It is used for comparing two correlated samples namely, two parallel sets of measurements which are paired off in some way. For comparison, the difference between each pair of observations is obtained, and then the significance of such differences is tested by the application of the Sign test. The word "Sign" is attached to this test since it uses plus and minus signs instead of quantitative measures as its data. This test makes useful contribution in situations where:

1. we need not consider any assumption regarding the form of distributions such as normality, homosedasticity and the like except when the variable under consideration has a continuous distribution;
2. we need not assume that all the subjects are drawn from the same population;

3. we are assigned the task of comparing two correlated samples, with the aim of testing the null hypothesis which states that the median difference between the pairs is zero;
4. in the correlated samples to be compared we must have two parallel sets of measurement that are paired off in some way (matched with respect to the relevant extraneous variables); and
5. the measurement in two parallel sets is neither on an interval nor on a ratio scale; but is available either in the form of ranking or simply showing the direction of differences in the form of positive or negative signs.

Illustration of the use of Sign test (small samples $N \leq 25$). A researcher selected 20 students for a study. He divided them into two groups in terms of their intelligence and socio-economic status. These two groups were given training in table manners and cleanliness in two different settings and were then rated for their behavioural performance by a panel of judges. Although the pooled rating scores were not so objective, they were quite enough to provide direction of differences between each pair. For this data, he wanted to know which one of the training set-ups was better. The pooled rating scores of the 10 matched pairs are given in Table 16.2.

Table 16.2 Pooled Rating Scores in Two Groups

Matched pair	*Group 1*	*Group 2*	*Sign of difference*
(a)	(b)	(c)	(d)
1	25	24	+
2	15	16	–
3	12	12	0
4	22	24	–
5	20	15	+
6	19	18	+
7	8	10	–
8	18	15	+
9	24	22	+
10	17	14	+

Method

Step 1. Determine the signs of differences and enter these as + and – signs in column (d). For zero differences, enter 0.

Step 2. Now, count the number of positive, negative and zero differences. Since the zero differences have neither plus nor minus signs, they can be eliminated from N (total number of pairs). As a result, in the present example we have 9 pairs (N = 9), out of which 6 are positive and 3 are negative. Use this formula for determining N (N = No. of matched pairs showing + and – signs).

Step 3. Establish a null hypothesis (H_0), i.e. the hypothesis of no difference:

H_0 = Median of differences between the pairs is zero

In a one-tailed test we can have

H_1 = Median of difference is positive or negative

In a two-tailed test we have

H_2 = Median of difference is significant (positive or negative)

In this case, we must know which one of the training set-ups is better since there are more positive signs. Thus we can establish H_1, that the first training set-up, is better than the second.

Step 4. Determine whether the sample of study is small or large. If N is smaller than 25, it should be taken as a small sample, but if it is larger than 25, it should be regarded as a large sample.

Step 5. The Sign test is based on the idea that under the null hypothesis, we expect the differences between the paired observations to be half-positive and half-negative. Hence the probability associated with the occurrence of a particular number +(p) and –(q) signs can be determined with reference to binomial distribution (the distribution with equal chances, i.e., $p = q = 1/2$, and $N = p + q$. For this purpose we have constructed binomial probabilities distribution table like Table J of the Appendix which gives the probabilities associated with the occurrence under the H_0 of values as small as x for N = 25.

Let us illustrate the use of Table J:

x = No. of fewer signs (whether +ve or –ve). In the present example

x = No. of fewer signs = No. of negative signs = 3

From Table J,

$$N = 9, \quad x = 3$$

The one-tailed probabilities of occurrence under H_0 are

$$p = 0.254.$$

Step 6. Examine the value of p. If it is equal to or lesser than (the given levels of significance, 0.01 at 1% level or 0.05 at 5% level), then reject H_0. In this example, p is 0.254. This value of p is greater than 0.05 at 5% level of significance. Hence, it does not lie in the area of rejection. It leads us to accept H_0 in favour of H_1, and we can safely conclude that the first training method was no better than the second.

Note. In the case of a two-tailed test, the values of p read from the table for the given N and x are doubled.

The procedure explained above for the Sign test is valid only for small samples, i.e. $N = 25$. If N is larger than 25 (total of + and – signs are more than 25), then we have to adopt a different procedure as explained now.

Sign test with large samples ($N > 25$)

If N (the total of the plus and minus signs) is larger than 25, the normal approximation to the binominal distribution or χ^2 may be used, preferably with Yates' correlation.

How to use normal approximation for bionomial distribution

Step 1. Compute the value of z by using the formula

$$z = \frac{x - N/2}{\frac{1}{2}\sqrt{N}}$$ (z is approximately normally distributed with zero mean and unit variance)

This approximation becomes excellent when correction for continuity (Yates' correction) is employed and the formula is modified as

$$z = \frac{(x \pm 0.5) - N/2}{\frac{1}{2}\sqrt{N}}$$

Here x corresponds to a total of + or – signs.

$x + 0.5$ is used when $x < 1/2\ N$

$x - 0.5$ is used when $x > 1/2\ N$

Step 2. After computing the value of z, Table K in the Appendix can be referred to. This table provides one-tailed probabilities (value of p) under H_0 of various values of z. If this value of $p \leq 0.05$ (at 5% level of significance) or 0.01 (at 1% level of significance), H_0 may be rejected at that level of significance. For a two-tailed test, the value of p read from the table is doubled for the required analysis. Let us illustrate this with an example.

Example 16.2: Instead of 10 pairs taken for study, as in Example 16.1, the researcher now has taken 50 pairs and analyzed the obtained data in terms of signs as follows:

No. of positive signs = 37

No. of negative signs = 12

No. of zero signs = 1

Can you conclude from this data that the first training method was better than the second or vice versa.

Solution. The null hypothesis in this case is that there exists no difference between the medians of the two treatments. Here, the value of N (the total No. of positive and negative signs) is:

$$N = 37 + 12 = 49$$

which is large and hence we have to consider the Sign tests meant for large samples.

Step 1. Calculation of the value of z as

$$z = \frac{(x \pm 0.5) - N/2}{\frac{1}{2}\sqrt{N}}$$

$$= \frac{(37 - 0.5) - 49/2}{\frac{1}{2}\sqrt{49}}$$

$$= \frac{2(36.5 - 24.5)}{7} = \frac{24}{7} = 3.43$$

Note. Here we have taken $x = 37$ (No. of positive signs). If we had taken $x = 12$ (No. of fewer signs), the calculation would have been

$$z = \frac{(12 + .5) - 49/2}{\frac{1}{2}\sqrt{49}} = \frac{2(12.5 - 24.5)}{7}$$

$$= \frac{-12 \times 2}{7} = \frac{-24}{7} = -3.43$$

In both the cases, the numerical value of z will be 3.43.

Step 2. After consulting Table K of the Appendix, we can read the one-tailed value of p associated with our computed z value of 3.43 as 0.0003.

Conclusion

This value of $p = 0.0003$ is much smaller than the value of α at 5% level, i.e. 0.05 or at 1% level or 0.01. Thus we can reject H_0 in favour of H_1 and can say that the first training method was better than the second.

Evaluation of Sign Test

The sign test proves to be a quite simple and a practicable test in situations where it is difficult to use parametric tests like 't' test for testing the difference between two related samples. It is a distribution-free test, does not require too many assumptions and can be used with small as well as large samples. The limitations of Sign test include the following:

1. It makes merely the use of signs—the positive or the negative—and, in this way, is unable to make use of all the available information regarding the quantitative values of the data. It takes into account only the direction and not the magnitude.
2. It is considered a less powerful test in comparison to 't' test for the same data and therefore its use is recommended in cases where it is not safe or practicable to use 't' or other parametric tests.

Wilcoxon Matched-Pairs Signed Ranks Test

In comparison to the Sign test discussed so far, the Wilcoxon's test is considered a more efficient and a powerful non-parametric test for finding the difference between two related samples that is pairs matched on some ground, or two sets of observations being made, either on the same or on the related subjects. It is on account of this fact that it uses more information than the Sign test. Whereas in the Sign test we make use only of the direction of differences between pairs, in the Wilcoxon test, the direction as well as magnitude of the differences are taken into account. Let us illustrate the use of this test with an example (first for small samples, i.e. not more than 25 pairs).

Use of Wilcoxon test for small samples

Example 16.3: To illustrate this test, eight children selected at random from an elementary school were rated on a seven-point scale with regard to some of their personality traits. The rating work was first done by their family members (three members including parents or guardians) and then by three teachers (class and subject teachers).

The pooled rating scores of both the sets of judges are given in the following tabular data. Can you conclude that no significant difference exists between these two different sets of ratings

Children	*Pooled ratings of scores of family members*	*Pooled rating of teachers*
A	6	3
B	18	15
C	14	16
D	10	12
E	20	13
F	17	11
G	12	8
H	8	9

Solution. In this example, each child pairs with its own identical pair to give two sets of observations measured on an ordinal scale.

Step 1. Setting up H_0 and the level of significance

H_0: There exists no significant difference between the ratings done by family members and teachers.

The level of significance is 0.05

Step 2. Computation of the observed T statistic. The observed T statistic can be obtained as in Table 16.3.

Table 16.3 Computation of Observed T Statistic

Children (1)	*Family ratings* (2)	*School ratings* (3)	*Difference* (4)	*Absolute rank of difference* (5)	*R(+)* (6)	*R(–)* (7)
A	6	3	3	4.5	4.5	
B	18	15	3	4.5	4.5	
C	14	16	–2	2.5		2.5
D	10	12	–2	2.5		2.5
E	20	13	7	8	8	
F	17	11	6	7	7	
G	12	8	4	6	6	
H	8	9	–1	1		1
$N = 8$					$R(+) = 30$	$R(-) = 6 = T$

Explanation. In the first three columns, the given data have been repeated. In column 4, the differences between the two sets of observations are recorded in both aspects—magnitude and direction. In column 5, the ranks of these differences have been shown, irrespective of their directions (positive or negative). Since these are tallies in the magnitude of differences, they are given ranks according to the set rule. The difference of –1 is given rank 1, whereas for –2, since it occurs in two places, the ranks are distributed equally, i.e. $(2 + 3)/2 = 2.5$. Similar is the case with the tallies of 3 which are given the ranks $(4 + 5)/2 = 4.5$ each. In column 6, all the ranks of differences which actually emerge from +ve differences are repeated and, in column 7, all the ranks of differences belonging to negative sign have been repeated. Both $R(+)$ and $R(-)$ have been summed up to give $R(+)$ and $R(-)$. The smaller of the $R(+)$ and $R(-)$ is then taken as T, Here it is 6. Thus our observed T statistic is 6.

Note. If there is a tie between the observations of a pair resulting in their difference (in column 4) as zero, such pairs are dropped, resulting in a decrease in the number of N.

Step 3: Interpretation or Decision. To decide whether to accept or reject the set hypothesis, we have to compare the computed and observed T statistic with the value of critical T read from Table L of the Appendix, the following rule is taken into account:

> *If the observed value of T is equal to or less than that read from the table for a particular significance level and a particular value of N, then we may reject H_0 at that level of significance. But in case it is larger than the table value, Then H_0 is to be retained.*

Now, in the present case if we take the row $N = 8$ in the table with the level of significance at 0.05, the critical value of T is 4. However, our observed value of T is 6, which is larger than the critical value of T. As a result, we have to accept the H_0 with the conclusion that there is no significant difference between the rating done by family members and teachers.

Use of Wilcoxon test in the case of large samples. In case the number of matched pairs is larger than 25, then the procedure differs some what from that adopted for small samples. Up to the computation of observed T statistics, the same steps as demonstrated in the previous example of small samples are followed. As the size of the sample that is, the number of matched pairs (N) increases beyond 25, the T distribution takes the form of a normal distribution. In this case, the T values need to be transformed into z function by using the following formula:

$$z = \frac{T - \frac{N(N+1)}{4}}{\sqrt{\frac{N(N+1)(2N+1)}{24}}}$$

The significance of z can then be tested by using Table K of the Appendix. This table gives the value of p under H_0 of z for one-tailed test. For a two-tailed test, this value of p is doubled. If the p thus read from the table is equal to or less than 0.05 (at 0.05 level of significance) or 0.01 (at 0.01 level of significance), we reject H_0 or, if greater than these, we accept H_0 at that level of significance.

Median Test

The Median test is that non-parametric test which is employed for knowing whether or not the two independent samples (not necessarily of the same size) have been drawn from the populations with the same median. In this way, it provides a technique for comparing the basic tendencies of two independent samples (much like the parametric t test). When we are unable to satisfy the assumptions and conditions necessary for employing a parametric t test, we can use the Median test and compare the basic tendencies of the two independent samples. However, this test demands that the observations or scores for these two samples be at least in an ordinal scale.

Procedure. We can apply the median test in the following manner:

Step 1. Setting the hypothesis. In the beginning, we can set the hypothesis as:

***Null hypothesis H_0*:** There is no difference between the median of the populations from which the samples are drawn or an alternative hypothesis like median of one population is different from that of the other (two-tailed test) or the median of one population is higher (or lower) than that of the other (one-tailed test).

Step 2. Determining the median score for the combination of the samples scores. The scores from both the samples are combined to determine the common median of these samples.

Step 3. Dichotomizing both sets of scores at the common median. Both sets of scores at the common median are then dichotomized and put in the contingency table.

These two steps can be well explained through a hypothetical example as follows:

Group I scores	*Group II* scores
6	7
6	2
14	12
13	13
15	8
6	6
8	4
7	2
10	2
14	12
10	
14	
$N_1 = 12$	$N_2 = 10$

The data given here belong to two independent samples of $N_1 = 12$ and $N_2 = 10$ observations. We have to combine these observations as 12 + 10 = 22 for computing the common median. In this case, the computed common median for all the 22 scores is 9. Hence we can dichotomize the combined group as scoring below 9 and scoring above 9 (as there is no score as 9 in both the groups). There are 5 scores below 9 in Group I and 7 in Group II. Similarly, there are 7 scores above 9 in Group I and 3 in Group II. We can then have the 2 × 2 contingency Table 16.4:

Table 16.4 Contingency Table for Computing χ^2

	Group I	*Group II*	*Total*
No. of scores above median	7(A)	3(B)	10(A + B)
No. of scores below median	5(C)	7(D)	12(C + D)
Total	12 (A + C)	10 (B + D)	N = (A) + (B) + (C) + (D) = 22

Step 4. Computing χ^2, a test of significance. From the contingency table, we can compute the value of χ^2 by using the formula (with Yates' correction)

$$\chi^2 = \frac{N(AD - BC - N/2)^2}{(A+B)(C+D)(A+C)(B+D)}$$

$$= \frac{22(49-15-22/2)^2}{10\times12\times12\times10} = \frac{22(34-11)^2}{10\times12\times12\times10}$$

$$= \frac{22\times23\times23}{10\times12\times12\times10} = 0.808$$

Step 5. Interpretation of χ^2 with reference to the set hypothesis. Now, we have to refer to Table F of the Appendix for a proper interpretation. Here, for the contingency 2 × 2 Table, *df* is 1, *N* is 22. The critical value of χ^2 at 0.05 level of significance is 33.924 and at 0.01 level of significance is 40.289. The computed value of χ^2 is 0.808. It is quite small for being significant at both the levels of significance. Hence H_0 is not to be rejected, and we can safely conclude that the two groups have been drawn from the populations with the same median.

Note. Sometimes there are scores in the samples or groups which fall at the common median. These are to be dealt with as follows:

1. If $N_1 + N_2$ is large and there are only a few cases that fall on the common median, these cases may be dropped from the analysis.
2. In other situations, we may dichotomize the scores as above the median and not above the median.

The use of χ^2 for testing the set hypothesis is quite safe in case the number of considered scores in the samples, i.e. $N_1 + N_2$ is larger. However, when this number is less than 20, the Fisher test is recommended.

Use of the Median test for more than two independent samples. The Median test can also be used for comparing more than two independent samples drawn from the respective populations. The procedure of employing the test remains the same. *First,* the scores of all the samples/groups are combined to find out a common median and then, these are dichotomized as below the median and above the median, and the data obtained are arranged into a contingency table of 3 × 2 if there are three samples, or 4 × 2 if there are four samples. From the contingency table, the value of χ^2 is computed and it is then interpreted in the light of degree of freedom (*df*), *N*, and the set level of significance for rejecting or accepting the null hypothesis.

The Mann-Whitney U Test

The Mann-Whitney U test is considered to be a more useful and a powerful non-parametric test than the Median test. Also, it is a very useful non-parametric alternative to the *t* test for assessing the difference between two independent samples having uncorrelated data, especially in the circumstances when the assumptions and conditions for applying the t test are not met.

Like the Median test, this test too is used to find out whether or not the two independent samples have been drawn from the same population. In this way, it is employed for comparing the population distributions from which samples under study have been drawn. Let us make it more clear through an example.

Let *A* be the population of class XII boys of some schools in Delhi and *B* be the population of class XII girls of some schools in Delhi. We have to compare them for their variable intelligence. We cannot approach each and every individual student. Hence, we have to draw appropriate samples from these two populations and then compare these two samples in relation to the variable under study to find out the difference in these two populations.

For the required comparison of the two populations *A* and *B* with regard to the variable intelligence, we can set the following types of hypothesis:

Null hypothesis (H_0) = *A* and *B* have the same distribution (two-tailed test)

Hypothesis H_1 = *A* is superior to *B* with regard to the distribution of intelligence, or *A* is inferior to *B* with regard to the distribution of intelligence (one-tailed test)

Thus, we try to find out the difference between population distributions, and not the difference between population means. This is why the Mann-Whitney U test is capable of providing significant difference between groups even when their means are the same.

Procedure for the U test. The U test can be used at three different levels according to the size of the samples, i.e. small samples, moderate samples, and large samples.

Procedure for small samples. When neither N_1 nor N_2, the number of cases in the two independent samples *A* and *B* are greater than 8, we can use the following steps of this test.

Step 1. Set the hypothesis, H_0 or H_1, as desired, and fix the level of significance for rejecting or accepting the hypothesis.

Step 2. All the scores of N_1 from *A* and N_2 from *B* are combined and arranged in the ascending order from lower to higher scores along with the identity of the group to which they belong.

Step 3. Find out U by counting how many scores from A precede (all lower than) each score of B.

Step 4. Find out U by counting how many scores from B precede (are lower than) each scores of A.

Step 5. Refer to Table M of the Appendix to determine the significance of computed U (with smaller value) at $p = .05$ of N_L (the group with larger number of cases) and N_S (the group with smaller number of cases), and read the value of U (critical value).

This table provides the critical value of U for testing H_0 (two-tailed test). If our computed U is equal to or smaller than the critical value of U read from the table, we reject H_0, but in case it is large, we accept the H_0.

Let us illustrate all these steps with the help of an example.

Example 16.4: Suppose there are two independent samples A and B with 4 and 5 cases. We have to establish that both samples have been drawn from the same population.

Scores of sample A and B

Sample A	*Sample B*
8	9
6	7
10	11
5	8
	12
$N_1 = 4$	$N_2 = 5$

Solution.

Step 1. (a) H_0: There is no difference between the distribution of the scores of sample A and sample B

(b) Level of significance 0.05 (5% level of significance).

Step 2. The process of combining the scores of the two samples and ranking them in ascending order (from the lowest to the highest) while maintaining their identity as scores of A and scores of B will provide the following arrangement:

Scores	5	6	7	8	8	9	10	11	12
Sample	*A*	*A*	*B*	*A*	*B*	*B*	*A*	*B*	*B*

Step 3. Determine U by counting how many scores from sample A precede (are lower than) each score of sample B. For this purpose, we shall consider each score of sample B.

(i) For B score 7, No. of A scores preceding it = 2

(ii) For B score 8, No. of A scores preceding it = 2 (one is equal)

(iii) For B score 9, No. of A scores preceding it = 3

(iv) For B score 11, No. of A scores preceding it = 4

(v) For B score 12, No. of A scores preceding it = 4

Therefore,

$$U = 2 + 2 + 3 + 4 + 4 = 15$$

Step 4. Determination of U by counting how many scores from sample B precede (are lower than) each score of sample A. For this purpose we have to consider each score of sample A:

(i) For A score 5, No. of B scores preceding it = 0

(ii) For A score 6, No. of B scores preceding it = 0

(iii) For A score 8, No. of B scores preceding it = 1

(iv) For A score 10, No. of B scores preceding it = 3

Here $U = 0 + 0 + 1 + 3 = 4$.

Step 5. We have to make use of the lower value of U, i.e. 4 for testing H_0.

From Table M(c) of the Appendix, the critical value of U for N_L (the large group of 5 Scores) and N_S (the small group of 4 scores) is 0.008, i.e. less than 1.

The computed value of U is 4. It is larger than the critical value obtained from the table. Thus H_0 is accepted and we conclude that both the samples are drawn from the same population.

Procedure for moderately large samples (where any one of the two samples has frequencies between 9 and 20)

Example 16.5: A researcher wanted to know the effect of environmental conditions on the growth of intelligence of children. For this purpose, he selected two groups—one from a Public School, and the other from a Corporation School. The IQ scores of these two groups are given in the Table 16.5.

Table 16.5 IQ Scores of Two Groups

Public School (Group A) IQ scores	*Corporation School (Group B)* IQ scores
120	115
118	94
116	90
106	110
117	97
110	118
125	112
121	99
108	110
98	116
105	
104	
108	
116	
112	
100	
$N_1 = 16$	$N_2 = 10$

Solution.

Step 1. Setting up of null hypothesis H_0

H_0: There is no difference between the distribution of intelligence in both the groups, in other word, the groups do not differ in terms of distribution of intelligence.

Level of significance = 0.05

Step 2. Combine the scores belonging to both the groups and rank them into a single group, giving rank one to the lowest. For the tied score, give the average of the tied ranks (as we do in the case of computation of rank correlation or ρ).

Step 3. The ranks for each group are then summed up. In the present example, we can rank and sum them up as in the Table 16.6.

Table 16.6 Worksheet for the Computation of Table of Ranks R_1 and R_2

Public School (Group A)		*Corporation School (Group B)*	
Score	Rank	Score	Rank
120	24	119	23
118	21.5	94	2
117	19.5	90	1
106	9	110	13.5
117	19.5	97	3
109	12	118	21.5
125	26	112	15.5
121	25	99	5
108	10.5	110	13.5
98	4	116	17.5
105	8		
104	7		
108	10.5		
116	17.5		
112	15.5		
	6		
R_1 = 235.5		R_2 = 115.5	

You can check the total of rank $R_1 + R_2 = 235.5 + 115.5 = 351$

by using the formula $\frac{N(N+1)}{2}$

Here,

$$N = N_1 + N_2 = 16 + 10 = 26$$

Therefore,

$$\text{Total} = \frac{26 \times 27}{2} = 351.$$

Step 4. Then the values of U are computed from formula I and formula II as follows:

$$U = N_1 N_2 + \frac{N_1(N_1+1)}{2} - R_1 \qquad \text{(Formula I)}$$

$$U' = N_1 N_2 + \frac{N_2(N_2+1)}{2} - R_2 \qquad \text{(Formula II)}$$

Let us use these formulae as follows:

$$U = 16 \times 10 + \frac{16(16+1)}{2} - 235.5$$

$$= 160 + 136 - 235.5$$

$$= 296 - 235.5 = 60.5$$

$$U' = 16 \times 10 + \frac{10(10+1)}{2} - 115.5$$

$$= 160 + 55 - 115.5 = 215 - 115.5 = 99.5$$

Actually, there is no need to compute both U and U' separately. We can find out the other if we have determined either of the two by using the formula

$$U + U' = N_1N_2 \quad \text{or} \quad U' = N_1N_2 - U$$

Let us apply the formula here.
Then,

$$60.5 = 16 \times 10 - U'$$

or

$$U' = 160 - 60.5 = 99.5$$

Step 5. Now we have to use Table N of the Appendix for the critical values of U to reject or accept H_0. In the table find N_L (larger group), i.e. $N_L = 16$ and N_S (smaller group), i.e. $N_S = 10$ at the 0.05 level. The critical value of U from the Table is 48. (at the intersection of $N_L = 16$ and $N_S = 10$ from the top) The computed smaller value of U (here we have to see which one, U or U', is smaller) is 60.5. It is larger than the critical value of U, i.e. 48 read from the Table for the significance at 0.05 level. Hence H_0 is to be accepted. Thus we may conclude that both the groups do not differ in terms of the distribution of intelligence on account of the environment influences.

For large samples. When one or both the independent samples drawn from the population are larger than 20, the tables used for finding the critical value of U (described for small and moderately large samples) are not much useful. With the increase in size, the sampling distribution of U takes the shape of a normal distribution. With normal distribution, we can safely use the z values (used very often in the case of parametric test).

The z values of sampling distribution of U can be computed with the use of the formula

$$z = \frac{U - \dfrac{N_1N_2}{2}}{\sqrt{\dfrac{N_1N_2(N_1 + N_2 + 1)}{12}}}$$

The procedure is as follows:

Step 1. Compute the value of U or U' with the help of any formula described, in the case of moderately large samples by combining and ranking the scores of both the groups.

Step 2. Use the computed value of U now in the given formula for determining z. (The only difference with the use of U or U' remains that for one of the values of U, z will be positive, while for the other, it will be negative. In both cases, the absolute value of z will remain the same.)

Step 3. Use the value of z for rejecting or accepting H_0 at a given level of significance.

(i) If the computed value of $z \geq 1.96$, U is considered significant at 0.05 level of significance (for two-tailed test) and hence H_0 stands rejected.
(ii) If the computed value of $z \geq 2.58$, U is considered significant at .01 level of significance (for two-tailed test), and hence H_0 stands rejected.
(iii) For one-tailed test, we have $z \geq 1.64$ and $z \geq 2.33$ at 0.05 and 0.01 levels of significance for rejecting H_1.

Wald-Wolfowitz-Runs Test

This is a general parametric test that can be used to test any sort of difference, and not some particular type of difference existing in a single sample or two independent samples. While non-parametric tests like Sign test and Median test are meant to find out a particular kind of difference between two independent samples or set of observations, the Runs test may be used to find any difference existing in a single sample (with regard to occurrence of events) or between two independent samples drawn from the population. The hypothesis to be tested through the Runs test in the single and in two independent samples may be stated in follows:

1. Sequence of events in a single sample occurs in a random order, i.e.
   (a) with the tossing of a coin a number of times, the occurrence of heads and tails will be in a random order or unpredictable in terms of showing head or tail.
   (b) In a co-ed class, the achievement scores of male and female students are in a random order.

2. Two independent samples are drawn from identical populations, i.e. there exists no difference in the two samples in their central tendencies, variability and skewness.

The Runs test owes its name on account of the term 'run' which it uses in its application. The term 'run' may be defined as *a succession of identical symbols or events which are followed and preceded by different symbols/events or by no symbols/events at all.*
Let us explain it with some examples.

1. In a series, the plus and minus signs occur as:

   + + + – – + – + + – – – +

   For counting the runs, we can group these into runs by underlining and numbering the consecutive identical symbols, as

+ + +	– –	+	–	+ +	– – –	+
1	2	3	4	5	6	7

   Here, we have a total of 7 runs. So N = No. of runs = 7
2. A coin shows the heads and tails sequence as follows:

   H H T H H T T T H T H H H H T T H T T T

   For counting, we proceed as follows:

H H	T	H H	T T T	H	T	H H H H	T T	H	T T T
1	2	3	4	5	6	7	8	9	10

Here, n = number of runs = 10. The total number of runs in a sample of any size gives indication of whether or not the sample is random, and the quality of run may be used for testing the randomness of a sample or identical nature of the two independent samples. The procedure adopted in the application of Runs test can be illustrated as follows:

Procedure using the Runs test.

Case I: **A single and small sample** A coin was tossed 20 times and the results obtained were:

H T H H T H H H T T H T T T H T H T H H

Test the hypothesis that the coin was not erratic.

Solution.

Step 1. H_0: Heads and tails occur randomly or the coin is not erratic
Level of significance = 0.05

Step 2. For counting the runs, the sequence of events H and T are marked and numbered as:

H	T	H H	T	H H H	T T	H	T T T	H	T	H	T	H H
1	2	3	4	5	6	7	8	9	10	11	12	13

Total No. of runs = 13

Step 3. It is a small sample (A sample is termed 'small' when the number of observations are equal to or less than 20).

Hence, we shall follow the procedure set for small samples. Here,

$$N_1 = \text{No. of first event}$$
$$= \text{No. of heads} = 11$$
$$N_2 = \text{No. of second event}$$
$$= \text{No. of tails} = 9$$
$$N = 11 + 9 = 20$$

Consult the Tables O_1 and O_2 given in the Appendix to find out the lower and higher values of critical r being significant at 0.05 level. Then,

with $N_1 = 11$ and $N_2 = 9$ from Table O_1, we get $r = 6$ (the lower value)
with $N_1 = 11$ and $N_2 = 9$ from Table O_2, we get $r = 16$ (the higher value)

Decision. The rejection or acceptance of H_0 based on the rule that if the obtained or computed value of r falls between the critical values (lower and higher) read from the tables, it cannot be regarded as significant. So we accept the H_0. But if it is equal to or more than one of these critical values, then we reject the hypothesis H_0 at 0.05 level. Here, $r = 13$, which lies well within the critical values of 6 and 16 read from the tables. It cannot be regarded as significant at 0.05 level, and hence H_0 cannot be rejected. We accept H_0 and conclude that the coin was not erratic and the heads and tails occur in a random fashion.

Note. In case of one-tailed test where the direction of the randomness is predicted, only one of the two tables given in the Appendix need to be referred. If the prediction is that too few runs will be observed, then refer the Table O_1 which says that r is equal to or smaller than read from table, reject H_0 at 0.025 level. If the prediction is that too many runs will be observed, then consult Table O_2.

Similarly, when we have observations recorded from two independent samples drawn from the populations, we make use of one table for finding out the critical value of r at 0.05 level.

Case II: **Two independent small samples.**

Example 16.5: 10 boys and 10 girls of class XI selected from a Boys' Higher Secondary School and a Grils' Higher Secondary School respectively, were examined in terms of their attitude towards population eduction. Their scores on the attitude scale are shown in the Table 16.7. Test the hypothesis that boys and girls do not differ in terms of their attitude towards population education.

Table 16.7 Attitude Scores of Boys and Girls

Boys	*Girls*
15	17
6	9
7	16
19	15
12	13
4	3
20	8
5	14
18	11
10	2
$N_1 = 10$	$N_2 = 10$

Step 1. H_0: There is no difference between boys and girls in respect of their attitude towards population education.
Level of significance = 0.05

Step 2. The two set of scores are combined and arranged in an ascending series from the lowest to the highest and their identities (to which group they belong), are maintained in the following way:

2 3	4 5 6 7	8 9	10	11	12	13 14	15	15 16 17	18 19 20
G G	B B B B	G G	B	G	B	G G	B	G G G	B B B
1	2	3	4	5	6	7	8	9	10

Total No. of runs = 10

Step 3. Referring to Table O_1 of the Appendix for $N_1 = 10$ and $N_2 = 10$, we find the critical value of r as 6 for being significant at 0.05 level. The computed value of r is 10. It is much larger than the critical value. Since it is not significant, H_0 cannot be rejected. Hence we accept the hypothesis H_0 that boys and girls do not differ in terms of their attitude towards population education.

Case III: **Large sample**

Example 16.6: On a Railway reservation window, there was a long queue of Men (M) and Women (W) standing in the order in which they have come, as depicted in the following displayed matter. Confirm, whether or not they were standing in a random order.

M   W M   W   M M M   W W   M   W   M   W
M   W   M M M M   W   M   W   M   W   M M
W W W   M   W   M   W   M   W   M M   W
M M   W   M M M M   W   M   W   M M

Step 1. H_0. The arrangement of standing was in random order.
Level of significance 0.01

Step 2. Total No. of runs = 35 $N_1 = 30$ (No. of Men)
$N_2 = 20$ (No. of Women)

Step 3. When the sample is large. A sample is considered large when either of N_1 or N_2 (No. of observations in any independent sample) is larger than 20. Here, N_1 (No. of Men) is equal to 30 and N_2 (No. of Women) is 20, and hence it is a case of large sample. Here, the tables employed in the case of small samples for the critical values of r are not applicable. As the size increases, the sampling distribution of r almost takes the form of a normal distribution and, therefore, the value of r (No. of total runs) needs to be converted into value of z for rejecting or accepting the set hypothesis. We can make use of following formula for converting r into z function

$$z = \frac{r - \mu_r}{\sigma_r}$$

Where μ_r = Mean of the distribution $= \dfrac{2N_1N_2}{N_1 + N_2} + 1$

and

σ_r = SD of the distribution $= \sqrt{\dfrac{2N_1N_2(2N_1N_2 - N_1 - N_2)}{(N_1 + N_2)^2(N_1 + N_2 - 1)}}$

r = Computed No. of runs.

Now let us use the formulae for converting r into z

Here

$$\mu_r = \frac{2N_1N_2}{N_1 + N_2} + 1 = \frac{2 \times 30 \times 20}{30 + 20} + 1$$

$$= \frac{1200}{50} + 1 = 24 + 1 = 25$$

$$\sigma_r = \sqrt{\frac{2N_1N_2\,(2N_1N_2 - N_1 - N_2)}{(N_1 + N_2)^2\,(N_1 + N_2 - 1)}}$$

$$= \sqrt{\frac{2 \times 30 \times 20\,(2 \times 30 \times 20 - 30 - 20)}{(30 + 20)^2\,(30 + 20 - 1)}}$$

$$= \sqrt{\frac{1200(1200 - 50)}{50 \times 50 \times 49}} = \sqrt{\frac{1200 \times 1150}{50 \times 50 \times 7 \times 7}} = \frac{\sqrt{1,380,000}}{350} = 3.35$$

Hence

$$z = \frac{r - \mu_r}{\sigma_r} = \frac{35 - 25}{3.35} = 2.98$$

Step 4. Interpretation of the value of z for H_0 at 0.01 level

Rules: 1. If the computed value of $z \geq 1.96$, r is considered significant at 0.05 level (for two-tailed test), H_0 stands rejected.

2. If $z \geq 2.58$, r is considered significant at 0.01 level (for two-tailed test), H_0 stands rejected.

3. For one-tailed test, we have $z \geq 1.64$, and $z \geq 2.33$, being significant at 0.05 and 0.01 levels of significance.

Here, our test is two-tailed, we have fixed the level of significance at 0.01 level. The computed value of z is 2.98. It is greater than the critical value of z, i.e. 2.58 at 0.01 level of significance. Therefore, it is regarded as significant for rejecting H_0 and we can conclude that the order of Men and Women in the queue was not random.

The Kolmogrov Smirnov Test (KS Test)

The Kolmogrov Smirnov test, described in short as KS test, is a popular parametric test that can be used to test both the nature of distribution in a single sample and the difference in the distribution of a particular trait in two independent samples. Let us discuss its uses with one sample as well as two independent samples.

KS One-Sample Test

The one-sample KS test is, in fact, a test of goodness of fit. Its counterpart in non-parametric tests is the χ^2 test. However, it does not require many assumption as in the case of the χ^2 test. The only assumptions required in KS test are: (i) the underlying dimension or variable should be continuous, and (ii) the data should be available at the nominal level of measurement.

The merits of KS test over the χ^2 test as a test of goodness of fit can be summarized as follows:

1. The χ^2 test assumes that cell frequencies should not be less than 5. Hence it tries to combine the categories to give more than 5 frequencies. Much information is lost in doing so. However, it is not required in the KS test, as it treats all the observations separately.
2. The χ^2 test, unlike the KS test, is not applicable to very small samples.
3. The KS test is more powerful and sensitive than the χ^2 test in its purpose as it gives good results with smallest samples and smallest frequencies.

What KS One-Sample Test Does?

As a test of goodness of fit, the KS test is concerned with the measurement of degree of agreement between the distribution of the scores or values in a given sample (observed scores) with some specified theoretical distribution (theoretical scores) based on the hypothesis of chance, equal probability and normal distribution.

Let us illustrate its use with some appropriate examples.

Example 16.7: (Small sample with N not larger than 20). Each child in a group of 20 was asked to give its preference for a particular type of dress out of four choices, differing only in terms of colour. The results can be listed as follows. Find out whether or not their choices are related to the colour of dress.

Children Choice of Dress

	Red dress	*Blue dress*	*Yellow dress*	*White dress*
No. of Children	4	8	2	6

Solution.

Step 1. Setting up the hypothesis and level of significance

H_0: The choices are not related to the colour of the dresses (It is a two-tailed test)

Level of significance = 0.05

Step 2. We have been given observed frequencies of choices of 20 children for four types of dresses. Theoretically, if we use the hypothesis of equal probability for the choice of four colours, then we must have 20/4, i.e. 5 frequencies for each type of dress. In this way, in the second step, we try to compute the expected frequencies based on some theoretical distribution and then arrange them as under in the name of f_o and f_e.

f_o	f_e
4	5
8	5
2	5
6	5

Step 3. Converting both types of frequencies into their respective cumulative frequencies and then dividing these by N to obtain cumulative proportions and naming them as C_{p_o} and C_{p_e}, i.e. cumulative proportions for observed frequencies and cumulative proportions for expected frequencies.

Step 4. The observed cumulative proportion C_{p_o} is then compared with the theoretically expected cumulative proportion C_{p_e} to get the value $|C_{p_o} - C_{p_e}|$.

Step 5. Out of the values of $|C_{p_o} - C_{p_e}|$, the maximum value is then taken for giving $|C_{p_o} - C_{p_e}|$, i.e. the greatest divergence between the observed and the theoretical proportions. It is denoted by D. Let us see how this value of D can be computed in the given example.

Table 16.8 Worksheet for the Computation of D

f_o	f_e	Cf_o	Cf_e	C_{p_o}	C_{p_e}	$\|C_{p_o} - C_{p_e}\|$	D
4	5	20	20	20/20	20/20	0	
8	5	16	15	16/20	15/20	1/20	
2	5	8	10	8/20	10/20	2/20	2/20
6	5	6	5	6/20	5/20	1/20	

$D = 2/20 = 1/10 = 0.1$

Step 6. The computed value of D is then compared with the critical value of D. The critical value of D is read from Table P of the Appendix for the given N.

Here, $N = 20$. Hence from the table, the critical value of D at the required level 0.05 of significance is 0.294.

Step 7. Decision about the rejection or acceptance of H_0 (two-tailed test) can be made by applying the following rule:

If the computed value of D is equal to or greater than the critical value of D at a particular level of significance, then it is taken as significant for rejecting H_0 at that level of significance, but if it is less, then H_0 is retained.

In the given example where the computed value of $D = 0.1$, it is much less than 0.294, the critical D at 0.05 level of significance. Thus, the hypothesis H_0 that the choice of dress is not related to the colour of dress is to be accepted.

Example 16.8: With large sample ($N > 20$). Apply the KS test to the following distribution to test the H_0 that the given distribution fits well in the normal distribution.

Scores	*20 and above*	*15–19*	*10–14*	*5–9*	*4 and <4*
f	6	14	55	20	5

$N = 100$

Solution.

Step 1. Setting up of H_0 and level of significance

H_0: There is no difference between the observed and theoretical distributions.

Level of significance = 0.05

Step 2. Computation of expected frequencies for the normal distribution fitted to the given distribution

Scores	*Expected frequencies*
20 and above	6.68
15–19	24.17
10–14	38.30
5–9	24.17
4 and < 4	6.68

Explanation. The baseline of the normal curve extended from -3σ to $+3\sigma$ (Total 6σ) is divided into 5 equal parts of 1.2σ and then we divide the total area of the curve into 5 parts and obtain the above frequencies.

Step 3. Computation of the value of D

Table 16.9 Worksheet for the Computation of D

f_o	f_e	C_{f_o}	C_{f_e}	C_{p_o}	C_{p_e}	$\lvert C_{p_o} - C_{p_e}\rvert$	D
6	6.68	100	100.00	1.00	1.00	0.00	
14	24.17	94	93.32	0.94	0.93	0.01	
55	38.30	80	69.15	0.80	0.69	0.11	0.11
20	24.17	25	30.85	0.25	0.31	0.06	
5	6.68	5	6.68	0.05	0.067	0.017	

Step 4. From Table P of the Appendix, the critical value of D for the value $N > 35$ at 0.05 level of significance can be obtained by using the formula

$$\text{Critical } D = \frac{1.36}{\sqrt{N}}$$

Here,

$$N = 100$$

Hence,

$$\text{Critical } D = \frac{1.36}{10} = 0.136$$

Step 5. Interpretation and Conclusion. The computed value of D is 0.11. It is less than the critical value 0.136 of D. It is not significant and, therefore, H_0 is not to be rejected. We thus accept the hypothesis H_0 that the given distribution fits well into normal distribution.

KS Two-Samples Test

Another useful non-parametric test for testing whether or not the two independent samples have been drawn from the same population or populations with the same distribution is the KS two-samples test. Like the one-sample KS test, it is also a test of goodness of fit as it is concerned with the measurement of degree of agreement between the distribution of scores or values of two independent samples. It has the same merits as outlined earlier in the one-sample test. It can be used with nominal data, grouped in continuous categories or arranged in a rank order. Like the one-sample KS test, it tries to compare two cumulative distributions of both the samples for drawing a conclusion about the populations of these two samples, the only difference lies in the fact that where as in the one-sample KS test, one distribution is observed, and the other, being theoretical, is expected. In the KS two-sample test, however, both these distributions are observed.

The procedure for the application of the KS test in two samples have variations with regard to the size of the samples (small or large) and the nature of the hypothesis to be tested (one-tailed or two-tailed test). This can be illustrated in the following manners.

Case I: KS test with small samples (when $N \ngtr 40$). Two groups of people from urban and rural populations were given an attitude scale for testing their attitude towards sex. Their scores are presented into two distributions (Table 16.10) to test the hypothesis that (i) both the groups do not differ significantly with regard to their attitude towards sex, or (ii) belonging to urban or rural society has no effect on a person's attitude towards sex.

Table 16.10 Distribution of Scores Showing Attitude Towards Sex

Scores	*0–4*	*5–9*	*10–14*	*15–19*	*20–24*	*25–29*	*30–34*
Group A (Urban)	0	3	5	2	0	4	1
Group B (Rural)	1	2	4	6	2	0	0

$N_1 = 15$ and $N_2 = 15$

Solution.

Step 1. Setting up the hypothesis and the level of significance

H_0: There is no difference between the urban and rural society with regard to the attitude towards sex or there is no significant difference between the two distributions (it is a two-tailed test).

Level of significance: 0.05

Step 2. Computation of the value of K for accepting or rejecting the set hypothesis. The procedure for the computation of K may be well understood through Table 16.11.

Table 16.11 Computation of K

Scores on attitude scale	*Frequencies (f)*		*Cumulative frequencies*		$\lvert K_D \rvert$	K
	Urban population	Rural population	Urban population	Rural population		
(1)	(2)	(3)	(4)	(5)	(6)	(7)
30–34	1	0	15	15	0	
25–29	4	0	14	15	1	
20–24	0	2	10	15	5	5
15–19	2	6	10	13	3	
10–14	5	4	8	7	1	
5–9	3	2	3	3	0	
0–4	0	1	0	1	1	

Here, we have first calculated $C'f$ for the two groups of urban and rural subjects in columns 4 and 5. In column 6, we have computed the value of K_D, i.e. the numerical difference (irrespective of direction – or +) between the cumulative frequencies of both the groups. In the last column, we have entered the value of K, i.e. the largest value among the values of K_D already listed in the previous column.

Step 3. Interpretation. We can now refer to Table Q of the Appendix with $N_1 = N_2 = 15$, and find (for a two-tailed test as in the present situation) that $K = 8$, which is significant at 0.05 level. The computed value is 5 which is quite less than the critical value of 8. Hence it is not significant and therefore, H_0 cannot be rejected. We accept the hypothesis H_0 that both the distributions do not differ and there is no difference between urban and rural populations with regard to their attitude towards sex.

Note. The set hypothesis H_0 presented here a two-tailed situation. In case our hypothesis had been that urban population shows more positive attitude towards sex, then it could have presented a one-tailed situation for testing. In such a case, we have to consult the given table for given N ($N = 15$) at 0.05 level under the column meant for one-tailed test. We could have found here the value of K as $K = 7$ which is significant at 0.05 level. Since our observed value $K = 5$ is much less, it should be taken as not significant by not rejecting H_0, the null hypothesis, in favour of H_1.

Case II: KS Test with large samples (when N_1 and N_2 are larger than 40)

Example 16.9: Two groups of students were rated on a nine-point scale for their habit of cleanliness. The data so obtained is given in the Table 16.12. Do the two groups differ significantly in terms of their habit of cleanliness?

Table 16.12 Rating Scores for the Habit of Cleanliness

Scores on scale	*Group A* (f)	*Group B* (f)
9	2	4
8	6	11
7	5	8
6	4	5
5	6	7
4	8	10
3	7	6
	9	4
1	3	5
	$N_1 = 50$	$N_2 = 60$

Solution.

Step 1. Setting up of the hypothesis and the level of significance

H_0: There is no significant difference between two groups regarding their habits of cleanliness.

Level of significance = both 0.05 and 0.01

Step 2. Computation of the value of D (Observed D). Here the value of D, $|C_{p_A} - C_{p_B}|$ is maximum, i.e. the greatest absolute divergence between the cumulative proportion of both the groups is computed. This computation process may become quite clear from Table 16.13.

Table 16.13 Worksheet for Computation of D

Group A (f)	*Group B* (f)	C_{f_A}	C_{f_B}	C_{p_A}	C_{p_B}	$\lvert C_{p_A} - C_{p_B}\rvert$	D
2	4	50	60	1.000	1.000	0.000	
6	11	48	56	0.960	0.933	0.027	
5	8	42	45	0.840	0.750	0.090	
4	5	37	37	0.740	0.617	0.123	
6	7	33	32	0.660	0.533	0.127	
8	10	27	25	0.540	0.417	0.123	
7	6	19	15	0.380	0.250	0.130	0.130
9	4	12	9	0.240	0.150	0.090	
3	5	3	5	0.060	0.083	0.023	
$N_1 = 50$	$N_2 = 60$						

Step 3. Obtaining critical value of D (Significant for rejecting the set hypothesis at a given level). In a two-tailed test, these values can be obtained for the given N_1 and N_2 from the formulae

$$\text{Critical value of } D \text{ (at 0.05 level)} = 1.36\sqrt{\frac{N_1 + N_2}{N_1 N_2}}$$

$$\text{Critical value of } D \text{ (at 0.01 level)} = 1.63\sqrt{\frac{N_1 + N_2}{N_1 N_2}}$$

We can compute now the critical value of D at both the levels 0.05 and 0.01.

$$\text{At 0.05 level, Critical } D = 1.36\sqrt{\frac{50+60}{50\times 60}}$$

$$= \frac{1.36}{10}\sqrt{\frac{110}{30}}$$

$$= 0.136\times\sqrt{11/3} = 0.136\times 1.91 = 0.259$$

$$\text{At 0.01 level, Critical } D = 1.63\sqrt{\frac{50+60}{50\times 60}}$$

$$= 0.163 \times 1.91 = 0.310$$

Step 4. Interpretation. The computed value of D is 0.130. It is much less than the critical values of D which is 0.259 at 0.05 level and 0.310 at 0.01 level. Hence, it cannot be regarded as significant at both the levels. Therefore, we cannot reject H_0. As a result, H_0 is accepted with the conclusion that both the groups do not differ with regard to their habits of cleanliness. With this analysis, it can also be concluded that both the groups or samples have been drawn from the same population.

Case III: KS two-sample test in one-tailed situation. As in Example 16.8, we set the hypothesis H_1 since Group A is superior to or better than Group B in terms of habits of cleanliness. Then certainly, we will require a one-tailed test for testing the set hypothesis. In such a situation, instead of obtaining the critical value of D for the required interpretation of the observed D, we make use of the χ^2 statistic. It is calculated from the use of the formula

$$\chi^2 = 4D^2\left(\frac{N_1 N_2}{N_1 + N_2}\right)$$

Here N_1 and N_2 are the number of cases in the two samples or groups and D is the greatest absolute divergence between the cumulative proposition of both the groups, viz. $|C_{p_A} - C_{p_B}|$. Let us make use of this formula in our given example.

Here,

$$D = 13, \quad N_1 = 50 \quad \text{and} \quad N_2 = 60$$

Therefore,

$$\chi^2 = 4 \times .13 \times .13 \times \left(\frac{50 \times 60}{50 + 60}\right)$$

$$= 4 \times 0.0169 \times \frac{3000}{110} = 1.84$$

As recommended by Goodman (1954) and referred to by Seigel (1956), we may determine the significance of an observed value of D with the above computed value of χ^2 with $df = 2$ by referring to Table F of the Appendix. We can see that our computed value $\chi^2 = 1.84$ is less than the critical value of χ^2 at 0.05 and 0.01 levels. Hence it is to be taken as "non-significant" for rejecting the null hypothesis. Thus, the null hypothesis H_0 is to be accepted and the H_1 hypothesis that Group A is superior to Group B in following cleanliness, stands rejected.

SUMMARY

1. **Non-parametric tests** are employed in those situations where parametric tests like t, z and F cannot be used to test the set hypothesis of a particular study at a given level of significance. These are called distribution-free tests as they may be used with the data, the distributions of which are not bound by specific requirements like normality, equality or known ratio of variance, large N and recording of observations only on ratio or on an interval scale. Their applicability even with very small samples, even on ordinal, nominal or even on + – signs and without needing any assumption make them quite popular and essential statistical tests to find the significance of statistics and differences. Some of the most common and popular non-parametric tests, e.g. McNemar test, Sign test, Wilcoxon test, Median test, U test, Runs test, and KS test have been discussed in this chapter.
2. **The McNemar test** is used for testing the significance of change, i.e. the change brought out in a randomly selected group of subjects on giving a particular treatment and on organizing the data into a "before" and "after" categories. It calls for the recording of observed frequencies into the cells of the 2 × 2 table, computation of χ^2 with the help of the formula $\chi^2 = \frac{(|A - D| - 1)^2}{A + D}$ (where A and D are the entries in cells A and D of the 2 × 2 table) and then testing the significance of χ^2 with df = 1 at the set level of significance. This test works well with nominal as well as ordinal data.
3. **The Sign test** may be used for testing the significance of differences between two correlated samples in which the data is available either in ordinal measurement or simply expressed in terms of positive and negative signs, showing the direction of differences existing between the observed scores of matched pairs. The null hypothesis test here is that the median change is zero, i.e. there are equal number of positive and negative signs. If the number of matched pairs are equal to or less than 10, a test of significance is applied using the binomninal probabilities distribution table. If the number is more than 10, then distribution is assumed as normal and the z values are used for rejecting or accepting H_0.
4. **Wilcoxon test** is considered more powerful than the Sign test as it takes into consideration the magnitude alongwith the direction of the differences existing between matched pairs.

Here we compute the statistic T and compare it with the critical value of T read from a given table for a particular significance level and particular value of N for drawing inferences about rejecting or accepting H_0. In case the number of matched pairs are more than 25, then we first convert the computed T into the z function and then, as usual, use this z for testing the significance.

5. **Median test** is used to test the difference between two unrelated samples more particularly, to test whether two independent samples have been drawn from populations with the same median. It may work well even with an ordinal scale. The available data for two sets of scales here can be dichotomized at the common median and arranged into a 2×2 contingency table and a value of χ^2 can be computed by using the formula,

$$\chi^2 = \frac{N(|AD - BC| - N/2)^2}{(A+B)(C+D)(A+C)(B+D)}$$

This value of χ^2 may then be compared to the critical value of χ^2 read from the given table with $df = 1$ and $N = N_1 \times N_2$ (the total number of observations in both the samples) for accepting or rejecting the H_0.

6. **The Mann-Whitney U test** is considered more powerful than Median test for comparing data of two unrelated samples. Where Median test helps only in comparing central tendencies of the populations from which these samples have been drawn, the U test is capable of testing the differences between population distributions in so many aspects other than the central tendencies. The null hypothesis to be tested in this is that there lies no difference between the distribution of two samples. The procedure requires first to determine the value of U by counting how many scores from sample A precede each score of sample B and then comparing it with the critical value of U read from a given table for a required level of significance for the given N_L and N_S. The procedure for computing U slightly differs with moderately large samples (having N_1 or N_2 between 9 and 20). For large samples, we first convert U into z function and then use the z value for accepting or rejecting H_0.

7. **Wald-Wolfowitz Runs test** is a general parametric test that can be used to test the general and not the particular differences existing in a single sample (with regard to occurrence of events) or between two unrelated samples where

the data may be recorded on an ordinal scale. H_0 is stated as the "sequence of events occurs in a random order" or "two independent samples are drawn from identical populations" while using this test for a single sample or two unrelated samples. The procedure requires first to convert the number of runs (r), the total frequencies of the succession of identical symbols or events in a given data and then compare this observed value of r with the critical values of r read from the table at the given level of significance for the given N_1 and N_2 to reject or accept H_0. In the case of large samples (N_1 or $N_2 > 20$), we first convert r into z function and then utilize the z value for testing the set hypothesis of the required level of significance.

8. **The Kolmogrov-Smirnov test (KS test)** is a test of goodness of fit like the χ^2 test. It is more powerful and sensitive than the χ^2 test as it may provide good results with smallest samples and smallest cell frequencies. It can be applied in a single sample to test the nature of distribution as well the differences in distribution of a particular trait in two independent samples. In one sample test, we try to compare two cumulative distributions, the one which is observed, and the other which is expected and derived on some theoretical basis. However, in the case of two independent samples, both the cumulative distributions are observed, i.e. available in the given data. The procedure lies in computing the value of D, i.e. the greatest absolute divergence between the cumulative proportions of two distributions and then compare it with the critical value of D for accepting or rejecting the set hypothesis.

To summarize, we can make use of the following table to know where and when it is appropriate to use one of the seven non-parametric tests (described in this chapter) including the χ^2 test (explained in Chapter 11).

Level of measurement	*Used with one sample*	*Used with two related samples*	*Used with two unrelated samples*
Nominal as well as ordinal	χ^2, one sample test	McNemar test	χ^2, two unrelated samples test
Ordinal	KS one sample test; one sample Runs test	Sign test; Wilcoxon test	Median test; U test; KS two samples test; two samples Runs test.

EXERCISES

1. What are non-parametric tests? How are they different from parametric tests? Discuss their merits and limitations.
2. When and where should we try to use parametric or non-parametric tests? Discuss.
3. What is the McNemar test for the significance of change? Discuss its application procedure with the help of a hypothetical example.
4. What is a Sign test? In which situations one tries to prefer it? Discuss its application procedure with the help of an example.
5. What is Wilcoxon test for matched pairs? How is it considered more powerful than the Sign test? Discuss its use with the help of an example.
6. What is Median test? For what purpose is it to be used and how? Discuss.
7. Analyze the process and use the Mann-Whitney U test for testing the difference between population distributions.
8. What is Runs test? How are runs counted in a given data? How is the computation of runs used for testing the significance by comparing it with the critical r? Illustrate with an example.
9. What is KS test? How is it used for testing H_0 in one-sample or two-sample cases? Illustrate with an example.
10. A random sample of 50 individuals were asked to give their opinion, whether they would like to donate their blood. Their responses were recorded. Afterwards, a lecture was given to them as a part of motivation and then they were asked the same question. Their responses were again noted down. The data thus obtained are shown in the following table:

		After lecture	
		Like	Dislike
Before lecture	Dislike	15	18
	Like	13	4

Can you conclude from the above data that there is a significant change in the attitude towards blood donation after the motivation lecture?

11. Fourteen students were rated by two different panels of judges for being selected as captain for a hockey team. Their pooled rating scores on the two occasions are given in the following

table. Can you conclude from the data by using the Sign test that the opinions of two panels differ significantly?

Students	*Rating scores of Panel 1*	*Rating scores of Panel 2*
1	15	13
2	10	12
3	9	8
4	11	13
5	8	6
6	12	14
7	13	13
8	6	5
9	9	8
10	14	11
11	18	16
12	16	14
13	4	3
14	17	12

12. There were nine pairs of matched individuals. In the beginning of the experiment, these individuals were matched and assigned to one of the two groups at random. One group was named as control group and the other, experimental. While the control group was taught through a traditional lecture method, the experimental group was taught by lecture-cum-demonstration method. The scores in both the situations were recorded through a common essay-cum-objective type test. These are given in the following table. Can you conclude from this data that there is a significant difference between the scores of both the groups by using Wilcoxon's test?

Pairs	*Control group scores*	*Experimental group scores*
1	45	39
2	40	48
3	21	30
4	32	33
5	25	31
6	12	23
7	16	25
8	9	15
9	26	30

13. Two groups of married men selected at random were given a self-evaluation marital adjustment rating scale and their scores were recorded as follows. Do you find any significant difference between the marital adjustment of these two groups by applying the Median test?

Group A	9	9	9	12	15	17	17	19	20	22	24	27
Group B	4	5	7	7	12	16	19	19	22			

14. An English teacher was interested in knowing the merits of structured approach over the traditional translation method. For this purpose, he randomly selected 20 students out of 150 students of Class IX and then divided them into two groups of equal size. The control group was taught by traditional method and the other experimental groups, by adopting structured approach. After a month, he tested both the groups on an achievement test and recorded the following scores. Test the hypothesis that the two groups do not differ significantly in terms of their scores by applying Median test:

Control group	*Experimental group*
15	22
21	21
18	19
14	23
16	19
21	22
15	17
18	19
20	17
17	16

15. A research student was interested to know whether children living in a rural environment were more physically fit than children living in an urban environment. He took two random samples, one from each environment and measured them on a test of physical fitness. The scores obtained are now tabulated. Can you conclude from the data by using the Mann-Whitney U test that rural and urban children do not differ in terms of physical fitness?

Scores on fitness test

Rural children	656259626751566869456664556070	$N_1 = 15$
Urban children	60624754604864505449	$N_2 = 10$

16. Twenty post graduate (M.Ed) students were given the choice of selecting their thesis from four given areas. The in charge and guide for these four areas were four teachers of the Education department. Their choices are shown as follows:

	Area 1	*Area 2*	*Area 3*	*Area 4*
No. of students	0	3	8	9

Can you conclude by using the KS test, that the students, choice of a particular area is not related to the teacher incharge of that area?

17. Another research scholar tried to verify the results obtained by his colleague in Problem 15 by taking some other samples. The scores obtained on the physical fitness test for the rural and urban children were listed as follows:

Scores obtained by urban children : 57, 60, 62, 56, 58, 54, 56, 64 52, 54, 56, 57, 53, 55, 52, 51, 63, 64, 61, 60, 59 ($N_1 = 21$)

Scores obtained by rural children : 68, 64, 65, 66, 62, 60, 58, 63, 63, 53 ($N_2 = 10$)

Test the hypothesis of no difference between the groups by using the Mann-Whitney U test.

18. A teacher Adjustment Inventory was administered to two different samples of a secondary school—male and female teachers, selected randomnly from the schools of a city. The scores so obtained are shown now in the following table. Can you conclude from this data by using the KS test that two groups do not differ in terms of their adjustment?

Scores on Adjustment

	60–64	*55–59*	*50–54*	*45–49*	*40–44*	*35–39*	*30–34*	*25–29*	*20–24*
Male Teachers (*f*)	6	10	12	20	16	6	4	2	4
Female Teachers (*f*)	0	0	0	10	8	16	20	26	20

19. A group of 30 teachers consisting of 21 male teachers and 9 female teachers were rated in terms of their teacher-effectiveness. Their scores were then ranked up in the strength of their effectiveness from least effective to most effective, as shown now.

F MM FF MMMMMMMMMMMM F MMMMM FF MM FFF

Apply the Runs test to test the hypothesis that the male and female teachers do not differ in teacher effectiveness.

20. Twelve adolescent girls and boys randomly selected from a coeducational Senior Secondary School were tested through a Personality Inventory. The scores so collected are given now. Can you conclude, using the Runs test that boys and girls differ significantly in terms of their personality make-up?

Scores on personality inventory

Girls	156,	139,	142,	135,	183,	135,	178,	115,	211,	174,	111,	120
Boys	125,	110,	92,	128,	86,	77,	79,	86,	96,	106,	90,	85

17

Analysis of Variance

NEED FOR THE TECHNIQUE OF ANALYSIS OF VARIANCE

In Chapter 10, we discussed the use of z and t tests for testing the significance of the difference between the means of two samples or groups. In practice, however, we often come across situations where we have several samples of the same general character drawn from a given population and wish to know whether there are any significant differences between the means of these samples. In such situations, instead of determining a single difference between two means, several differences between several means are determined. Let us illustrate such a situation with an example.

In a research study, localities are divided into four classes ranging from 'best' to 'worst', according to their social environment. A group test of general mental ability is administered to four random samples of 10 boys (studying in class VIII) each from four schools of the locality. We thus have four means for these samples drawn from the four localities. Now, if we wish to test the significance of the differences between these four means (by formulating a null hypothesis that no difference exists between the means) and apply the z or t test, it will be difficult, cumbersome and unwise on the following grounds:

1. The z or t test can be used for testing the significance of the difference between means by taking two means at a time. Here we have to test the significance of the difference between four means and so we have to take

$$\frac{n(n-1)}{2}, \quad \text{i.e.} \quad \frac{4(4-1)}{2} = 6$$

pairs for comparison. The work will be done in six rounds and thus may involve too much a labour and complication. The degree of complication and the amount of labour will gradually increase with an increase in the number of groups or samples, e.g. for 8 samples we will have 28, for 10 samples 45, and for 15 samples 105 separate z or t tests.

2. However, after we decide to do so much labour, there is no guarantee that we would get the desired results. There is a possibility that none of the differences between pairs could prove to be significant and in such a case, the cumbersome exercise of computing a number of z or t values for testing the significance between several pairs of means will be complete waste.
3. In the above situation, while testing the significance of the difference between 6 pairs of sample means we may find that one of them is significant at the 0.01 level, the other at the 0.05 level, and the remaining four differences significant neither at 0.05 level nor at the 0.01 level. Thus, we may conclude that none of these six differences is significant. This conclusion is erroneous. Unless we have a single composite test for testing the differences within the given means at a time, we cannot conclude that the whole distribution of obtained sampling statistics has occurred by chance.
4. There could be a serious limitation in this case regarding the omission of the element of interaction existing between the different samples or groups included in the study. The various differences between means are not independent of each other. If we know the difference between sample means A and B, and A and C, we can automatically tell the difference between B and C because the difference between B and C is related to the difference between A and B, and A and C. In other words, if we have to test the difference between three sample means, one difference is not independent of the other two differences. Similarly, if we have to test the difference between four sample means, at least two differences in the six pairs are not independent of the other four differences. Thus, there is a need to take into account the dependence of the differences while deciding about their significance. However, as know, both t and z tests are tied to a distribution of the differences between pairs of means of independent random samples. As a result, the use of z or t test cannot provide us any satisfactory result.

Thus we may conclude that, the usual procedure of testing the significance between two means by the t or z test definitely needs a substitute in the form of a single composite test for simultaneously testing the differences between the means of several samples of groups. The solution to the problem lies in a statistical technique known by the name *analysis of variance* in which all the data are treated together and a general null hypothesis of no difference among the means of the various samples or groups is tested.

MEANING OF THE TERM 'ANALYSIS OF VARIANCE'

A composite procedure for testing simultaneously the difference between several sample means is known as the *analysis of variance*. It helps us to know whether any of the differences between the means of the given samples are significant. If the answer is 'yes', we examine pairs (with the help of the t test) to see just where the significant differences lie. If the answer is 'no', we do not proceed further.

In such a test, as the name implies, we usually deal with the analysis of the variances. Variance is simply the arithmetic average of the squared deviation from their means. In other words, it is the square of the standard deviation (variance = σ^2). Variance has a quality which makes it specially useful. It has an additive property, which the standard deviation with its square root does not possess. Variance on this account can be added up and broken down into components. Hence, the term 'analysis of variance' deals with the task of analyzing of breaking up the total variance of a large sample or a population consisting of a number of equal groups or sub-samples into two components (two kinds of variances), given as follows:

1. *"Within-groups" variance*. This is the average variance of the members of each group around their respective group means, i.e. the mean value of the scores in a sample (as members of each group may vary among themselves).
2. *"Between-groups" variance*. This represents the variance of group means around the total or grand mean of all groups, i.e. the best estimate of the population mean (as the group means may vary considerably from each other).

Let us make this clearer with the help of the example cited in the beginning of this chapter.

In this study, there were 40 boys in all, belonging to four different localities. If we add the IQ scores of these 40 boys and divide the sum by 40, we get the value of the grand or general mean, i.e. the best estimate of the population mean. There are 4 groups (samples) of 10 boys each. The mean of the IQ scores of 10 boys in each group is called the *group mean* and in this way, there will be 4 group means, which will vary considerably from each other.

Now the question arises, as to how far does an IQ score of a particular boy belonging to a particular sample or group deviate from the grand mean for 40 boys. We may observe that the deviation has two parts, i.e. deviation of the score from the mean of that particular group and the deviation of the mean of the group from the grand mean.

For deriving more useful results, we can use variance as a measure of dispersion (deviation from the mean) in place of some useful measures like standard deviation. Consequently, the variance of an individual's score from the grand mean may be broken into two parts (as pointed out earlier), viz. within-groups variance and between-groups variance. Commenting on the above aspects regarding the meaning and nature of analysis of variance and the subsequent procedure adopted in the analysis of variance technique, Lindquist (1970) writes:

> The basic proposition is that from any set of *r* groups of *n* cases each, we may, on the hypothesis that all groups are random samples from the same population, derive two independent estimates of the population variance, one of which is based on the variance of group means, the other on the average variance of within groups. The test of this hypothesis then consists of determining whether or not the ratio (*F*) between these estimates lies below the value in the table for *F* that corresponds to the selected level of significance.

In this way, the technique of analysis of variance as a single composite test of significance, for the difference between several group means demands the derivation of two independent estimates of the population variance, one based on variance of group means (between groups variance) and the other on the average variance within the groups (within groups variance.) Ultimately, the comparison of the size of between groups variance and within-groups variance called F-ratio denoted by

$$\frac{\text{between-groups variance}}{\text{within-groups variance}}$$

is used as a critical ratio for determining the significance of the difference between group means at a given level of significance.

PROCEDURE FOR CALCULATING THE ANALYSIS OF VARIANCE

As already pointed out, the deviation of an individual's score belonging to a sample or a group of population from the grand mean can be divided into two parts: (i) deviation of the individual's score from his group mean; and (ii) deviation of the group mean from the grand mean. Consequently, the total variance of the scores of all individuals included in the study may be partitioned into within-group variance and between-groups variance. The formula used for the computation of variance (σ^2) is $\Sigma x^2/N$, i.e. sum of the squared deviation from the mean value divided by total frequencies. Hence, by taking N as the common denominator, the total sum of the squared deviation of scores around the grand or general mean for all groups combined can be made equal to the sum of the two partitioned, between-groups and within-groups sum of squares. Mathematically,

Total sum of squares (around the general mean)

= between-groups sum of squares + within-groups sum of squares

or

$$S_t^2 = S_b^2 + S_w^2$$

Hence the procedure for the analysis of variance involves the following main tasks:

(i) Computation of total sum of squares (S_t^2)
(ii) Computation of between-groups sum of squares (S_b^2)
(iii) Computation of within-groups sum of squares (S_w^2)
(iv) Computation of F-ratio
(v) Use of t test (if the need for further testing arises).

All these tasks may be carried out in a series of systematic steps. Let us try to understand these steps by adopting the following terminology:

X = Raw score of any individual included in the study (any score entry in the given table)

ΣX = Grand Sum

$\dfrac{\Sigma X}{N}$ = Grand or general mean

$X_1, X_2, \ldots$ denote scores within first group, second group, ...

n_1, n_2, n_3 = No. of individuals in first, second and third groups

$\dfrac{\Sigma X_1}{N}, \dfrac{\Sigma X_2}{N}, \ldots$ denote means of the first group, second group, ...

N = total No. of scores or frequencies

$= n_1 + n_2 + n_3 + \ldots$

Let us now outline the steps.

Step 1. Arrangement of the given table and computation of some initial values. In this step, the following values needed in computation are calculated from the experimental data arranged in proper tabular form:

(i) Sum of squares, ΣX_1, ΣX_2, ... and the grand sum, ΣX

(ii) Group means, $\frac{\Sigma X_1}{N}$, $\frac{\Sigma X_2}{N}$, ..., and the grand mean $\frac{\Sigma X}{N}$

(iii) Correction term C computed by the formula

$$C = \frac{(\Sigma X)^2}{N} = \frac{\text{Square of the grand sum}}{\text{Total No. of cases}}$$

Step 2. Arrangement of the given table into squared-form table and calculation of some other values. The given table is transformed into a squared-form table by squaring the values of each score given in the original table and then the following values are computed:

(i) $\Sigma X_1^2, \Sigma X_2^2, \Sigma X_3^2, \ldots$

(ii) ΣX^2

Step 3. Calculation of total sum of squares. The total sum of squares around the general mean is calculated with the help of the following formula:

$$S_t^2 = \Sigma X^2 - \text{Correction value } (C)$$

$$= \Sigma X^2 - \frac{(\Sigma X)^2}{N}$$

Step 4. Calculation of between-group sum of squares. The value of the between-groups sum of squares may be computed with the help of the following formula:

$$S_b^2 = \frac{(\Sigma X_1)^2}{n_1} + \frac{(\Sigma X_2)^2}{n_2} + \frac{(\Sigma X_3)^2}{n_3} + \cdots + \frac{(\Sigma X_n)^2}{n_n} - C$$

$$= \frac{(\text{sum of scores in group I})^2}{\text{No. of scores in group I}}$$

$$+ \frac{(\text{sum of scores in group II})^2}{\text{No. of scores in group II}}$$

$$+ \cdots - C \text{ (correction value)}$$

Step 5. Calculation of within-groups sum of squares. Between-groups and within-groups sum of squares constitute the total sum of squares. Therefore, after steps 3 and 4, the value of within-groups sum of squares (sum of squares of deviation within each group about their respective group means) may be calculated by subtracting the value of between-groups sum of squares from the total sum of squares. Its formula, therefore, goes thus:

Within-groups sum of squares,

$$S_w^2 = S_t^2 - S_b^2$$

Step 6. Calculation of the number of degrees of freedom. All these sums of squares calculated in steps 3–5 possess different degrees of freedom given by

Total sum of squares, $(S_t^2) = N - 1$

Between-groups sum of squares, $(S_b^2) = K - 1$

Within-groups sum of squares, $(S_w^2) = (N - 1) - (K - 1) = N - K$

where N represents the total number of observations, scores or frequencies and K, the number of groups in the research study.

Step 7. Calculation of F-ratio. The value of F-ratio furnishes a comprehensive or overall test of significance of the difference between means. For its computation, we have to arrange the data and computation work in the following manner:

Source of variance	*Sum of squares*	*df*	*Mean square variance*
Between-groups	S_b^2 (computed in step 4)	$K - 1$	$\frac{S_b^2}{K-1}$
Within-groups	S_w^2 (computed in step 5)	$N - K$	$\frac{S_w^2}{N-K}$

$$F = \frac{\text{Mean square variance between-groups}}{\text{Mean square variance within-groups}}$$

Step 8. Interpretation of F-ratio. F-ratios are interpreted by the use of the critical value of F-ratios given in Table R of the Appendix. This table has the number of degrees of freedom for the greater mean square variance across the top and the number of degrees of freedom in the smaller mean square variance on the left-hand side. If our computed value of F is equal to or greater than the critical tabled value of F at a given level of significance 0.05 or 0.01, it is assumed to be significant and consequently, we reject the null hypothesis of no difference among these means at that level of significance. However, a significant F does not tell us which of the group means differ significantly; it merely tells us that at least one mean is relatively different from some other. Consequently, there arises a need for further testing to determine which of the differences between means are significant.

In case our computed value of F is less than the critical tabled value of F at a given level of significance, it is taken as non-significant and consequently, the null hypothesis cannot be rejected. Then there is no reason for further testing (as none of the differences between means will be significant). In a summarized form, the above analysis may be represented as follows:-

F → Significant → Null hypothesis rejected → Need for further testing

F → Non-significant → Null hypothesis not rejected → No need for further testing

Generally, as and when we get the value of F as less than 1, we straightaway interpret it as non-significant resulting in the non-rejection of the null hypothesis.

Step 9. Testing differences between means with the t test. When F is found significant, the need for further testing arises. We take pairs of the group means one by one for testing the significance of differences. The t test provides an adequate procedure for testing the significance when we have means of only two samples or groups at a time for consideration. Therefore, we make use of the t test to test the differences between pairs of means.

As we have seen in Chapter 10, the usual formula for computation of t values is

$$t = \frac{D}{\sigma_D} = \frac{\text{Difference between two means}}{\text{Standard error of the difference between the means}}$$

and σ_D is computed by the formula

$$\sigma_D = \sigma\left(\frac{1}{n_1} + \frac{1}{n_2}\right)$$

where

σ = Pooled SD of the samples drawn from the same population

n_1, n_2 = Total No. of cases in samples I and II, respectively

In the analysis of variance technique, within-groups means square variance provides us the value of σ^2, the square root of which can give us the required pooled SD of the samples or groups included in our study.

The degrees of freedom for within-groups sum of squares are given by the formula $N - K$. With these degrees of freedom we can read the t values from Table C given in the Appendix, at the 0.05 and 0.01 levels of significance. If the computed value of t is found to be equal to or greater than the critical tabled value of t at 0.05 or 0.01 levels, we can reject the null hypothesis at that level of significance.

Proceeding similarly, we take other pairs for testing the difference between means and arrive at conclusions.

Let us illustrate now the whole process of using the analysis of variance technique with the help of an example.

Example 17.1: The aim of an experimental study was to determine the effect of three different techniques of training on the learning of a particular skill. Three groups, each consisting of seven students of class IX, assigned randomly, were given training through these different techniques. The scores obtained on a performance test were recorded as follows:

Group I	*Group II*	*Group III*
3	4	5
5	5	5
3	3	5
1	4	1
7	9	7
3	5	3
6	5	7

Test the difference between groups by adopting the analysis of variance technique.

Solution.

Step 1. Original table computation

Table 17.1 Organization of Data Given in Example 17.1

Rating of the coaching experts			*Total*
Group I (X_1)	Group II (X_2)	Group III (X_3)	
3	4	5	12
5	5	5	15
3	3	5	11
1	4	1	6
7	9	7	23
3	5	3	11
6	5	7	18
$\Sigma X_1 = 28$	$\Sigma X_2 = 35$	$\Sigma X_3 = 33$	$\Sigma X = 96$ Grand Total

Here,

$$n_1 = n_2 = n_3 = 7, \quad N = n_1 + n_2 + n_3 = 21$$

$$\text{Group means} = \frac{\Sigma X_1}{n_1} = \frac{28}{7} = 4$$

$$\frac{\Sigma X_2}{n_2} = \frac{35}{7} = 5$$

$$\frac{\Sigma X_3}{n_3} = \frac{33}{7} = 4.71$$

$$\text{Correction term } C = \frac{(\Sigma X)^2}{N} = \frac{96 \times 96}{21} = \frac{9216}{21} = 438.85$$

Step 2. Squared-table computation

Table 17.2 Squared Values of the Original Data

X_1^2	X_2^2	X_3^2	*Total*
9	16	25	50
25	25	25	75
9	9	25	43
1	16	1	18
49	81	49	179
9	25	9	43
36	25	49	110
$\Sigma X_1^2 = 138$	$\Sigma X_2^2 = 197$	$\Sigma X_3^2 = 183$	$\Sigma X^2 = 518$

Step 3. Total sum of squares (S_t^2):

$$S_t^2 = \Sigma X^2 - \frac{(\Sigma X)^2}{N} = \Sigma X^2 - C = 518 - 438.85 = 79.15$$

Step 4. Between-groups sum of squares (S_b^2):

$$S_b^2 = \frac{(\Sigma X_1)^2}{n_1} + \frac{(\Sigma X_2)^2}{n_2} + \frac{(\Sigma X_3)^2}{n_3} - C$$

$$= \frac{28 \times 28}{7} + \frac{35 \times 35}{7} + \frac{33 \times 33}{7} - 438.85$$

$$= \frac{784 + 1225 + 1089}{7} - 438.85$$

$$= 442.57 - 438.85 = 3.72$$

Step 5. Within-groups sum of squares (S_w^2). This is obtained as

$$S_w^2 = S_t^2 - S_b^2 = 79.15 - 3.72 = 75.43$$

Step 6. Number of degrees of freedom

For total sum of squares,

$$(S_t^2) = N - 1 = 21 - 1 = 20$$

For between-groups sum of squares,

$$(S_b^2) = K - 1 = 3 - 1 = 2$$

For within-groups sum of squares,

$$(S_w^2) = N - K = 21 - 3 = 18$$

Step 7. Calculation of F-ratio

Table 17.3 Computation of Values of Mean Square Variance

Source of variation	*Sum of squares*	*df*	*Mean square variance*
Between-groups	$S_b^2 = 3.72$	2	3.72/2 = 1.86
Within-groups	$S_w^2 = 75.43$	18	75.43/18 = 4.19

$$F = \frac{\text{Mean square variance between-groups}}{\text{Mean square variance within-groups}} = \frac{1.86}{4.19} = 0.444$$

Step 8. Interpretation of F-ratio. The *F*-ratio table (Table R given in the Appendix) is referred to for 2 degrees of freedom for smaller mean square variance on the left-hand side, and for 18 degrees of freedom for greater mean square variance across the top. The critical values of *F* obtained by interpolation are as follows:

Critical value of F = 19.43 at 0.05 level of significance

Critical value of F = 99.44 at 0.01 level of significance

Our computed value of *F* (.444) is not significant at both the levels of significance and hence, the null hypothesis cannot be rejected and we may confidently say that the differences between means are not significant and therefore, there is no need for further testing with the help of t test.

Example 17.2: In a study, the effectiveness of the methods of memorization was to be determined. For this purpose, three groups of 10 students, each randomly selected from class VII of a school were taken and each group was made to adopt a particular method of memorization. In the end, the performance was tested. The number of nonsense syllables correctly recalled by the students of these groups is presented below:

Group I : 12, 10, 11, 11, 8, 10, 7, 9, 10, 6
Group II : 14, 8, 19, 15, 10, 11, 13, 12, 9, 12
Group III : 8, 11, 13, 9, 7, 5, 6, 8, 7, 10

Apply the analysis of variance technique for testing the significance of the difference between group means.

Solution.

Step 1. Arrangement of the data into a proper table and initial computation (Table 17.4).

Table 17.4 Organization of Data Given in Example 17.2

Group I (X_1)	*Group II* (X_2)	*Group III* (X_3)	*Total*
12	14	8	34
10	8	11	29
11	19	13	43
11	15	9	35
8	10	7	25
10	11	5	26
7	13	6	26
9	12	8	29
10	9	7	26
6	12	10	28
$\Sigma X_1 = 94$	$\Sigma X_2 = 123$	$\Sigma X_3 = 84$	$\Sigma X = 301$

Here,

$$n_1 = n_2 = n_3 = 10$$

$$N = n_1 + n_2 + n_3 = 30$$

$$\text{Group means} = \frac{\Sigma X_1}{n_1} = 9.4, \quad \frac{\Sigma X_2}{n_2} = 12.3, \quad \frac{\Sigma X_3}{n_3} = 8.4$$

$$\text{Correction term } C = \frac{(\Sigma X)^2}{N} = \frac{301 \times 301}{30} = \frac{90{,}601}{30} = 3020$$

Step 2. Squared table computation. This can be obtained as in Table 17.5.

Table 17.5 Squared Values of the Original Data

X_1^2	X_2^2	X_3^2	*Total*
144	196	64	404
100	64	121	285
121	361	169	651
121	225	81	427
64	100	49	213
100	121	25	246
49	169	36	254
81	144	64	289
100	81	49	230
36	144	100	280
$\Sigma X_1^2 = 916$	$\Sigma X_2^2 = 1605$	$\Sigma X_3^2 = 758$	$\Sigma X^2 = 3279$

Step 3. *Total sum of squares* (S_t^2). This is given by

$$S_t^2 = \Sigma X^2 - \frac{(\Sigma X)^2}{N} = X^2 - C$$

$$= 3279 - 3020 = 259$$

Step 4. *Between-groups sum of squares* (S_b^2). This is obtained as

$$S_b^2 = \frac{(\Sigma X_1)^2}{n_1} + \frac{(\Sigma X_2)^2}{n_2} + \frac{(\Sigma X_3)^2}{n_3} - C$$

$$= \frac{94 \times 94}{10} + \frac{123 \times 123}{10} + \frac{84 \times 84}{10} - 3020$$

$$= 883.6 + 1512.9 + 705.6 - 3020$$

$$= 3102.1 - 3020 = 82.1$$

Step 5. *Within-groups sum of squares* (S_w^2). This is given by

$$S_w^2 = S_t^2 - S_b^2 = 259 - 82.1 = 176.9$$

Step 6. *Number of degrees of freedom*

$$df \text{ for } S_t^2 = N - 1 = 30 - 1 = 29$$

$$df \text{ for } S_b^2 = K - 1 = 3 - 1 = 2$$

$$df \text{ for } S_w^2 = N - K = 30 - 3 = 27$$

Step 7. Calculation of F-ratio

Table 17.6 Computation of the Values of Mean Square Variance

Source of variance	*Sum of squares*	*df*	*Mean square variance*
Between-groups	$S_b^2 = 82.1$	2	$\frac{82.1}{2} = 41.05$
Within-groups	$S_w^2 = 176.9$	27	$\frac{176.9}{27} = 6.55$

$$F = \frac{\text{Mean square variance between-groups}}{\text{Mean square variance within-groups}} = \frac{41.05}{6.55} = 6.27$$

Step 8. Interpretation of F-ratio. The F-ratio table (Table R in the Appendix) is now referred for 2 degrees of freedom for greater mean square variance and 27 degrees of freedom for smaller mean square variance.

Critical values of F = 3.35 at 0.05 level of significance

Critical values of F = 5.49 at 0.01 level of significance

The computed value of F, i.e. 6.27, is much higher than both the critical values of F at 0.05 and 0.01 levels of significance. Hence, it should be taken as quite significant. Consequently, we have to reject the null hypothesis. Thus, a significant difference definitely exists between the group means. Let us further test to find out where these differences exist.

Step 9. Application of t test. The group means in our study are as follows:

$$M_1 = 9.4, \quad M_2 = 12.3, \quad M_3 = 8.4$$

Let us first test the difference between M_1 and M_2, i.e.

$$12.3 - 9.4 = 2.9$$

$$t = \frac{D}{\sigma_D} = \frac{2.9}{\sigma_D}$$

$$\sigma_D = \sigma\left(\frac{1}{n_1} + \frac{1}{n_2}\right)$$

where σ, the square root of the value of within-groups mean square variance, is

$$\sqrt{6.55} = 2.559$$

and $$n_1 = n_2 = 10$$

Hence,

$$\sigma_D = 2.559\left(\frac{1}{10}+\frac{1}{10}\right)$$
$$= 2.559 \times .2 = 0.5118$$
$$= 0.52 \text{ (approx.)}$$

Therefore,

$$t = \frac{2.9}{0.52} = 5.57$$

and *df* for within-groups sum of squares is

$$N - K = 27$$

From the *t*-distribution table (Table C of the Appendix):

Critical values of t = 2.05 at 0.05 level of significance
Critical values of t = 2.77 at 0.01 level of significance

The computed value of t, i.e. 5.57, is much higher than the critical values of t at both these levels. Hence it is to be regarded as quite significant and thereby null hypothesis stands rejected, the result being that the difference between M_1 and M_2 is quite significant and real.

Now, take M_2 and M_3. Here,

$$D = M_2 - M_3 = 12.3 - 8.4 = 3.9$$

$$t = \frac{D}{\sigma_D} = \frac{3.9}{0.52} = 7.5$$

This computed t value is quite significant at both levels of significance, the result being given by that the difference between M_2 and M_3 is also quite significant and real.

Finally, we take M_1 and M_3

$$D = M_1 - M_3 = 9.4 - 8.4 = 1$$

$$t = \frac{D}{\sigma_D} = \frac{1}{0.52} = 1.92$$

It can be seen that the computed value of t, i.e. 1.92, is much lesser than the critical values 2.05 and 2.77 at 0.05 and 0.01 levels of significance. Hence it is not significant and, consequently, the null hypothesis cannot be rejected. Thus, it can be said that the difference between M_1 and M_3 is not significant and real. It may occur by chance or due to sampling fluctuation.

In conclusion, it can be said that of the total three, only two of the difference, $M_1 - M_2$ and $M_2 - M_3$ are significant and trustworthy.

TWO-WAY ANALYSIS OF VARIANCE

So far, we have dealt with one-way analysis of variance involving one experimental variable. However, experiments may be conducted in the fields of education and psychology for the simultaneous study of two experimental variables. Such experiments involve two-way classification based on two experimental variables. Let us make some distinction between the need for carrying out one-way and two-way analyses of variance through some illustrations.

Suppose that we want to study the effect of four different methods of teaching. Here, the method of teaching is the experimental variable (independent variable which is to be applied at four levels). We take four groups of students randomly selected from a class. These four groups are taught by the same teacher in the same school but by different methods. At the end of the session, all the groups are tested through an achievement test by the teacher. The mean scores of these four groups are computed. If we are interested in knowing the significance of the differences between the means of these groups, the best technique is the analysis of variance. Since only one experimental variable (effect of the method of teaching) is to be studied, we have to carry out one-way analysis of variance.

Let us assume, that there is one more experimental or independent variable in the study, in addition to the method of teaching. Let it be the school system at three levels which means that three school systems are chosen for the experiment. These systems can be: government school, government-aided school and public school. Now the experiment will involve the study of 4 × 3 groups. We have 4 groups each in the three types of schools (all randomly selected). The achievement scores of these groups can then be compared by the method of analysis of variance by establishing a null hypothesis that neither the school system nor the methods have anything to do with the achievement of pupils. In this way, we have to simultaneously study the impact of two experimental variables, each having two or more levels, characteristics or classifications and hence we have to carry out the two-way analysis of variance.

In the two-way classification situation, an estimate of population variance, i.e. total variance is supposed to be broken into: (i) variance due to methods alone, (ii) variance due to school alone, and (iii) the residual variance in the groups called *interaction variance* ($M \times S$;

M = methods, S = schools) which may exist on account of the following factors:

1. Chance
2. Uncontrolled variables like lack of uniformity in teachers
3. Relative merits of the methods (which may differ from one school to another).

In other words, there may be interaction between methods and schools which means that although no method may be regarded as good or bad in general, yet it may be more suitable (or unsuitable) for a particular school system. Hence, the presence of interaction variance is a unique feature with all the experimental studies involving two or more experimental variables. In such problems, requiring two or more ways of analysis of variance, we will have to take care of the residual or interaction variance in estimating their population variance. If the null hypothesis is true, variance in terms of the method should not be significantly different from the interaction variance. Similarly, the variance due to schools may also be compared with the interaction variance. For all such purposes of comparison, the F-ratio test is used, as explained later in this chapter.

The design of the above two-way classification experiment can be further elaborated by having more experimental or independent variables, each considered at several levels. As the number of variables increases, the order of interaction also increases. For example, if school (S), teacher (T), and methods (M) are taken as three independent variables, there will be 3 first-order interactions: $S \times T$, $T \times M$, and $S \times M$, and the second-order interaction $S \times T \times M$. We will have $4 \times 3 \times 4$ (if there are 4 levels of teacher variable), i.e. 48 randomized groups in this study and the problem of testing the difference between means will require three-way analysis of variance technique.

According to the needs and requirements of the experiment, a research worker has to select a particular experimental design involving two or more independent or experimental variables. A discussion of these designs in terms of their construction, administration and analysis is beyond the scope of the book. Hence, the readers are advised to consult some of the books given in the reference section like Edwards (1961), Hicks (1964), Lindquist (1968) and Guilford (1973). However, let us briefly study the method of carrying out two-way analysis of variance for testing the difference between group means. As an illustration, let us take the case of an experimental design where a single group is being assessed more than once.

Example 17.3: In a research study, there were two experimental or independent variables: a seven-member group of player and three coaches who were asked to rate the players in terms of a particular trait on a ten-point scale. The data were recorded as under:

Rating by three coaches	*Players*						
	1	2	3	4	5	6	7
A	3	5	3	1	7	3	6
B	4	5	3	4	9	5	5
C	5	5	5	1	7	3	7

Apply the technique of analysis of variance for analyzing these data.

Step 1. Arrangement of the data in a proper table and computation of essential initial values (Table 17.7).

Table 17.7 Organization of Data Given in Example 17.3

Players	*Rating of coaches*			*Total of rows*	*Square of the total of rows*
	By A (X_1)	By B (X_2)	By C (X_3)		
1	3	4	5	12	144
2	5	5	5	15	225
3	3	3	5	11	121
4	1	4	1	6	36
5	7	9	7	23	529
6	3	5	3	11	121
7	6	5	7	18	324
Total of columns	$\Sigma X_1 = 28$	$\Sigma X_2 = 35$	$\Sigma X_3 = 33$	$\Sigma X = 96$ (Grand total)	
Square of the totals of the column	$(\Sigma X_1)^2 = 784$,	$(\Sigma X_2)^2 = 1225$,	$(\Sigma X_3)^2 = 1089$,	$(\Sigma X)^2 = 9216$	

Here,

$$N = n_1 + n_2 + n_3 = 7 + 7 + 7 = 21$$

$$C = \frac{(\Sigma X)^2}{N} = \frac{9216}{21} = 438.85$$

Step 2. Arrangement of the table in square form and computation of some essential values (Table 17.8).

Table 17.8 Squared Values of Original Data

	X_1^2	X_2^2	X_3^2	*Total*
	9	16	25	50
	25	25	25	75
	9	9	25	43
	1	16	1	18
	49	81	49	179
	9	25	9	43
	36	25	49	110
Total	$\Sigma X_1^2 = 138$	$\Sigma X_2^2 = 197$	$\Sigma X_3^2 = 183$	$\Sigma X^2 = 518$

Step 3. Calculation of the total sum of squares (S_t^2) (around grand mean).

$$S_t^2 = \Sigma X^2 - \frac{(\Sigma X)^2}{N} = \Sigma X^2 - C$$

$$= 518 - 438.85 = 79.15$$

Step 4. Calculation of the sum of squares for rows (S_r^2) (between the means of players to be rated by three coaches).

$$S_r^2 = \frac{144 + 225 + 121 + 36 + 529 + 121 + 324}{3} - C$$

$$= \frac{1500}{3} - 438.85 = 61.15$$

Step 5. Calculation of the sum of squares for columns (S_c^2) between the means of coaches rating 7 players).

$$S_c^2 = \frac{784 \times 1225 \times 1089}{7} - C$$

$$= 442.57 - 438 \cdot 85 = 3.72$$

Step 6. Calculation of the interaction or residual sum of squares (S_i^2). The interaction sum of squares is given by

$$(S_i^2) = S_t^2 - (S_r^2 + S_c^2)$$

$$= 79.15 - (61.15 + 3.72) = 14.28$$

Step 7. Computation of F-ratios. Table 17.9 illustrates the computation of mean square variance value.

Table 17.9 Computation of the Values of Mean Square Variance

Source of variation	*df*	*Sum of squares*	*Mean square variance*
Rows (players)	$(r - 1) = 6$	61.15	$\frac{61.15}{6} = 10.19$
Columns (coaches)	$(c - 1) = 2$	3.72	$\frac{3.72}{2} = 1.86$
Interaction or residual	$(r - 1)(c - 1) = 12$	14.28	$\frac{14.28}{12} = 1.19$

$$F \text{ (for rows)} = \frac{\text{Mean square variance between rows (players)}}{\text{Mean square variance in terms of interaction}}$$

$$= \frac{10.19}{1.19} = 8.56$$

$$F \text{ (for columns)} = \frac{\text{Mean square variance between columns (coaches)}}{\text{Mean square variance in terms of interaction}}$$

$$= \frac{1.86}{1.19} = 1.56$$

Step 8. Interpretation of F-ratios. Table 17.10 gives the critical values of *F*.

Table 17.10 Critical Values of *F* and Significance of Computed *F*

Kind of F	*df for greater mean square variance*	*df for smaller mean square variance*	*Critical values of F at 0.05 level*	*Critical values of F at 0.01 level*	*Judgement about the significance of computed F*	*Conclusion*
F (for rows)	2	12	3.88	6.93	Significant at both levels	Null hypothesis rejected
F (for columns)	6	12	3.00	4.82	Not significant at both levels	Null hypothesis not rejected

Here, *F* (for rows) is highly significant and hence null hypothesis is rejected. It indicates that the coaches did discriminate among the players. The second *F* (for columns) is insignificant and hence, the null hypothesis cannot be rejected. It indicates that the coaches did not differ significantly among themselves in their ratings of the players. In other words, their ratings may be taken as trustworthy and reliable.

UNDERLYING ASSUMPTIONS IN ANALYSIS OF VARIANCE

The following are the fundamental assumptions for the use of analysis of variance technique:

1. The dependent variable which is measured should be normally distributed in the population.
2. The individuals being observed should be distributed randomly in the groups.
3. Within-groups variances must be approximately equal.
4. The contributions to variance in the total sample must be additive.

SUMMARY

In performing experiments and carrying out studies in the fields of education and psychology, we often come across situations where we are required to test the significance of the differences among the means of several samples instead of only two sample means, capable of testing with the help of z or t tests. In such situations, a technique known as analysis of variance proves quite useful. It provides a composite test to find out, simultaneously, the difference between several sample means and thus helps us tell, whether any of the differences between means of the given samples are significant. If the answer is 'yes' we examine pairs of sample means (with the help of the usual *t* test) to see just where the significant differences lie. If the answer is 'no', we do not require further testing.

The technique of analysis of variance demands the analysis or breaking apart of the total squared deviation scores or variance of the scores of all individuals (σ^2) included in the study around the grand mean (mean of the total scores) into two parts—(i) within-groups variance, i.e. the squared deviation scores of the individuals from their group means and, (ii) between-groups variance, i.e. the squared deviation scores of the group mean from the grand mean. In actual computation work:

1. The total variance S_t^2 is first calculated and then the S_b^2, the difference between the two automatically gives S_w^2. The formulae run as follows:

$$S_t^2 = \Sigma X^2 - \frac{(\Sigma X)^2}{N}$$

$$S_b^2 = \frac{(\Sigma X_1)^2}{n_1} + \frac{(\Sigma X_2)^2}{n_2} + \frac{(\Sigma X_3)^2}{n_3} + \cdots + \frac{(\Sigma X_n)^2}{n_n} - C$$

$$S_w^2 = S_t^2 - S_b^2$$

2. The degrees of freedom for S_b^2 and S_w^2 are $K - 1$ and $N - K$, where K represents the number of groups and N, total observations.
3. Then, the F-ratios desired for testing the significance is calculated by the formula

$$F = \frac{\text{Mean square variance between-groups}}{\text{Mean square variance within-groups}} = \frac{S_b^2/K - 1}{S_w^2/N - K}$$

4. The computed F-ratios are then interpreted by the use of critical F values read from the table with the degrees of freedom at the given level of significance. In case our computed F is found non-significant, then there is no need for further testing but if it is found significant then the use of t test is made for testing further the difference between sample means taken two at a time.

In the experiments involving two experimental or independent variables instead of one, the significance of the difference between several means is tested with the help of two-way analysis of variance instead of one-way analysis of variance. In the two-way analysis total variance is supposed to be broken into three parts instead of two as done in the one-way analysis. These are: (i) variance due to one variable, (ii) variance due to other variable, and (iii) interaction or residual variance on account of the supposed interaction between variables. Here, instead of one, two F-ratios are computed with the help of the formulae:

$$F \text{ (for one variable)} = \frac{\text{Mean square variance between one variable}}{\text{Mean square variance in terms of interaction}}$$

$$F \text{ (for the other variable)} = \frac{\text{Mean square variance between other variable}}{\text{Mean square variance in terms of interaction}}$$

and then the interpretation is made by comparing these F-ratios with the critical F values read from the table for computed degrees of freedom at a given level of significance.

For its successful application, the analysis of variance needs the fulfilment of assumptions like the normal distribution of the dependent variable, random distribution in the groups of individuals under study, homogeneity of the within-groups variances and the analysis of total variances into component variances.

EXERCISES

1. What do you understand by the technique, analysis of variance, used for the analysis of statistical data?
2. In which circumstances is the technique of analysis of variance preferred to the usual z or t tests for testing the significance of the difference between means? Discuss with the help of examples.
3. Discuss the various steps involved in the application of analysis of variance for testing the difference between groups. Illustrate with the help of a hypothetical example.
4. What is analysis of variance? Point out the underlying assumptions in its application.
5. The following are error scores on a psychomotor test for four groups of equal subjects tested under four experimental conditions:

Group I	*Group II*	*Group III*	*Group IV*
4	9	2	7
5	10	2	7
1	9	6	4
0	6	5	2
2	6	2	7

   Apply the analysis of variance to test the null hypothesis.

6. The following data represent the scores of six students (selected randomly) in each of the five sections of class VIII of a school on a vocabulary test:

Section A	*Section B*	*Section C*	*Section D*	*Section E*
32	19	17	12	12
17	26	26	15	15
28	30	30	10	36
24	17	35	20	17
21	34	20	18	20
38	15	15	30	25

   Test the null hypothesis for vocabulary ability of the different sections of class VIII.

7. In a research study, a Marital Adjustment Inventory was administered on four random samples of the individual. Test the hypothesis that they are from the same population.

Sample I	*Sample II*	*Sample III*	*Sample IV*
16	24	16	25
7	6	15	19
19	15	18	16
24	25	19	17
31	32	6	42
	24	13	45
	29	18	

8. The following data were collected from the students of three groups in terms of correctly recalled nonsense syllables under three methods of memorization:

Method I	*Method II*	*Method III*
18	20	7
29	17	15
28	21	9
26	19	13
24	29	5
31	26	11
30	25	
27		

Compute the means for separate groups and apply the analysis of variance technique to test the significance of the difference between groups.

9. In a learning experiment, three subjects made the following number of correct responses in a series of 7 trials.

Subjects	*Trials*						
	1	2	3	4	5	6	7
A	5	9	3	7	9	3	7
B	6	8	4	5	2	4	3
C	5	7	3	5	9	3	7

Apply the technique of two-way analysis to test the difference between means.

10. The following data represent the marks of eight students by three teachers in terms of their performances on a particular skill:

Students	*Marks given by the teachers*		
	A	B	C
1	8	4	2
2	6	3	6
3	8	4	8
4	10	8	8
5	12	6	8
6	14	10	9
7	16	8	10
8	20	11	8

Apply the technique of analysis of variance to answer the following questions:

(a) Did the teachers discriminate among the students in their markings?

(b) Did the teachers differ among themselves in their markings?

18 Analysis of Covariance

MEANING AND PURPOSE

Analysis of covariance may be looked upon as a special provision or procedure for exercising necessary statistical control over the variable or variables that have been left uncontrolled at the start of the experiment or study on account of the practical limitations and difficulties associated with the conducting such experiments or studies. In one sense, it may be regarded as a remedy or a solution for what has been left undone or what was quite impossible or difficult in doing experimentally at the start of the study.

In its procedure or methodology, the work of analysis of covariance may be equated with that of partial correlation, where we seek a measure of correlation between two sets of variables—independent and dependent—by partialling out the effects of the intervening variables. Here, we try to exercise statistical control instead of experimental control, over the intervening variables, after having conducted the actual study or experiment. Similar is the case with the analysis of covariance. By using this technique, we try to partial out the side effects if any, on our study, due to lack of exercising proper experimental control over the intervening variables or covariates (covariables). Let us make the idea clearer with the help of some concrete examples.

1. A researcher wants to study the effectiveness of praise or blame as a technique for behaviour modification. As a part of the experimental study, he should try to have three equivalent groups: one controlled, and two experimental. The equivalence of these groups may either be achieved through randomness or matched pairs or groups techniques. If a researcher does not try to equate these groups or is unable to do so on account of serious limitations or difficulties faced by him, he can take them for his study as natural groups or sections or classes, existing in the school environment or social set-up. Even if he divides them

into three groups by selecting them randomly from a single population, it does not guarantee their equivalence in terms of so many other variates or variables. In this way, the basic differences among these three groups are bound to remain there from the very start of the experiment. Now, if the experimentor selects the first group as control group (neither praises nor blames), the second group as experimental group 1 (praises), and the third group as experimental group 2 (blames), then the differences measured at the end of the experiment cannot be treated as valid for drawing inferences regarding the comparative role of praise or blame on behaviour modification. It may be possible that these differences have been generated due to the initial differences in their behaviour. The experimentor must have ensured the equivalence of these three groups before starting the experiment, i.e. providing treatments. The solution lies now in exercising some genuine statistical control over the uncontrolled variates through the technique of analysis of covariance. This technique helps in the task of making necessary adjustments or corrections in the final measures or scores of behaviour for eliminating the uncontrolled differences existing in the initial behaviour scores. As a result, we can now partial out or root out the effect of initial differences that exist in the behaviour of these three groups, and thus we will be able to draw valid inferences regarding the comparison of two entirely different treatments—praise or blame—in behaviour modification.

2. In another study, a research worker wanted to compare the relative effectiveness of three different methods, say lecture, leture-cum-demonstration, and laboratory experiments, for teaching science. He took three sections of Class IX of a school for this purpose. These classes were used to be taught by a single science teacher. At the start of the experiment, he conducted an achievement test and recorded the initial scores. There were significant differences in terms of mean and SD. He might have tried to equate these three groups in terms of mean and SD by including or excluding some students in one group or the other. But it would have been a difficult task and practically quite impossible to do so. Hence, he accepted those initial differences with regard to academic potential in science. In addition to such academic potential differences, these students might have differed in intelligence, a powerful covariate of academic potential. For

exercising proper control, these three groups might have been equated also in terms of this powerful covariate. Since such equivalence was neither feasible nor practicable, the sections A, B and C of the school were taken as three different groups, and each taught by a different method. At the end of one month, they were again tested in terms of their achievement, and their final scores were recorded. The means of these scores were then computed and analysed by the technique of analysis of variance for testing the significant differences existing among them. The differences were quite significant. However, the researcher was in a fix whether or not to draw valid inferences on the comparative effectiveness of the three methods. He was not certain whether these differences exist due to the comparative effectiveness of teaching methods or due to the initial differences existing among these groups for one or the other reasons (differences in initial achievement potential or intelligence, and so on. There was a need to have necessary correction or adjustment in the final scores for eliminating the differences in initial scores, and the researcher, for this purpose, used the technique of analysis of covariance. He then became successful in finding out the significant differences existing among the three means of final scores, by partialling out or rooting out the effect of the initial differences that existed on account of some intervening or uncontrolled covariates or covariables.

Thus, the role of analysis of covariance as a statistical technique or procedure, adopted in a particular research study, may be summed up as follows:

1. Analysis of covariance represents an extension of the method of analysis of variance, to allow a correlation between initial and final scores.
2. After the study or experiment has been performed, it helps the researcher in exercising proper statistical control over the uncontrolled covariates or covarying variables that have been left uncontrolled at the start of the experiment or study.
3. It enables the researcher to get rid of the difficulties and limitations he may face in adopting randomization or matching of groups techniques for studying the relative effectiveness of one or the other treatments and secure the same increase in precise evaluation.
4. It may serve other purposes like testing the homogeneity of a set of regression coefficients and related hypotheses.

How to Make Use of the Analysis of Covariance

Let us illustrate the use of the technique of Analysis of covariance with the help of some hypothetical data given in the following example.

Example 18.1: Three groups of five students each (randomly selected from a Class VIII of a school) were initially rated for their leadership qualities, and their scorse were recorded. Then they were subjected to different treatments (three different approaches or training techniques for leadership), and after 15 days of such training, they were again evaluated for their leadership qualities, and these final scores were also recorded. The data so collected are given in the following table.

Group A		*Group B*		*Group C*	
Initial scores X_1	Final scores Y_1	Initial scores X_2	Final scores Y_2	Initial scores X_3	Final scores Y_3
4	6	8	8	7	9
3	5	6	5	9	8
5	6	7	9	10	11
2	4	4	7	12	12
1	4	5	6	12	15

Use this data to compare the relative effectiveness of the treatments given to the groups.

Solution. There were many observable differences among the initial scores of the three groups, but no attempt was made to make these groups as equivalent groups at the start of the study, i.e. before subjecting these to different treatments. In the absence of such an experimental control, the researcher was forced to exercise statistical control by applying the technique of analysis of covariance. The procedure may be understood through computation. Let us begin with arranging the given data as in Table 18.1.

Table 18.1 Computational Work for Covariance Analysis

	Group A					*Group B*					*Group C*				
	X_1	Y_1	X_1Y_1	X_1^2	Y_1^2	X_2	Y_2	X_2Y_2	X_2^2	Y_2^2	X_3	Y_3	X_3Y_3	X_3^2	Y_3^2
	4	6	24	16	36	8	8	64	64	64	7	9	63	49	81
	3	5	15	9	25	6	5	30	36	25	9	8	72	81	64
	5	6	30	25	36	7	9	63	49	81	10	11	110	100	121
	2	4	8	4	16	4	7	28	16	49	12	12	144	144	144
	1	4	4	1	16	5	6	30	25	36	12	15	180	144	225
Sums	15	25	81	55	129	30	35	215	190	255	50	55	569	518	635
M's	3	5				6	7				10	11			

For all the three groups,

$$\Sigma X = \Sigma X_1 + \Sigma X_2 + \Sigma X_3 = 15 + 30 + 50 = 95$$

$$\Sigma Y = \Sigma Y_1 + \Sigma Y_2 + \Sigma Y_3 = 25 + 35 + 55 = 115$$

$$\Sigma X^2 = \Sigma X_1^2 + \Sigma X_2^2 + \Sigma X_3^2 = 55 + 190 + 518 = 763$$

$$\Sigma Y^2 = \Sigma Y_1^2 + \Sigma Y_2^2 + \Sigma Y_3^2 = 129 + 255 + 635 = 1019$$

$$\Sigma XY = \Sigma X_1Y_1 + \Sigma X_2Y_2 + \Sigma X_3Y_3 = 81 + 215 + 569 = 865$$

After computing various sums and means thus, the following steps can be adopted:

Step 1. Computation of correction terms (C's). Different corrections are applied to different sums of squares as in the case of analysis of variance. These can be computed by using the following formulae:

(i) $C_X = \dfrac{(\Sigma X)^2}{N} = \dfrac{95 \times 95}{15} = 601.67$

(ii) $C_Y = \dfrac{(\Sigma Y)^2}{N} = \dfrac{115 \times 115}{15} = 881.67$

(iii) $C_{XY} = \dfrac{\Sigma X\ \Sigma Y}{N} = \dfrac{95 \times 115}{15} = 728.33$

Step 2. Computation of total sum of squares (total SS).

(i) $SS_X = \Sigma X^2 - C_X = 763 - 601.67 = 161.33$

(ii) $SS_Y = \Sigma Y^2 - C_Y = 1019 - 881.67 = 137.33$

(iii) $SS_{XY} = \Sigma XY - C_{XY} = 865 - 728.33 = 136.67$

Step 3. Computation of sum of squares (SS) among the means of the groups.

(i) SS among-means for $X = \dfrac{\Sigma X_1^2}{N_1} + \dfrac{\Sigma X_2^2}{N_2} + \dfrac{\Sigma X_3^2}{N_3} - C_X$

$$= \frac{15^2 + 30^2 + 50^2}{5} - 601.67$$

$$= 123.33$$

(ii) SS among-means for $Y = \dfrac{\Sigma Y_1^2}{N_1} + \dfrac{\Sigma Y_2^2}{N_2} + \dfrac{\Sigma Y_3^2}{N_3} - C_Y$

$$= \frac{25^2 + 35^2 + 55^2}{5} - 881.67$$

$$= 93.33$$

(iii) SS among-means for

$$XY = \frac{\Sigma X_1Y_1}{N_1} + \frac{\Sigma X_2Y_2}{N_2} + \frac{\Sigma X_3Y_3}{N_3} - C_{XY}$$

$$= \frac{15 \times 25 + 30 \times 35 + 50 \times 55}{5} - 728.33$$

$$= 106.67$$

Step 4. Computation of sum of squares (SS) within-group

(i) Within-groups SS for $X = SS_X$ – SS among-means for X
$= 161.33 - 123.33 = 38$

(ii) Within-groups SS for $Y = SS_Y$ – SS among-means for Y
$= 137.33 - 93.33 = 44$

(iii) Within-groups SS for $XY = SS_{XY}$ – SS among-means for XY
$= 136.67 - 106.67 = 30$

Step 5. Calculation of the number of degrees of freedom.

(i) Among-means $(df) = K - 1$ = No. of groups $= 3 - 1 = 2$

(ii) Within-groups $(df) = N - K = 15 - 3 = 12$

Step 6. Analysis of variance of X and Y scores taken separately (Table 18.2).

Table 18.2 Worksheet for Analysis of Variance (ANOVA)

Source of variation	*df*	SS_X *(Sum of squares for X)*	SS_Y *(Sum of squares for Y)*	MS_X *(Mean square variance for X or* $\sqrt{X}$*)*	MS_Y *(Mean square variance for Y or* $\sqrt{Y}$*)*
Among-means	2	123.33	93.33	$\frac{123.33}{2} = 61.66$	$\frac{93.33}{2} = 46.66$
Within-groups	12	38	44	$\frac{38}{12} = 3.17$	$\frac{44}{12} = 3.67$
Total	14	161.33	137.33		

$$F_X = \frac{\text{Mean square variance of among-groups (for } X)}{\text{Mean square variance of within-groups}}$$

$$= \frac{61.66}{3.17} = 19.45$$

$$F_Y = \frac{\text{Mean square variance of among-groups (for } Y)}{\text{Mean squares variance of within-groups}}$$

$$= \frac{46.66}{3.67} = 12.71$$

where

F_X = F ratio for X scores

F_Y = F ratio for Y scores

From Table *R* of the Appendix for *df* (2, 12), we can have the critical value of F at 0.05 level = 3.88 and at 0.01 level = 6.93

Rule: If F_X is significant the H_0 is to be rejected showing that initially groups were different. Hence covariance is needed. If not significant, we can have only analysis of variance.

The computed value of F for X scores is significant at both levels, and similar is the case with the computed F for Y scores. Hence H_0 for X scores as well as Y scores are rejected, leading to the conclusion that (i) there are significant differences in initial (X) scores, and (ii) there are significant differences in final (Y) scores.

Step 7. Computation of adjusted sum of squares (SS for Y, i.e. SS_{YX}*).* The initial differences in the groups X scores may cause variability in their final scores measured after giving treatment. It needs to be checked and controlled. For this purpose, necessary adjustments are made in various Sum of Squares (SS) for Y by using the following general formula:

$$SS_{YX} = SS_Y - \frac{(SS_{XY})^2}{SS_X}$$

(Here, SS_{YX} stands for the sum of squares of Y adjusted for X differences). The specific adjusted SS for Y may be computed as follows:

(a) Adjusted sum of squares for total, i.e.,

$$SS_{YX} \text{ (total)} = \text{Total } SS_Y - \frac{\text{Total } (SS_{XY})^2}{\text{Total } SS_X}$$

$$= 137.33 - \frac{(136.67)^2}{161.33}$$

$$= 137.33 - 115.77 = 21.56$$

(b) Adjusted sum of squares for within-groups means, i.e.

$$SS_{YX} \text{ (within-mean)} = \text{within } SS_Y - \frac{\text{within } (SS_{XY})^2}{\text{within } SS_X}$$

$$= 44 - \frac{(30)^2}{38} = 44 - 23.68 = 20.32$$

(c) Adjusted sum of squares for among-group means, i.e.

$$SS_{YX} \text{ (among-mean)} = SS_{YX} \text{ (Total)} - SS_{YX} \text{ (within)}$$

$$= 21.56 - 20.32 = 1.24$$

Step 8. Computation of Analysis of Covariance: It is carried out as shown in Table 18.3

Table 18.3 Worksheet for the Computation of Analysis of Covariance (ANCOVA)

Source of variation	*df*	SS_X	SS_Y	S_{XY}	SS_{YX}	MS_{YX} or V_{YX}	SD_{YX}
Among-groups means	2	123.33	93.33	106.67	0.44	0.22	
Within-groups means	11*	38	44	30	20.32	1.76	$\sqrt{1.76} = 1.32$
Total	13	161.33	137.33	136.67	20.76		

(*1 *df* is lost because of regression of Y on X)

$$F_{YX} = \frac{V_{YX}\text{(among)}}{V_{YX}\text{(within)}} = \frac{0.22}{1.76} = 0.125$$

From Table R of the Appendix for *df* (2, 11).

Critical F at 0.05 level = 3.98

and

Critical F at 0.01 level = 7.20

The computed value of F (F_{YX}) is not significant at both the levels. Hence, H_0 is to be accepted with the conclusion that groups do not differ significantly after giving treatments. Hence, out of the three treatments (techniques of training for leadership) one treatment cannot be termed better than another.

As far as this example is concerned, the matter ends with drawing inferences from the collected data. However, if H_0 is rejected, concluding that there are significant differences among the means of the final scores, then our objective will be analyse these differences and conclude which of the treatment is better than others.

In such a case, further steps taken can be outlined in the following manner: For the sake of illustration, let us take the data from the present example.

Step 9. Computation of regression coefficient for within-groups. An unbiased estimate of the regression of Y on X can be computed by the use of the formula:

$$b = \frac{\Sigma XY}{\Sigma X^2} = \frac{\text{within-groups SS for } XY}{\text{within-groups SS for } X}$$

$$= \frac{30}{38} = 0.79$$

Step 10. Computation of adjusted Y means. The work is carried out as shown in Table 18.4.

Table 18.4 Worksheet for the Computation of Adjusted Y Means

Groups	*N*	M_X *(means for X)*	M_Y *(unadjusted)*	M_{YX} *(Adjusted)*
A	5	3	5	7.63
B	5	6	7	7.26
C	5	10	11	8.08

In the last column, we have M_{YX} (Means of final Y scores after ruling out the initial differences in X scores). M_{YX} for groups A, B and C have been computed as follows by using the general formula:

$$M_{YX} = M_Y - b(M_X - GM_X)$$

where

M_Y = Unadjusted means for Y scores

M_X = Mean for X scores

b = Regression coefficient for within-groups (computed in step 9)

$$GM_X = \text{General mean for } X$$

$$= (3 + 6 + 10)/3 = 19/3 = 6.33$$

Hence

For group A, $M_{YX} = 5 - 0.79(3 - 6.33)$

$= 5 - 0.79(-3.33) = 7.63$

For group B, $M_{YX} = 7 - 0.79(6 - 6.33)$

$= 7 - 0.79(-.33) = 7.26$

For group C, $M_{YX} = 11 - 0.79\ (10 - 6.33)$

$= 11 - 0.79 \times 3.67 = 8.08$

Step 11. Significance of differences among adjusted Y means. Apparently, there is no significant differences among the Y mean of group A, B and C, especially between A and B. Let us further examine it by applying the 't' test as we did in the analysis of variance (Chapter 17) for testing the separate differences between group means. As we know,

$$t = \frac{D}{SE_D} = \frac{\text{Differences between means}}{\text{Standard Error of the difference between means}}$$

Here, SE of the difference between any two adjusted means can be computed by using the formula

$$SE_D = SD_{YX}\sqrt{\frac{1}{N_1} + \frac{1}{N_2}}$$

where, SD_{YX} is the standard deviation of the adjusted Y scores. It can be computed by the formula

$$SD_{YX} = \sqrt{\text{within-group variance}} = \sqrt{\text{within-group } V_{YX}}$$

$$= \sqrt{1.76} = 1.32 \quad \text{(already computed in Table 18.3)}$$

Hence,

$$SE_D = 1.32\sqrt{\frac{1}{5} + \frac{1}{5}} = 1.32\sqrt{.4} = 1.32 \times 0.63 = 0.83$$

For $df = 11$, from Table C of the Appendix, we have

Critical value of t at 0.05 level = 2.20

Critical value of t at 0.01 level = 3.11

The computed value of t is

(i) $$\frac{M_1 - M_2}{SE_D} = \frac{7.63 - 7.26}{0.83} = \frac{0.37}{0.83} = 0.44 \text{ for } M_1 - M_2$$

(Difference between adjusted means of group A and group B)

(ii) $$\frac{8.08 - 7.26}{0.83} = \frac{0.82}{0.83} = 0.99 \text{ for } M_3 - M_2$$

(iii) $$\frac{8.08 - 7.63}{0.83} = \frac{0.45}{0.83} = 0.54 \text{ for } M_3 - M_1$$

The computed values of t for all the differences in means are not significant at both the levels (0.05 and 0.01) of significance. Hence H_0 cannot be rejected. We accept H_0 here too since that the groups, after having different leadership training programmes, do not differ in final scores.

Assumptions Underlying Analysis of Covariance

The method of analysis of covariance requires some basic assumptions for its application, which are now enumerated:

1. The dependent variable which is under measurement should be normally distributed in the population.
2. The treatment groups should be selected at random from the same population.
3. Within-groups variances must be approximately equal.
4. The contributions of variance in the total sample must be additive.
5. The regression of the final scores (Y) on initial scores (X) should be basically the same in all groups.
6. There should exist a linear relationship between X and Y.

SUMMARY

1. Analysis of covariance is a statistical procedure or a method for exercising post-experiment or post-study control over the intervening variables or covariates that have been left uncontrolled at the start of the experiment or study due to administrative difficulties or through ignorance of their relationship with criterion measures. Its use may enable us to dispense with the inconvenient procedure of matching of individuals and groups to have controlled and experimental subjects or groups for study and to secure the same increase in precision by exercising statistical control.
2. In its application procedure, it is just an extension devised by R.A. Fisher for his method of analysis of variance. In brief, it involves the following steps:
   (a) Arranging the data into a suitable tabular form for computing various sums like ΣX, ΣY, ΣXY, ΣX^2, ΣY^2 and group means for the variate Y and covariate X.
   (b) Computation of correction terms C_X, C_Y and C_{XY}.
   (c) Computation of total sum of square and squares among-means of the groups and within-groups for X, Y and the product XY by using correction terms.
   (d) Carrying out analysis of variance with the help of usual formulae and procedure (partitioning of total sum of squares in two sources—among groups and within-groups)—and determining the need for adjusting the means of the final scores Y in view of the significant differences in initial scores X.

(e) Computation of adjusted sum of squares (SS) for Y, i.e. SS_{YX} separately for both within-group and among-group means.

(f) If H_0 is rejected, then computing the regression coefficient for within-groups, i.e. b, to help calculate the values of adjusted means for both X and Y scores of every group.

(g) Carrying out analysis of covariance and obtain the variance estimates, i.e. the values of V_{YX} (among) and V_{YX} (within) for computing F_{YX} and then comparing it with the critical table value of F for accepting or rejecting H_0.

(h) Using the t test for determining the significance of differences among adjusted means. We can then conclude about the differences generated through varying treatments after partialling out the initial difference, if any.

EXERCISES

1. What is analysis of covariance? Why and where is it to be used? Illustrate with examples.
2. What assumptions are required for the use of analysis of covariance?
3. Discuss the process of using analysis of covariance by taking a hypothetical example involving simple calculations.
4. A researcher wanted to know the relative effectiveness of grammar, translation and structural methods of teaching English. He performed the experiment with the help of 12 students by dividing them at random into three groups. The initial scores (before starting the experiment and final scores (after teaching each group by different methods) were recorded as follows. Find the relative effectiveness of these three methods.

Group A		*Group B*		*Group C*	
X_1 (Initial)	Y_1 (Final)	X_2 (Initial)	Y_2 (Final)	X_3 (Initial)	Y_3 (Final)
33	18	34	31	34	15
42	34	55	45	4	8
40	22	9	1	12	18
31	24	50	33	16	15

5. A researcher wanted to study the relative effectiveness of three methods of behaviour modification for the treatment of *problem children*. He selected 15 students for this study. He administered an Adjustment Inventory and recorded the scores as X. He then divided them randomly into three groups. Three different treatments were given to these three groups and after two months, he again administered the same Adjustment Inventory and recorded their scores as Y. What can you conclude about the relative effectiveness of the three treatments from the following data.

Group A		*Group B*		*Group C*	
X_1	Y_1	X_2	Y_2	X_3	Y_3
6	8	8	10	3	2
3	7	6	15	6	2
8	5	3	14	2	3
2	3	8	8	2	1
1	2	5	3	2	2

6. An experiment was conducted to know the relative effectiveness of three methods of teaching science at the elementary level. The nursery children were taken as available in the different three sections. Their achievement scores (X) were recorded and then they were taught by different methods by the same teacher. Their final achievement scores (Y) were recorded after three months. Find out the relative effectiveness of the three methods of teaching science from the given data:

Section A		*Section B*		*Section C*	
X_1	Y_1	X_2	Y_2	X_3	Y_3
5	5	5	6	7	4
6	11	7	6	8	5
9	12	12	7	3	7
12	26	10	12	4	9
15	28	8	14	10	10
16	24	4	9	5	6
18	11	15	8		
20	27	9	12		
4	12				
12	20				
$N_1 = 10$		$N_2 = 8$		$N_3 = 6$	

Answers

Chapter 1

3. (a) to (d) continuous, (e) and (f) discrete, (g) continuous
4. 13.5–14.5, 21.5–22.5, 45.5–46.5, 71.5–72.5, 84.5–85.5
6. (a) and (b) nominal, (c) interval, (d) and (e) ratio, (f) ordinal, (g) and (h) interval, (i) and (j) ratio
7. (a) 52.73, (b) 0.32, (c) 0.84, (d) 2.37, (e) 8.68, (f) 23.73

Chapter 2

5. (a) (i) Class interval = 4
   (ii) 6.5, 10.5, 14.5, 18.5, 22.5
   (iii) 4.5–8.5, 8.5–12.5, 12.5–16.5, 16.5–20.5 and 20.5–24.5
   (b) (i) 3
   (ii) 17, 20, 23, 26, 29
   (iii) 15.5–18.5, 18.5–21.5, 21.5–24.5, 24.5–27.5, 27.5–30.5
   (c) (i) 10
   (ii) 34.5, 44.5, 54.5, 64.5 and 74.5
   (iii) 29.5–39.5, 39.5–49.5, 49.5–59.5, 59.5–69.5, 69.5–79.5
6. Class interval = 3

Frequency distribution table

Class interval	*Frequencies (f)*
85–87	1
82–84	3
79–81	1
76–78	3
73–75	2
70–72	6
67–69	5
64–66	2
61–63	2
	N = 25

7.

Class interval	f
57–59	2
54–56	3
51–53	8
48–50	3
45–47	4
42–44	3
39–41	8
36–38	5
33–35	3
30–32	1
	$N = 40$

9.

Class interval	f	cf	Cumulative percentage frequencies
85–89	2	40	100.00
80–84	2	38	95.00
75–79	4	36	90.00
70–74	6	32	80.00
65–69	5	26	65.00
60–64	4	21	52.50
55–59	5	17	42.50
50–54	2	12	30.00
45–49	2	10	25.00
40–44	4	8	20.00
35–39	1	4	10.00
30–34	2	3	7.50
25–29	1	1	2.50
	$N = 40$		

Chapter 4

6. (a) Mean (b) Mode (c) Median

7. 104

8. (a) 9 (b) 71

9. (a) 14 (b) 4

10. $M = 72.66$ and $M_d = 72.25$

11.

	(a)	(b)	(c)	(d)
M	19.9	15.6	20.4	10.8
M_d	20.5	14.2	21.0	10.3
M_o	—	14.0	—	10.0

12.

	(a)	(b)	(c)	(d)
M	61.11	106.00	25.05	99.3
M_d	61.21	105.83	25.17	99.3
M_o	61.41	105.49	25.41	99.3

13.

	(a)	(b)	(c)	(d)
M	77.5	41.9	34.6	66.58
M_d	80.9	41.7	34.25	67.36
M_o	87.7	41.3	33.55	68.92

Chapter 5

5.

	(c)	(d)
Q_1	20.3	90.40
Q_3	29.3	108.14
D_1	15.8	82.29
P_{90}	33.6	115.75

6.

	(i)	(ii)	(iii)
(a) P_{30}	24.13	11.53	40.82
P_{70}	30.5	18.37	52.54
P_{85}	33.2	21.22	58.77
P_{90}	34.4	24.80	62.00
(b) PR of 14	3	45	—
PR of 20	17	79	—
PR of 26	40	97	1
PR of 38	99	—	19

7.

Scores:	42	60	31	50	71
PR:	30	70	10	50	90

Chapter 6

7. Problem 12 of Chapter 4

	(a)	(b)	(c)	(d)
SD	5.02	7.23	7.7	13.4
Q	3.1	4.5	4.51	8.86

Problem 13 of Chapter 4

	(a)	(b)	(c)	(d)
SD	13.55	7.3	9.61	11.84
Q	9.79	5.72	5.7	7.92

8. $AD = 3.9$, $SD = 4.68$
9. $AD = 2.04$
10. (a) 10.22 (b) 4.16 (c) 14.9

Chapter 7

10. (a) 0.86 (b) 0.96 (c) 0.79
11. (a) 0.65 (b) 0.76
12. (a) 0.14 (b) 0.65
13. (a) 0.524 (b) 0.56 (c) 0.508

Chapter 8

6. 1.25σ and 3.78σ; he did better in Physics
7. (a) 32.79 percent (b) 16.9 percent (c) 11.51 percent
8. (a) 50.65 and 57.35
   (b) 50.65 and 57.35
   (c) 435
9. (a) 10.46 percent (b) 24.6 and 32.4
10. (a) 0.99 percent (b) 9.18 percent
    (c) 25.14 percent (d) 90.50 percent
11. (a) 119 (b) 96 (c) 75 percent
    (d) 107 (e) 85 to 115
12. 1.036σ, 0, -0.253σ, -0.675σ
13. 22 percent
14. 7, 28, 79, 160, 226, 226, 160, 79, 28, 7
15.

Grade	*Score interval*	*Grade*	*Score interval*
A	62.8	*D*	37.2–44.8
B	55.2–62.8	*E*	–37.2
C	44.8–55.2		

Chapter 9

9.

	Sample A	*Sample B*	*Sample C*
At 0.05	18.087–61.913	44.412–45.588	58.935–61.065
At 0.01	11.156–68.844	44.226–45.774	58.525–61.475

	Sample D	*Sample E*	*Sample F*
At 0.05	49.479–50.521	28.764–31.236	79.06–80.94
At 0.01	49.314–50.686	28.320–31.680	78.76–81.24

10. (a) Not significantly different from zero at both 0.05 and 0.01 levels.
(b) Significantly different from zero at 0.05 level but not at 0.01 level.

11. (a) SE_r = 0.107 Interval at 0.05 = 0.270–0.690
at 0.01 = 0.204–0.756
(b) At 0.05 = 0.24–0.665, at 0.01 = 0.15–0.71
(c) 0.273 and 0.354, significant at both 0.05 and 0.01 levels.

12. At 0.05 level 29.418–31.382
At 0.01 level 29.107–31.693

Chapter 10

5. z = 4.12; significant at both 5 percent and 1 percent levels.

6. t = 3.70; null hypothesis rejected; the weight gain is significant.

7. z = 1.91; not significant, null hypothesis is not rejected; we have insufficient evidence of any sex difference in the attitudes as assessed by the given attitude scale.

8. (a) z = 1.5, not significant.
(b) Difference should be 7.22 for being significant at 0.01 level.

9. t = 0.80, not significant at 0.05 level; null hypothesis not rejected.

10. t = 4.81, not significant at both the levels.

11. z = 2.86, significant at both 0.05 and 0.01 levels.

12. t = 3.75, significant, null hypothesis rejected.

13. z = 2.34, significant at 0.05 level. Praise has a significant effect in increasing the scores.

14. t = 3.04, significant at both levels, null hypothesis rejected.

Chapter 11

6. χ^2 = 4, significant at 5% level; hypothesis rejected.

7. χ^2 = 7.20, significant, hypothesis rejected.

8. $\chi^2 = 5.71$, significant.
9. $\chi^2 = 6$, significant, hypothesis rejected.
10. $\chi^2 = 3$, not significant.
11. $\chi^2 = 15.56$, significant, hypothesis rejected.
12. $\chi^2 = 5.90$, not significant, hypothesis not rejected.
13. $\chi^2 = 34.209$, significant, opinions are not independent.
14. $\chi^2 = 32.473$, $C = 0.37$, significant.
15. $\chi^2 = 1.24$, non-significant, preference independent of class.
16. $\chi^2 = 2.08$, (after making Yates' correction), not significant, hypothesis not rejected.
17. $\chi^2 = 0.17$, not significant, preference of a method independent of the sex of the teacher educator.
18. $\chi^2 = 0.633$, not significant, independent of the treatment applied.
19. $\chi^2 = 14.10$, significant, hypothesis of no difference rejected implying that preference for a drink depends upon the status of the employee.

Chapter 12

6. $r_{\text{bis}} = 0.71$
7. (a) $r_{\text{bis}} = 0.508$ (b) $r_{\text{bis}} = 0.34$
8. (a) $r_{p,\text{bis}} = 0.54$ (b) $r_{p,\text{bis}} = 0.56$
9. (a) $r_t = 0.59$ (b) $r_t = 0.326$
10. (a) $\phi = -0.12$ (b) $\phi = 0.36$

Chapter 13

3. 0.72
4. (i) 0.04 (ii) 0.38
5. 0.67
6. 0.79

Chapter 14

2. (a) $Y = 0.9X + 7.5$ (b) 43.5 (c) 45
   $X = Y - 5$

3. (a) $Y = 0.72X + 68.95,$ (b) 45.16
$X = 0.37Y + 8.16$

4. (a) $Y = 2.8X - 14$ (b) 28 (c) 7
$X = 0.318Y - 5.548$

6. (a) $\overline{X}_1 = 0.533X_2 + 0.96X_3 + 16.2$ (b) $\overline{X}_1 = 86.58$

7. (a) $\overline{X}_1 = 0.35X_2 + 0.25X_3 + 54.5$ (b) $\overline{X}_1 = 72$

Chapter 15

6. (i) Sweeti (ii) Rani, Anita, and Sweeti performed better in grammar.

7. Sweeti (She scored 183 while Rani and Anita scored 180 and 182, respcetively).

10. Ajay performed better than Vijay with a total scores of 160 in comparison to Vijay who earned scores of 151.

Chapter 16

10. There is a significant change in attitude after the motivation lecture at 0.05 level.

11. There is a significant difference between the ratings of the two panels at 0.05 level.

12. There is a significant difference between the scores of two groups at 0.05 level.

13. There is no significant difference between the medians of the adjustment scores of the two groups at 0.05 level.

14. There is no significant difference between the scores of two groups at 0.05 level.

15. Rural and urban children differ significantly in terms of physical fitness at the 0.05 level.

16. Null hypothesis is rejected. The student's choice of a particular area is significantly related to the in-charge of that area.

17. Rural and urban children differ significantly in terms of physical fitness at the 0.05 as well as 0.01 levels

18. Male and female teachers differ significantly in terms of their adjustment at 0.05 level.

19. Male and female teachers differ significantly with regard to teacher effectiveness at 0.05 level.

20. Boys and girls differ significantly in terms of their personality make-up at 0.05 level.

Chapter 17

5. F = 6.38, significant; null hypothesis rejected.
6. F = 1.18, not significant; null hypothesis not rejected.
7. F = 2.06, significant; null hypothesis rejected.
8. F = 29.47, significant; null hypothesis rejected.
9. F = 2.48 and 1.29, not significant; null hypothesis not rejected in both cases.
10. F = 4.63 and 10.65, significant; null hypothesis rejected in both cases.

Chapter 18

4. Methods differences are not significant.
5. Treatment differences are significant. Treatment two is better than others.
6. Methods differences are not significant.

Appendix

Table A Square and Square Roots of Numbers from 1 to 1000

Number	*Square*	*S.R.*	*Number*	*Square*	*S.R.*
1	1	1.0000	41	1681	6.4031
2	4	1.4142	42	1764	6.4807
3	9	1.7321	43	1849	6.5574
4	16	2.0000	44	1936	6.6332
5	25	2.2361	45	2025	6.7082
6	36	2.4495	46	2116	6.7823
7	49	2.6458	47	2209	6.8557
8	64	2.8284	48	2304	6.9282
9	81	3.0000	49	2401	7.0000
10	100	3.1623	50	2500	7.0711
11	121	3.3166	51	2601	7.1414
12	144	3.4641	52	2704	7.2111
13	169	3.6056	53	2809	7.2801
14	196	3.7417	54	2916	7.3485
15	225	3.8730	55	3025	7.4162
16	256	4.0000	56	3136	7.4833
17	289	4.1231	57	3249	7.5498
18	324	4.2426	58	3364	7.6158
19	361	4.3589	59	3481	7.6811
20	400	4.4721	60	3600	7.7460
21	441	4.5826	61	3721	7.8102
22	484	4.6904	62	3844	7.8740
23	529	4.7958	63	3969	7.9373
24	576	4.8990	64	4096	8.0000
25	625	5.0000	65	4225	8.0623
26	676	5.0990	66	4356	8.1240
27	729	5.1962	67	4489	8.1854
28	784	5.2915	68	4624	8.2462
29	841	5.3852	69	4761	8.3066
30	900	5.4772	70	4900	8.3666
31	961	5.5678	71	5041	8.4261
32	1024	5.6569	72	5184	8.4863
33	1089	5.7446	73	5329	8.5440
34	1156	5.8310	74	5476	8.6023
35	1225	5.9161	75	5625	8.6603
36	1296	6.0000	76	5776	8.7178
37	1369	6.0828	77	5929	8.7750
38	1444	6.1644	78	6084	8.8318
39	1521	6.2450	79	6241	8.8882
40	1600	6.3245	80	6400	8.9443

Table A Square and Square Roots of Numbers from 1 to 1000 (*cont.*)

Number	*Square*	*S.R.*	*Number*	*Square*	*S.R.*
81	6561	9.0000	132	17424	11.4891
82	6724	9.0554	133	17689	11.5326
83	6889	9.1104	134	17956	11.5758
84	7056	9.1652	135	18225	11.6190
85	7225	9.2195	136	18496	11.6619
86	7396	9.2736	137	18769	11.7047
87	7569	9.3274	138	19044	11.7473
88	7744	9.3808	139	19321	11.7898
89	7921	9.4340	140	19600	11.8322
90	8100	9.4868	141	19881	11.8743
91	8281	9.5394	142	20164	11.9164
92	8464	9.5917	143	20449	11.9583
93	8649	9.6437	144	20736	12.0000
94	8836	9.6954	145	21025	12.0416
95	9025	9.7468	146	21316	12.0830
96	9216	9.7980	147	21609	12.1244
97	9409	9.8489	148	21904	12.1655
98	9604	9.8995	149	22801	12.2066
99	9801	9.9499	150	22500	12.2474
100	10000	10.0000	151	22801	12.2882
101	10201	10.0499	152	23104	12.3288
102	10404	10.0995	153	23409	12.3693
103	10609	10.1489	154	23716	12.4097
104	10816	10.1980	155	24025	12.4499
105	11025	10.2470	156	24336	12.4900
106	11236	10.2956	157	24649	12.5300
107	11449	10.3441	158	24964	12.5698
108	11664	10.3923	159	25281	12.6095
109	11881	10.4403	160	25600	12.6491
110	12100	10.4881	161	25921	12.6886
111	12321	10.5357	162	26244	12.7279
112	12544	10.5830	163	26569	12.7671
113	12769	10.6301	164	26896	12.8062
114	12996	10.6771	165	27225	12.8452
115	13225	10.7238	166	27556	12.8841
116	13456	10.7703	167	27889	12.9228
117	13689	10.8167	168	28224	12.9615
118	13924	10.8628	169	28561	13.0000
119	14161	10.9087	170	28900	13.0384
120	14400	10.9545	171	29241	13.0767
121	14641	11.0000	172	29584	13.1149
122	14884	11.0454	173	29929	13.1529
123	15129	11.0905	174	30276	13.1909
124	15376	11.1355	175	30625	13.2288
125	15625	11.1803	176	30976	13.2665
126	15876	11.2250	177	31329	13.3041
127	16129	11.2694	178	31684	13.3417
128	16384	11.3137	179	32041	13.3791
129	16641	11.3578	180	32400	13.4164
130	16900	11.4018	181	32761	13.4536
131	17161	11.4455	182	33124	13.4907

Table A Square and Square Roots of Numbers from 1 to 1000 (*cont.*)

Number	*Square*	*S.R.*	*Number*	*Square*	*S.R.*
183	33489	13.5277	235	55225	15.3297
184	33856	13.5647	236	55696	15.3623
185	34225	13.6015	237	56169	15.3948
186	34596	13.6382	238	56644	15.4272
187	34969	13.6748	239	57121	15.4596
188	35344	13.7113	240	57600	15.4919
189	35721	13.7477	241	58081	15.5242
190	36100	13.7840	242	58564	15.5563
191	36481	13.8203	243	59049	15.5885
192	36864	13.8564	244	59536	15.6205
193	37249	13.8924	245	60025	15.6525
194	37636	13.9284	246	60516	15.6844
195	38025	13.9642	247	61009	15.7162
196	38416	14.0000	248	61504	15.7480
197	38809	14.0357	249	62001	15.7797
198	39204	14.0712	250	62500	15.8114
199	39601	14.1067	251	63001	15.8430
200	40000	14.1421	252	63504	15.8745
201	40401	14.1774	253	64009	15.9060
202	40804	14.2127	254	64516	15.9374
203	41209	14.2478	255	65025	15.9687
204	41616	14.2829	256	65536	16.0000
205	42025	14.3178	257	66049	16.0322
206	42436	14.3527	258	66564	16.0624
207	42849	14.3875	259	67081	16.0935
208	43264	14.4222	260	67600	16.1245
209	43681	14.4568	261	68121	16.1555
210	44100	14.4914	262	68644	16.1864
211	44521	14.5258	263	69169	16.2173
212	44944	14.5602	264	69696	16.2481
213	45369	14.5945	265	70225	16.2788
214	45796	14.6287	266	70756	16.3095
215	46225	14.6629	267	71289	16.3401
216	46656	14.6969	268	71824	16.3707
217	47089	14.7309	269	72361	16.4012
218	47524	14.7648	270	72900	16.4317
219	47961	14.7986	271	73441	16.4621
220	48400	14.8324	272	73984	16.4924
221	48841	14.8661	273	74529	16.5227
222	49284	14.8997	274	75076	16.5529
223	49729	14.9332	275	75625	16.5831
224	50176	14.9666	276	76176	16.6132
225	50625	15.0000	277	76729	16.6433
226	51076	15.0333	278	77284	16.6733
227	51529	15.0665	279	77841	16.7033
228	51984	15.0997	280	78400	16.7332
229	52441	15.1327	281	78961	16.7631
230	52900	15.1658	282	79524	16.7929
231	53361	15.1987	283	80089	16.8226
232	53824	15.2315	284	80756	16.8523
233	54289	15.2643	285	81225	16.8819
234	54756	15.2971	286	81796	16.9115

Table A Square and Square Roots of Numbers from 1 to 1000 (*cont.*)

Number	*Square*	*S.R.*	*Number*	*Square*	*S.R.*
287	82369	16.9411	338	114244	18.3848
288	82944	16.9706	339	114921	18.4120
289	83521	17.0000	340	115600	18.4391
290	84100	17.0294	341	116281	18.4662
291	84681	17.0587	342	116964	18.4932
292	85264	17.0880	343	117649	18.5303
293	85849	17.1172	344	118336	18.5472
294	86436	17.1464	345	119025	18.5742
295	87025	17.1756	346	119716	18.6011
296	87616	17.2047	347	120409	18.6279
297	88209	17.2337	348	121104	18.6548
298	88804	17.2627	349	121801	18.6815
299	89401	17.2916	350	122500	18.7083
300	90000	17.3205	351	123201	18.7350
301	90601	17.3494	352	123904	18.7617
302	91204	17.3781	353	124609	18.7883
303	91809	17.4069	354	125316	18.8149
304	92416	17.4356	355	126025	18.8414
305	93025	17.4642	356	126736	18.8680
306	93636	17.4929	357	127449	18.8944
307	94249	17.5214	358	128164	18.9209
308	94864	17.5499	359	128881	18.9473
309	95481	17.5784	360	129600	18.9737
310	96100	17.6068	361	130321	19.0000
311	96721	17.6352	362	131044	19.0263
312	97344	17.6635	363	131769	19.0526
313	97969	17.6918	364	132496	19.0788
314	98596	17.7200	365	133225	19.1050
315	99225	17.7482	366	133956	19.1311
316	99856	17.7764	367	134689	19.1572
317	100489	17.8045	368	135424	19.1833
318	101124	17.8326	369	136161	19.2094
319	101761	17.8606	370	136900	19.2354
320	102400	17.8885	371	137641	19.2614
321	103041	17.9165	372	138384	19.2873
322	103684	17.9444	373	139129	19.3132
323	104329	17.9722	374	139876	19.3391
324	104976	18.0000	375	140625	19.3649
325	105625	18.0278	376	141376	19.3907
326	106276	18.0555	377	142129	19.4165
327	106929	18.0831	378	142884	19.4422
328	107584	18.1108	379	143641	19.4679
329	108241	18.1384	380	144400	19.4936
330	108900	18.1659	381	145161	19.5192
331	109561	18.1934	382	145924	19.5448
332	110224	18.2209	383	146689	19.5704
333	110889	18.2483	384	147456	19.5959
334	111556	18.2757	385	148225	19.6214
335	112225	18.3030	386	148996	19.6469
336	112896	18.3303	387	149769	19.6723
337	113569	18.3576	388	150544	19.6977

Table A Square and Square Roots of Numbers from 1 to 1000 (*cont.*)

Number	*Square*	*S.R.*	*Number*	*Square*	*S.R.*
389	151321	19.7231	441	194481	21.0000
390	152100	19.7484	442	195364	21.0238
391	152881	19.7737	443	196249	21.0476
392	153664	19.7990	444	197136	21.0713
393	154449	19.8242	445	198025	21.0950
394	155236	19.8494	446	198916	21.1187
395	156025	19.8746	447	199809	21.1424
396	156816	19.8997	448	200704	21.1660
397	157609	19.9249	449	201601	21.1896
398	158404	19.9499	450	202500	21.2132
399	159201	19.9750	451	203401	21.2368
400	160000	20.0000	452	204304	21.2603
401	160801	20.0250	453	205209	21.2818
402	161604	20.0499	454	206116	21.3073
403	162409	20.0749	455	207025	21.3307
404	163216	20.0998	456	207936	21.3542
405	164025	20.1246	457	208849	21.3776
406	164836	20.1494	458	209764	21.4009
407	165649	20.1742	459	210681	21.4243
408	166464	20.1990	460	211600	21.4476
409	167281	20.2237	461	212521	21.4709
410	168100	20.2485	462	213444	21.4942
411	168921	20.2731	463	214369	21.5174
412	169744	20.2978	464	215296	21.5407
413	170569	20.3224	465	216225	21.5639
414	171396	20.3470	466	217156	21.5870
415	172225	20.3715	467	218089	21.6102
416	173056	20.3961	468	219024	21.6333
417	173889	20.4206	469	219961	21.6564
418	174724	20.4450	470	220900	21.6795
419	175561	20.4695	471	221841	21.7025
420	176400	20.4939	472	222784	21.7256
421	177241	20.5183	473	223729	21.7486
422	178024	20.5436	474	224676	21.7715
423	178929	20.5670	475	225625	21.7945
424	179976	20.5913	476	226576	21.8174
425	180625	20.6155	477	227529	21.8403
426	181476	20.6398	478	228484	21.8632
427	182329	20.6640	479	229441	21.8861
428	183184	20.6882	480	230400	21.9089
429	184041	20.7123	481	231361	21.9317
430	184900	20.7364	482	232324	21.9545
431	185761	20.7605	483	233289	21.9773
432	186624	20.7846	484	234256	22.0000
433	187489	20.8087	485	235225	22.0327
434	188356	20.8327	486	236196	22.0454
435	189225	20.8567	487	237169	22.0681
436	190096	20.8806	488	238144	22.0907
437	190969	20.9245	489	239121	22.1133
438	191844	20.9284	490	240100	22.1359
439	192721	20.9523	491	241081	22.1585
440	193600	20.9762	492	242064	22.1811

Table A Square and Square Roots of Numbers from 1 to 1000 (*cont.*)

Number	*Square*	*S.R.*	*Number*	*Square*	*S.R.*
493	243049	22.2036	544	295936	23.3238
494	244036	22.2261	545	297025	23.3452
495	245025	22.2486	546	298116	23.3666
496	246016	22.2711	547	299209	23.3880
497	247009	22.2935	548	300304	23.4094
498	248004	22.3159	549	301401	23.4307
499	249001	22.3383	550	302500	23.4521
500	250000	22.3607	551	303601	23.4734
501	251001	22.3830	552	304704	23.4947
502	252004	22.4054	553	305809	23.5160
503	253009	22.4277	554	306916	23.5372
504	254016	22.4499	555	308025	23.5584
505	255025	22.4722	556	309136	23.5797
506	256036	22.4944	557	310249	23.6008
507	257049	22.5167	558	311364	23.6220
508	258064	22.5389	559	312481	23.6432
509	259081	22.5610	560	313600	23.6643
510	260100	22.5832	561	314721	23.6854
511	261121	22.6053	562	315844	23.7065
512	262144	22.6274	563	316969	23.7276
513	263169	22.6495	564	318059	23.7487
514	264196	22.6716	565	319225	23.7697
515	265225	22.6936	566	320356	23.7908
516	266256	22.7156	567	321489	23.8118
517	267289	22.7376	568	322624	23.8328
518	268324	22.7596	569	323761	23.8537
519	269361	22.7816	570	324900	23.8747
520	270400	22.8035	571	326041	23.8956
521	271441	22.8254	572	327184	23.9165
522	272484	22.8473	573	328329	23.9374
523	273529	22.8692	574	329476	23.9583
524	274576	22.8910	575	330625	23.9792
525	275625	22.9129	576	331776	24.0000
526	276676	22.9347	577	332929	24.0208
527	277729	22.9565	578	334084	24.0416
528	278784	22.9783	579	335241	24.0624
529	279841	23.0000	580	336400	24.0832
530	280900	23.0217	581	337561	24.1039
531	281961	23.0434	582	338724	24.1247
532	283024	23.0651	583	339889	24.1454
533	284089	23.0868	584	341056	24.1661
534	285156	23.1084	585	342225	24.1868
535	286225	23.1301	586	343396	24.2074
536	287296	23.1517	587	344569	24.2281
537	288369	23.1733	588	345844	24.2487
538	289444	23.1948	589	346921	24.2693
539	290521	23.2164	590	348100	24.2899
540	291600	23.2379	591	349281	24.3105
541	292681	23.2594	592	350464	24.3311
542	293764	23.2809	593	351649	24.3516
543	294849	23.3024	594	352836	24.3721

Table A Square and Square Roots of Numbers from 1 to 1000 (*cont.*)

Number	*Square*	*S.R.*	*Number*	*Square*	*S.R.*
595	354025	24.3926	647	418609	25.4362
596	355216	24.4131	648	419904	25.4558
597	356409	24.4336	649	421201	25.4755
598	357604	24.4540	650	422500	25.4951
599	358890	24.4745	651	423801	25.5147
600	360000	24.4949	652	425104	25.5343
601	361201	24.5153	653	426409	25.5539
602	362404	24.5357	654	427716	25.5734
603	363609	24.5561	655	429025	25.5930
604	364816	24.5764	656	430336	25.6125
605	366025	24.5967	657	431649	25.6320
606	367236	24.6171	658	432964	25.6515
607	368449	24.6374	659	434281	25.6710
608	369664	24.6577	660	435600	25.6905
609	370881	24.6779	661	436921	25.7099
610	372100	24.6982	662	438244	25.7294
611	373321	24.7184	663	439569	25.7488
612	374544	24.7385	664	440896	25.7682
613	375769	24.7588	665	442225	25.7876
614	376996	24.7790	666	443556	25.8070
615	378225	24.7992	667	444889	25.8263
616	379456	24.8193	668	446224	25.8457
617	380689	24.8395	669	447461	25.8650
618	381924	24.8596	670	448900	25.8844
619	383161	24.8997	671	450241	25.9037
620	384400	24.8998	672	451584	25.9230
621	385641	24.9199	673	452929	25.9422
622	386884	24.9399	674	454276	25.9615
623	388129	24.9600	675	455625	25.9808
624	389376	24.9800	676	456976	26.0000
625	390625	25.0000	677	458329	26.0192
626	391876	25.0200	678	459684	26.0384
627	393129	25.0400	679	461041	26.0576
628	394384	25.0599	680	462400	26.0768
629	395641	25.0796	681	463761	26.0960
630	396900	25.0998	682	465124	26.1151
631	398161	25.1197	683	466489	26.1343
632	399424	25.1396	684	467856	26.1534
633	400689	25.1595	685	469225	26.1725
634	401956	25.1794	686	470596	26.1916
635	403225	25.1992	687	471969	26.2107
636	404496	25.2190	688	473344	26.2298
637	405769	25.2389	689	474721	26.2488
638	407044	25.2587	690	476100	26.2679
639	408321	25.2784	691	477481	26.2869
640	409600	25.2982	692	478864	26.3059
641	410881	25.3180	693	480249	26.3249
642	412164	25.3377	694	481636	26.3439
643	413449	25.3574	695	483025	26.3629
644	414736	25.3772	696	484416	26.3818
645	416025	25.3969	697	485809	29.4008
646	417316	25.4165	698	487204	26.4197

Table A Square and Square Roots of Numbers from 1 to 1000 (*cont.*)

Number	*Square*	*S.R.*	*Number*	*Square*	*S.R.*
699	488601	26.4386	750	562500	27.3861
700	490000	26.4575	751	564001	27.4044
701	491401	26.4764	752	565504	27.4226
702	492804	26.4953	753	567009	27.4408
703	494209	26.5141	754	568516	27.4591
704	495616	26.5330	755	570025	27.4773
705	497025	26.5518	756	571536	27.4955
706	498436	26.5707	757	573049	27.5136
707	499849	26.5895	758	574564	27.5318
708	501264	26.6083	759	576081	27.5500
709	502681	26.6271	760	577600	27.5681
710	504100	26.6458	761	579121	27.5862
711	505521	26.6646	762	580644	27.6043
712	506944	26.6833	763	582169	27.6225
713	508369	26.7021	764	583696	27.6405
714	509796	26.7208	765	585225	27.6586
715	511225	26.7395	766	586756	27.6767
716	512656	26.7582	767	588289	27.6948
717	514089	26.7769	768	589824	27.7128
718	515524	26.7955	769	591361	27.7308
719	516961	26.8142	770	592900	27.7489
720	518400	26.8328	771	594441	27.7669
721	519841	26.8514	772	595984	27.7849
722	521284	26.8701	773	597529	27.8029
723	522729	26.8887	774	599076	27.8209
724	524176	26.9072	775	600625	27.8388
725	525625	26.9258	776	602176	27.8568
726	527076	26.9444	777	603729	27.8747
727	528529	26.9629	778	605284	27.8927
728	529984	26.9815	779	606841	27.9106
729	531441	27.0000	780	608400	27.9285
730	532900	27.0185	781	609961	27.9464
731	534361	27.0370	782	611524	27.9643
732	535824	27.0555	783	613089	27.9821
733	537289	27.0740	784	614656	28.0000
734	538756	27.0924	785	616225	28.0179
735	540225	27.1109	786	617796	28.0353
736	541696	27.1293	787	619369	28.0535
737	543169	27.1477	788	620944	28.0713
738	544644	27.1662	789	622521	28.0891
739	546127	27.1846	790	624100	28.1069
740	547600	27.2029	791	625681	28.1247
741	549081	27.2213	792	627264	28.1425
742	550564	27.2397	793	628849	28.1603
743	552049	27.2580	794	630436	28.1780
744	553536	27.2764	795	632025	28.1957
745	555025	27.2947	796	633616	28.2135
746	556516	27.3130	797	635209	28.2312
747	558009	27.3313	798	636804	28.2489
748	559504	27.3496	799	638401	28.2666
749	561001	27.3675	800	640000	28.2843

Table A Square and Square Roots of Numbers from 1 to 1000 (*cont.*)

Number	*Square*	*S.R.*	*Number*	*Square*	*S.R.*
801	641601	28.3019	853	727609	29.2062
802	643204	28.3196	854	729316	29.2233
803	644809	28.3373	855	731025	29.2404
804	646416	28.3549	856	732736	29.2575
805	648025	28.3725	857	734449	29.2746
806	649636	28.3901	858	736164	29.2916
807	651249	28.4077	859	737881	29.3087
808	652864	28.4253	860	739600	29.3258
809	654481	28.4429	861	741321	29.3428
810	656100	28.4605	862	743044	29.3598
811	657721	28.4781	863	744769	29.3769
812	659344	28.4956	864	746496	29.3939
813	660969	28.5132	865	748225	29.4109
814	662596	28.5307	866	749956	29.4279
815	664225	28.5482	867	751689	29.4449
816	665856	28.5657	868	753424	29.4618
817	667489	28.5832	869	755161	29.4788
818	669124	28.6007	870	756900	29.4958
819	670761	28.6082	871	758641	29.5127
820	672400	28.6356	872	760384	29.5296
821	674041	28.6531	873	762129	29.5466
822	675684	28.6705	874	763876	29.5635
823	677329	28.6880	875	765625	29.5804
824	678976	28.7054	876	767376	29.5973
825	680625	28.7228	877	769129	29.6142
826	682276	28.7402	878	770884	29.6311
827	683929	28.7576	879	772641	29.6479
828	685584	28.7750	880	774400	29.6648
829	687241	28.7924	881	776161	29.6816
830	688900	28.8097	882	777924	29.6984
831	690561	28.8271	883	779689	29.7153
832	692224	28.8444	884	781456	29.7321
833	693889	28.8617	885	783225	29.7489
834	695556	28.8791	886	784996	29.7658
835	697225	28.8964	887	786769	29.7825
836	698896	28.9137	888	788544	29.7993
837	700569	28.9310	889	790321	29.8161
838	702244	28.9482	890	792100	29.8329
839	703921	28.9655	891	793881	29.8496
840	705600	28.9828	892	795664	29.8664
841	707281	29.0000	893	797449	29.8831
842	708964	29.0172	894	799236	29.8998
843	710649	29.0345	895	801025	29.9166
844	712336	29.0517	896	802816	29.9333
845	714025	29.0689	897	804609	29.9500
846	715716	29.0861	898	806404	29.9666
847	717409	29.1033	899	808201	29.9833
848	719104	29.1204	900	810000	30.0000
849	720801	29.1376	901	811801	30.0167
850	722500	29.1548	902	813604	30.0333
851	724201	29.1719	903	815409	30.0500
852	725904	29.1890	904	817216	30.0666

Table A Square and Square Roots of Numbers from 1 to 1000 (*cont.*)

Number	*Square*	*S.R.*	*Number*	*Square*	*S.R.*
905	819025	30.0832	953	908209	30.8707
906	820836	30.0998	954	910116	30.8869
907	822649	30.1164	955	912025	30.9031
908	824464	30.1330	956	913936	30.9192
909	826281	30.1496	957	915849	30.9354
910	828100	30.1662	958	917764	30.9516
911	829921	30.1828	959	919681	30.9677
912	831744	30.1993	960	921600	30.9839
913	833569	30.2159	961	923521	31.0000
914	835396	30.2324	962	925444	31.0161
915	837225	30.2490	963	927369	31.0322
916	839056	30.2655	964	929296	31.0483
917	840889	30.2820	965	931225	31.0644
918	842724	30.2985	966	933156	31.0805
919	844561	30.3150	967	935089	31.3966
920	846400	30.3315	968	937024	31.1127
921	848241	30.3480	969	938961	31.1288
922	850084	30.3645	970	940900	31.1448
923	851929	30.3809	971	942841	31.1609
924	853776	30.3974	972	944784	31.1769
925	855625	30.4138	973	946729	31.1929
926	857476	30.4302	974	948676	31.2090
927	859329	30.4467	975	950625	31.2250
928	861184	30.4631	976	952576	31.2410
929	863041	30.4795	977	954529	31.2570
930	864900	30.4959	978	956484	31.2730
931	866761	30.5123	979	958441	31.2890
932	868624	30.5287	980	960400	31.3050
933	870489	30.5450	981	962361	31.3209
934	872356	30.5614	982	964324	31.3369
935	874225	30.5778	983	966289	31.3528
936	876096	30.5941	984	968256	31.3688
937	877969	30.6105	985	970225	31.3847
938	879844	30.6268	986	972197	31.4006
939	881721	30.6431	987	974169	31.4166
940	883600	30.6594	988	976144	31.4325
941	885481	30.6757	989	978121	31.4484
942	887364	30.6920	990	980100	31.4643
943	889249	30.7083	991	982081	31.4802
944	891136	30.7246	992	984064	31.4960
945	893025	30.7409	993	986049	31.5119
946	894916	30.7581	994	988036	31.5278
947	896809	30.7734	995	990025	31.5436
948	898704	30.7896	996	992016	31.5595
949	900601	30.8058	997	994009	31.5753
950	902500	30.8221	998	996004	31.5911
951	904401	30.8383	999	998001	31.6070
952	906304	30.8545	1000	1000000	31.6228

Table B Areas of the Normal Curve (proportions out of 10,000) and Critical Values of z (i.e. x/σ)

x/σ	.00	.01	.02	.03	.04	.05	.06	.07	.08	.09
0.0	0000	0040	0080	0120	0160	0199	0239	0279	0319	0359
0.1	0398	0438	0478	0517	0557	0596	0636	0675	0714	0753
0.2	0793	0832	0871	0910	0948	0987	1026	1064	1103	1141
0.3	1179	1217	1255	1293	1331	1368	1406	1443	1480	1517
0.4	1554	1591	1628	1664	1700	1736	1772	1808	1844	1879
0.5	1915	1950	1985	2019	2054	2088	2123	2157	2190	2224
0.6	2257	2291	2324	2357	2389	2422	2454	2486	2517	2549
0.7	2580	2611	2642	2673	2704	2734	2764	2794	2823	2852
0.8	2881	2910	2939	2967	2995	3023	3051	3078	3106	3133
0.9	3159	3186	3212	3238	3264	3290	3315	3340	3365	3389
1.0	3413	3438	3461	3485	3508	3531	3554	3577	3599	3621
1.1	3643	3665	3686	3708	3729	3749	3770	3790	3810	3830
1.2	3849	3869	3888	3907	3925	3944	3962	3980	3997	4015
1.3	4032	4049	4066	4082	4099	4115	4131	4147	4162	4177
1.4	4192	4207	4222	4236	4251	4265	4279	4292	4306	4319
1.5	4332	4345	4357	4370	4383	4394	4406	4418	4429	4441
1.6	4452	4463	4474	4484	4495	4505	4515	4525	4535	4545
1.7	4554	4564	4573	4582	4591	4599	4608	4616	4625	4633
1.8	4641	4649	4656	4664	4671	4678	4686	4693	4699	4706
1.9	4713	4719	4726	4732	4738	4744	4750	4756	4761	4767
2.0	4772	4778	4783	4788	4793	4798	4803	4808	4812	4817
2.1	4821	4826	4838	4834	4838	4842	4846	4850	4854	4857
2.2	4861	4864	4868	4871	4875	4878	4881	4884	4887	4890
2.3	4893	4896	4898	4901	4904	4906	4909	4911	4913	4916
2.4	4918	4920	4922	4925	4927	4929	4931	4932	4934	4936
2.5	4938	4940	4941	4943	4945	4946	4948	4949	4951	4952
2.6	4953	4955	4956	4957	4959	4960	4961	4962	4963	4964
2.7	4965	4966	4967	4968	4969	4970	4971	4972	4973	4974
2.8	4974	4975	4976	4977	4977	4978	4979	4979	4980	4981
2.9	4981	4982	4982	4983	4984	4984	4985	4985	4986	4986
3.0	4986.5	4986.9	4987.4	4987.8	4988.2	4988.6	4988.9	4989.3	4989.7	4990.0
3.1	4990.3	4990.0	4991.0	4991.3	4991.6	4991.8	4992.1	4992.4	4992.6	4992.9
3.2	4993.129									
3.3	4995.166									
3.4	4996.631									
3.5	4997.674									
3.6	4998.409									
3.7	4998.922									
3.8	4999.277									
3.9	4999.519									
4.0	4999.683									
4.5	4999.966									
5.0	4999.997133									

Table C Critical Values of t

Degrees of freedom	Probability P 0.10	0.05	0.02	0.01
1	t = 6.34	t = 12.71	t = 31.82	t = 63.66
2	2.92	4.30	6.96	9.92
3	2.35	3.18	4.54	5.84
4	2.13	2.78	3.75	4.60
5	2.02	2.57	3.36	4.03
6	1.94	2.45	3.14	3.71
7	1.90	2.36	3.00	3.50
8	1.86	2.31	2.90	3.36
9	1.83	2.26	2.82	3.25
10	1.81	2.23	2.76	3.17
11	1.80	2.20	2.72	3.11
12	1.78	2.18	2.68	3.06
13	1.77	2.16	2.65	3.01
14	1.76	2.14	2.62	2.98
15	1.75	2.13	2.60	2.95
16	1.75	2.12	2.58	2.92
17	1.74	2.11	2.57	2.90
18	1.73	2.10	2.55	2.88
19	1.73	2.09	2.54	2.86
20	1.72	2.09	2.53	2.84
21	1.72	2.08	2.52	2.83
22	1.72	2.07	2.51	2.82
23	1.71	2.07	2.50	2.81
24	1.71	2.06	2.49	2.80
25	1.71	2.06	2.48	2.79
26	1.71	2.06	2.48	2.78
27	1.70	2.05	2.47	2.77
28	1.70	2.05	2.47	2.76
29	1.70	2.04	2.46	2.76
30	1.70	2.04	2.46	2.75
35	1.69	2.03	2.44	2.72
40	1.68	2.02	2.42	2.71
45	1.68	2.02	2.41	2.69
50	1.68	2.01	2.40	2.68
60	1.67	2.00	2.39	2.66
70	1.67	2.00	2.38	2.65
80	1.66	1.99	2.38	2.64
90	1.66	1.99	2.37	2.63
100	1.66	1.98	2.36	2.63
125	1.66	1.98	2.36	2.62
150	1.66	1.98	2.35	2.61
200	1.65	1.97	2.35	2.60
300	1.65	1.97	2.34	2.59
400	1.65	1.97	2.34	2.59
500	1.65	1.96	2.33	2.59
1000	1.65	1.96	2.33	2.58
∞	1.65	1.96	2.33	2.58

Table D Conversion of the Value *r* into Fisher's *z* Coefficient

r	*z*	*r*	*z*	*r*	*z*	*r*	*z*	*r*	*z*	*r*	*z*
.25	.26	.40	.42	.55	.62	.70	.87	.85	1.26	.950	1.83
.26	.27	.41	.44	.56	.63	.71	.89	.86	1.29	.955	1.89
.27	.28	.42	.45	.57	.65	.72	.91	.87	1.33	.960	1.95
.28	.29	.43	.46	.58	.66	.73	.93	.88	1.38	.965	2.01
.29	.30	.44	.47	.59	.68	.74	.95	.89	1.42	.970	2.09
.30	.31	.45	.48	.60	.69	.75	.97	.90	1.47	.975	2.18
.31	.32	.46	.50	.61	.71	.76	1.00	.905	1.50	.980	2.30
.32	.33	.47	.51	.62	.73	.77	1.02	.910	1.53	.985	2.44
.33	.34	.48	.52	.63	.74	.78	1.05	.915	1.56	.990	2.65
.34	.35	.49	.54	.64	.76	.79	1.07	.920	1.59	.995	2.99
.35	.37	.50	.55	.65	.78	.80	1.10	.925	1.62		
.36	.38	.51	.56	.66	.79	.81	1.13	.930	1.66		
.37	.39	.52	.58	.67	.81	.82	1.16	.935	1.70		
.38	.40	.53	.59	.68	.83	.83	1.19	.940	1.74		
.39	.41	.54	.60	.69	.85	.84	1.22	.945	1.78		

Note: *r*'s under .25 may be taken as equivalent to *z*'s.

Table E Critical Values of *r*

Example: Where *N* is 72 and *df* is 70, an *r* must be 0.232 to be significant at 0.05 level, and 0.302 to be significant at 0.01 level

Degrees of freedom (N – 2)	*0.05*	*0.01*	*Degrees of freedom (N – 2)*	*0.05*	*0.01*
1	0.997	1.000	24	0.388	0.496
2	0.950	0.990	25	0.381	0.487
3	0.878	0.959	26	0.374	0.478
4	0.811	0.917	27	0.367	0.470
5	0.754	0.874	28	0.361	0.463
6	0.707	0.834	29	0.355	0.456
7	0.666	0.798	30	0.349	0.449
8	0.632	0.765	35	0.325	0.418
9	0.602	0.735	40	0.304	0.393
10	0.576	0.708	45	0.288	0.372
11	0.553	0.684	50	0.273	0.354
12	0.532	0.661	60	0.250	0.325
13	0.514	0.641	70	0.232	0.302
14	0.497	0.623	80	0.217	0.283
15	0.482	0.606	90	0.205	0.267
16	0.468	0.590	100	0.195	0.254
17	0.456	0.575	125	0.174	0.228
18	0.444	0.561	150	0.159	0.208
19	0.433	0.549	200	0.138	0.181
20	0.423	0.537	300	0.113	0.148
21	0.413	0.526	400	0.098	0.128
22	0.404	0.515	500	0.088	0.115
23	0.396	0.505	1000	0.062	0.081

Adapted from: H.E. Garrett, *Statistics in Pyschology and Education*, Vakils, Feffer and Simon, Bombay, 1971, p. 201.

Table F Critical Values of χ^2

	Levels of significance			
df	*0.10*	*0.05*	*0.02*	*0.01*
1	2.706	3.841	5.412	6.635
2	4.605	5.991	7.824	9.210
3	6.251	7.815	9.837	11.345
4	7.779	9.488	11.668	13.277
5	9.236	11.070	13.388	15.086
6	10.645	12.592	15.033	16.812
7	12.017	14.067	16.622	18.475
8	13.362	15.507	18.168	20.090
9	14.684	16.919	19.679	21.666
10	15.987	18.307	21.161	23.209
11	17.275	19.675	22.618	24.725
12	18.549	21.026	24.054	26.217
13	19.812	22.362	25.472	27.688
14	21.064	23.685	26.873	29.141
15	22.307	24.996	28.259	30.578
16	23.542	26.296	29.633	32.000
17	24.569	27.587	30.995	33.409
18	25.989	28.869	32.346	34.805
19	27.204	30.144	33.687	36.191
20	28.412	31.410	35.020	37.566
21	29.615	32.671	36.343	38.932
22	30.813	33.924	37.659	40.289
23	32.007	35.172	38.968	41.638
24	33.196	36.415	40.270	42.980
25	34.382	37.652	41.566	44.314
26	35.563	38.885	42.856	45.642
27	36.741	40.113	44.140	46.963
28	37.916	41.337	45.419	48.278
29	39.087	42.557	46.693	49.588
30	40.256	43.773	47.962	50.892

Table G Standard Scores (or Deviates) and Ordinates Corresponding to Divisions of the Area under the Normal Curve into a Larger Proportion (p) and a Smaller Proportion (q) alongwith the Value $\sqrt{pq}$

The larger area p	*Standard score z*	*Ordinate y*	*The smaller area q*	$\sqrt{pq}$
.500	.0000	.3989	.500	.5000
.505	.0125	.3989	.195	.5000
.510	.0251	.3988	.190	.4999
.515	.0376	.3987	.485	.4998
.520	.0502	.3984	.480	.4996
.525	.0627	.3982	.475	.4994
.530	.0753	.3978	.470	.4951
.535	.0878	.3974	.465	.4988
.540	.1004	.3969	.460	.4984
.545	.1130	.3964	.455	.4980

Table G Standard Scores (or Deviates) and Ordinates Corresponding to Divisions of the Area under the Normal Curve into a Larger Proportion (p) and a Smaller Proportion (q) alongwith the Value $\sqrt{pq}$ *(cont.)*

The larger area p	*Standard score z*	*Ordinate y*	*The smaller area q*	$\sqrt{pq}$
.550	.1257	.3958	.450	.4975
.555	.1383	.3951	.445	.4970
.560	.1510	.3944	.440	.4964
.565	.1637	.3936	.435	.4958
.570	.1764	.3928	.430	.4951
.575	.1891	.3919	.425	.4943
.580	.2019	.3909	.420	.4936
.585	.2147	.3899	.415	.4927
.590	.2275	.3887	.410	.4918
.595	.2404	.3876	.405	.4909
.600	.2533	.3863	.400	.4899
.605	.2663	.3850	.395	.4889
.610	.2793	.3837	.390	.4877
.615	.2924	.3822	.385	.4867
.620	.3055	.3808	.380	.4854
.625	.3186	.3792	.375	.4841
.630	.3319	.3776	.370	.4828
.635	.3451	.3759	.365	.4814
.640	.3585	.3741	.360	.4800
.645	.3719	.3723	.355	.4785
.650	.3853	.3704	.350	.4770
.655	.3989	.3684	.345	.4754
.660	.4125	.3664	.340	.4737
.665	.4261	.3643	.335	.4720
.670	.4399	.3621	.330	.4702
.675	.4538	.3599	.325	.4684
.680	.4677	.3576	.320	.4665
.685	.4817	.3552	.315	.4645
.690	.4959	.3528	.310	.4625
.695	.5101	.3503	.305	.4604
.700	.5244	.3477	.300	.4583
.705	.5388	.3450	.295	.4560
.710	.5534	.3423	.290	.4538
.715	.5681	.3395	.285	.4514
.720	.5828	.3366	.280	.4490
.725	.5978	.3337	.275	.4465
.730	.6128	.3306	.270	.4440
.735	.6280	.3275	.265	.4413
.740	.6433	.3244	.260	.4386
.745	.6588	.3211	.255	.4359
.750	.6745	.3178	.250	.4330
.755	.6903	.3144	.245	.4301
.760	.7063	.3109	.240	.4271
.765	.7225	.3073	.235	.4240
.770	.7388	.3036	.230	.4208
.775	.7554	.2999	.225	.4176
.780	.7722	.2961	.220	.4142

Table G Standard Scores (or Deviates) and Ordinates Corresponding to Divisions of the Area under the Normal Curve into a Larger Proportion (p) and a Smaller Proportion (q) alongwith the Value $\sqrt{pq}$ *(cont.)*

The larger area p	*Standard score z*	*Ordinate y*	*The smaller area q*	$\sqrt{pq}$
.785	.7892	.2922	.215	.4108
.790	.8064	.2882	.210	.4073
.795	.8239	.2841	.205	.4037
.800	.8416	.2800	.200	.4000
.805	.8596	.2757	.195	.3962
.810	.8779	.2714	.190	.3923
.815	.8965	.2669	.185	.3883
.820	.9154	.2624	.180	.3842
.825	.9346	.2578	.175	.3800
.830	.9542	.2531	.170	.3756
.835	.9741	.2482	.165	.3712
.840	.9945	.2433	.160	.3666
.845	1.0152	.2383	.155	.3619
.850	1.0364	.2332	.150	.3571
.855	1.0581	.2279	.145	.3521
.860	1.0803	.2226	.140	.3470
.865	1.1031	.2171	.135	.3417
.870	1.1264	.2115	.130	.3363
.875	1.1503	.2059	.125	.3307
.880	1.1750	.2000	.120	.3250
.885	1.2004	.1941	.115	.3190
.890	1.2265	.1880	.110	.3129
.895	1.2536	.1818	.105	.3066
.900	1.2816	.1755	.100	.3000
.905	1.3106	.1690	.095	.2932
.910	1.3408	.1624	.090	.2862
.915	1.3722	.1556	.085	.2789
.920	1.4051	.1487	.080	.2713
.925	1.4395	.1416	.075	.2634
.930	1.4757	.1343	.070	.2551
.935	1.5141	.1268	.065	.2465
.940	1.5548	.1191	.060	.2375
.945	1.5982	.1112	.055	.2280
.950	1.6449	.1031	.050	.2179
.955	1.6954	.0948	.045	.2073
.960	1.7507	.0862	.040	.1960
.965	1.8119	.0773	.035	.1838
.970	1.8808	.0680	.030	.1706
.975	1.9600	.0584	.025	.1561
.980	2.0537	.0484	.020	.1400
.985	2.1701	.0379	.015	.1226
.990	2.3263	.0267	.010	.0995
.995	2.5758	.0145	.005	.0705
.996	2.6521	.0118	.004	.0631
.997	2.7478	.0091	.003	.0547
.998	2.8782	.0063	.002	.0447
.999	3.0902	.0034	.001	.0316
.9995	3.2905	.0018	.0005	.0224

Table H Values of r_t Taken as the Cosine of an Angle

Example: Suppose that r_t = cos 45°. Then cos 45° = 0.707, and r_t = 0.71 (to two decimals)

Angle	*Cosine*	*Angle*	*Cosine*	*Angle*	*Cosine*
0°	1.000	41°	.755	73°	.292
		42	.743	74	.276
5	.996	43	.731	75	.259
		44	.719	76	.242
10	.985	45	.707	77	.225
		46	.695	78	.208
		47	.682	79	.191
15	.966	48	.669	80	.174
16	.961	49	.656		
17	.956	50	.643	81	.156
18	.951			82	.139
19	.946	51	.629	83	.122
20	.940	52	.616	84	.105
		53	.602	85	.087
21	.934	54	.588		
22	.927	55	.574		
23	.921	56	.559	90	.000
24	.914	57	.545		
25	.906	58	.530		
26	.899	59	.515		
27	.891	60	.500		
28	.883				
29	.875	61	.485		
30	.866	62	.469		
		63	.454		
31	.857	64	.438		
32	.848	65	.423		
33	.839	66	.407		
34	.829	67	.391		
35	.819	68	.375		
36	.809	69	.358		
37	.799	70	.342		
38	.788				
39	.777	71	.326		
40	.766	72	.309		

Table I Direct Calculation of T Scores

(The percents refer to the percentage of the total frequency below a given score +1/2 of the frequency on that scores. T scores are read directly from the given percentages.*)

Percent	*T score*	*Percent*	*T score*
.0032	10	53.98	51
.0048	11	57.93	52
.007	12	61.79	53
.011	13	65.54	54
.016	14	69.15	55
.023	15	72.57	56
.034	16	75.80	57
.048	17	78.81	58
.069	18	81.59	59
.097	19	84.13	60
.13	20	86.43	61
.19	21	88.49	62
.26	22	90.32	63
.35	23	91.92	64
.47	24	93.32	65
.62	25	94.52	66
.82	26	95.54	67
1.07	27	96.41	68
1.39	28	97.13	69
1.79	29	97.72	70
2.28	30	98.21	71
2.87	31	98.61	72
3.59	32	98.93	73
4.46	33	99.18	74
5.48	34	99.38	75
6.68	35	99.53	76
8.08	36	99.65	77
9.68	37	99.74	78
11.51	38	99.81	79
13.57	39	99.865	80
15.87	40	99.903	81
18.41	41	99.931	82
21.19	42	99.952	83
24.20	43	99.966	84
27.43	44	99.997	85
30.85	45	99.984	86
34.46	46	99.9890	87
38.21	47	99.9928	88
42.07	48	99.9952	89
46.02	49	99.9968	90
50.00	50		

*T scores under 10 or above 90 differ so slightly that they cannot be read as different two-place numbers.

Table J Table of Probabilities Associated with Values as Small as Observed Values of x in the Binomial Test*

(Given in the body of this table are one-tailed probabilities under H_0 for the binomial test when $P = Q = 1/2$. To save space, decimal points are omitted in the p's.)

N \ x	0	1	2	3	4	5	6	7	8	9	10	11	12	13	14	15
5	031	188	500	812	969	†										
6	016	109	344	656	891	984	†									
7	008	062	227	500	773	938	992	†								
8	004	035	145	363	637	855	965	996	†							
9	002	020	090	254	500	746	910	980	998	†						
10	001	011	055	172	377	623	828	945	989	999	†					
11		006	033	113	274	500	726	887	967	994	†	†				
12		003	019	073	194	387	613	806	927	981	997	†	†			
13		002	011	046	133	291	500	709	867	954	989	998	†	†		
14		001	006	029	090	212	395	605	788	910	971	994	999	†	†	
15			004	018	059	151	304	500	696	849	941	982	996	†	†	†
16			002	011	038	105	227	402	598	773	895	962	989	998	†	†
17			001	006	025	072	166	315	500	685	834	928	975	994	999	†
18			001	004	015	048	119	240	407	593	760	881	952	985	996	999
19				002	010	032	084	180	324	500	676	820	916	968	990	998
20				001	006	021	058	132	252	412	588	748	868	942	979	994
21				001	004	013	039	095	192	332	500	668	808	905	961	987
22					002	008	026	067	143	262	416	584	738	857	933	974
23					001	005	017	047	105	202	339	500	661	798	895	953
24					001	003	011	032	076	154	271	419	581	729	846	924
25						002	007	002	054	115	212	345	500	655	788	885

*Adapted from Table IV, B, of Walker Helen, and Lev, J. 1953. *Statistical Inference*. New York: Holt, p. 458,

†1.0 or approximately 1.0.

Table K One-tailed Probabilities of z (Values of p) in the Normal Distribution

(The body of the table gives one-tailed probabilities under H_0 of z. The left-hand marginal column gives various values of z to one decimal place. The top row gives various values to the second decimal place. Thus, for example, the one-tailed p of $z \geq .11$ or $z \leq -.11$ is $p = .4562$.)

z	.00	.01	.02	.03	.04	.05	.06	.07	.08	.09
.0	.5000	.4960	.4920	.4880	.4840	.4801	.4761	.4721	.4681	.4641
.1	.4602	.4562	.4522	.4483	.4443	.4404	.4364	.4325	.4286	.4247
.2	.4207	.4168	.4129	.4090	.4052	.4013	.3974	.3936	.3897	.3859
.3	.3821	.3783	.3745	.3707	.3669	.3632	.3594	.3557	.3520	.3483
.4	.3446	.3409	.3372	.3336	.3300	.3264	.3228	.3192	.3156	.3121
.5	.3085	.3050	.3015	.2981	.2946	.2912	.2877	.2843	.2810	.2776
.6	.2743	.2709	.2676	.2643	.2611	.2578	.2546	.2514	.2483	.2451
.7	.2420	.2389	.2358	.2327	.2296	.2266	.2236	.2206	.2177	.2148
.8	.2119	.2090	.2061	.2033	.2005	.1977	.1949	.1922	.1894	.1867
.9	.1841	.1814	.1788	.1762	.1736	.1711	.1685	.1660	.1635	.1611
1.0	.1587	.1562	.1539	.1515	.1492	.1469	.1446	.1423	.1401	.1379
1.1	.1357	.1335	.1314	.1292	.1271	.1251	.1230	.1210	.1190	.1170
1.2	.1151	.1131	.1112	.1093	.1075	.1056	.1038	.1020	.1003	.0985
1.3	.0968	.0951	.0934	.0918	.0901	.0885	.0869	.0853	.0838	.0823
1.4	.0808	.0793	.0778	.0764	.0749	.0735	.0721	.0708	.0694	.0681
1.5	.0668	.0655	.0643	.0630	.0618	.0606	.0594	.0582	.0571	.0559
1.6	.0548	.0537	.0526	.0516	.0505	.0495	.0485	.0475	.0465	.0455
1.7	.0446	.0436	.0427	.0418	.0409	.0401	.0392	.0384	.0375	.0367
1.8	.0359	.0351	.0344	.0336	.0329	.0322	.0314	.0307	.0301	.0294
1.9	.0287	.0281	.0274	.0268	.0262	.0256	.0250	.0244	.0239	.0233
2.0	.0228	.0222	.0217	.0212	.0207	.0202	.0917	.0192	.0188	.0183
2.1	.0179	.0174	.0170	.0166	.0162	.0158	.0154	.0150	.0146	.0143
2.2	.0139	.0136	.0132	.0129	.0125	.0122	.0119	.0116	.0113	.0110
2.3	.0107	.0104	.0102	.0099	.0096	.0094	.0091	.0089	.0087	.0084
2.4	.0082	.0080	.0078	.0075	.0073	.0071	.0069	.0068	.0069	.0064
2.5	.0062	.0060	.0059	.0057	.0055	.0054	.0052	.0051	.0049	.0048
2.6	.0047	.0045	.0044	.0043	.0041	.0040	.0039	.0038	.0037	.0036
2.7	.0035	.0034	.0033	.0032	.0031	.0030	.0029	.0028	.0027	.0026
2.8	.0026	.0025	.0024	.0023	.0023	.0022	.0021	.0021	.0020	.0019
2.9	.0019	.0018	.0018	.0017	.0016	.0016	.0015	.0015	.0014	.0014
3.0	.0013	.0013	.0013	.0012	.0012	.0011	.0011	.0011	.0010	.0010
3.1	.0010	.0009	.0009	.0009	.0008	.0008	.0008	.0008	.0007	.0007
3.2	.0007									
3.3	.0005									
3.4	.0003									
3.5	.00023									
3.6	.00016									
3.7	.00011									
3.8	.00007									
3.9	.00005									
4.0	.00003									

Table L Critical Values of T in the Wilcoxon Matched-Pairs Signed-Ranks Test*

N	*Level of significance for one-tailed test*		
	.025	.01	.005
	Level of significance for two-tailed test		
	.05	.02	.01
6	0	—	—
7	2	0	—
8	4	2	0
9	6	3	2
10	8	5	3
11	11	7	5
12	14	10	7
13	17	13	10
14	21	16	13
15	25	20	16
16	30	24	20
17	35	28	23
18	40	33	28
19	46	38	32
20	52	43	38
21	59	49	43
22	66	56	49
23	73	62	55
24	81	69	61
25	89	77	68

*Adapted from Table I of Wilcoxon, F. 1949. *Some rapid approximate statistical procedures*. New York: American Cyanamid Company, p. 13.

Table M Probabilities Associated with Values as Small as Observed Values of U in the Mann-Whitney Test

(a) $N_L = 3$

U \ N_S	1	2	3
0	.250	.100	.050
1	.500	.200	.100
2	.750	.400	.200
3		.600	.350
4			.500
5			.650

(b) $N_L = 4$

U \ N_S	1	2	3	4
0	.200	.067	.028	.014
1	.400	.133	.057	.029
2	.600	.267	.114	.057
3		.400	.200	.100
4		.600	.314	.171
5			.429	.243
6			.571	.343
7				.443
8				.557

Table M Probabilities Associated with Values as Small as Observed Values of U in the Mann-Whitney Test (*cont.*)

(c) $N_L = 5$

U \ N_S	1	2	3	4	5
0	.167	.047	.018	.008	.004
1	.333	.095	.036	.016	.008
2	.500	.190	.071	.032	.016
3	.667	.286	.125	.056	.028
4		.429	.196	.095	.048
5		.571	.286	.143	.075
6			.393	.206	.111
7			.500	.278	.155
8			.607	.365	.210
9				.452	.274
10				.548	.345
11					.421
12					.500
13					.579

(d) $N_L = 6$

U \ N_S	1	2	3	4	5	6
0	.143	.036	.012	.005	.002	.001
1	.286	.071	.024	.010	.004	.002
2	.428	.143	.048	.019	.009	.004
3	.571	.214	.083	.033	.015	.008
4		.321	.131	.057	.026	.013
5		.429	.190	.086	.041	.021
6		.571	.274	.129	.063	.032
7			.357	.176	.089	.047
8			.452	.238	.123	.066
9			.548	.305	.165	.090
10				.381	.214	.120
11				.457	.268	.155
12				.545	.331	.197
13					.396	.242
14					.465	.294
15					.535	.350
16						.409
17						.469
18						.531

(e) $N_L = 7$

U \ N_S	1	2	3	4	5	6	7
0	.125	.028	.008	.003	.001	.001	.000
1	.250	.056	.017	.006	.003	.001	.001
2	.375	.111	.033	.012	.005	.002	.001
3	.500	.167	.058	.021	.009	.004	.002
4	.625	.250	.092	.036	.015	.007	.003
5		.333	.133	.055	.024	.011	.006
6		.444	.192	.082	.037	.017	.009
7		.556	.258	.115	.053	.026	.013
8			.333	.158	.074	.037	.019
9			.417	.206	.101	.051	.027
10			.500	.264	.134	.069	.036
11			.583	.324	.172	.090	.049
12				.394	.216	.117	.064
13				.464	.265	.147	.082
14				.538	.319	.183	.104
15					.378	.223	.130
16					.438	.267	.159
17					.500	.314	.191
18					.562	.365	.228
19						.418	.267
20						.473	.310
21						.527	.355
22							.402
23							.451
24							.500
25							.549

Table M Probabilities Associated with Values as Small as Observed Values of U in the Mann-Whitney Test* (*cont.*)

(f) $N_L = 8$

U \ N_S	1	2	3	4	5	6	7	8	*t*	*Normal*
0	.111	.022	.006	.002	.001	.000	.000	.000	3.308	.001
1	.222	.044	.012	.004	.002	.001	.000	.000	3.203	.001
2	.333	.089	.024	.008	.003	.001	.001	.000	3.098	.001
3	.444	.133	.042	.014	.005	.002	.001	.001	2.993	.001
4	.556	.200	.067	.024	.009	.004	.002	.001	2.888	.002
5		.267	.097	.036	.015	.006	.003	.001	2.783	.003
6		.356	.139	.055	.023	.010	.005	.002	2.678	.004
7		.444	.188	.077	.033	.015	.007	.003	2.573	.005
8		.556	.248	.107	.047	.021	.010	.005	2.468	.007
9			.315	.141	.064	.030	.014	.007	2.363	.009
10			.387	.184	.085	.041	.020	.010	2.258	.012
11			.461	.230	.111	.054	.027	.014	2.153	.016
12			.539	.285	.142	.071	.036	.019	2.048	.020
13				.341	.177	.091	.047	.025	1.943	.026
14				.404	.217	.114	.060	.032	1.838	.033
15				.467	.262	.141	.076	.041	1.733	.041
16				.533	.311	.172	.095	.052	1.628	.052
17					.362	.207	.116	.065	1.523	.064
18					.416	.245	.140	.080	1.418	.078
19					.472	.286	.168	.097	1.313	.094
20					.528	.331	.198	.117	1.208	.113
21						.377	.232	.139	1.102	.135
22						.426	.268	.164	.998	.159
23						.475	.306	.191	.893	.185
24						.525	.347	.221	.788	.215
25							.389	.253	.683	.247
26							.433	.287	.578	.282
27							.478	.323	.473	.318
28							.522	.360	.368	.356
29								.399	.263	.396
30								.439	.158	.437
31								.480	.052	.481
32								.520		

*Adapted from Mann, H.B., and Whitney, D.R. 1947. On a test of whether one of two random variables is stochastically larger than the other. *Ann. Math. Statist.*, 18, 52–54.

Table N Critical Values of the Mann-Whitney U for Significance at α = .05 in a One-tail Test and α = .10 in a Two-Tail test.

N_S \ N_L	9	10	11	12	13	14	15	16	17	18	19	20
1											0	0
2	1	1	1	2	2	2	3	3	3	4	4	4
3	3	4	5	5	6	7	7	8	9	9	10	11
4	6	7	8	9	10	11	12	14	15	16	17	18
5	9	11	12	13	15	16	18	19	20	22	23	25
6	12	14	16	17	19	21	23	25	26	28	30	32
7	15	17	19	21	24	26	28	30	33	35	37	39
8	18	20	23	26	28	31	33	36	39	41	44	47
9	21	24	27	30	33	36	39	42	45	48	51	54
10	24	27	31	34	37	41	44	48	51	55	58	62
11	27	31	34	38	42	46	50	54	57	61	65	69
12	30	34	38	42	47	51	55	60	64	68	72	77
13	33	37	42	47	51	56	61	65	70	75	80	84
14	36	41	46	51	56	61	66	71	77	82	87	92
15	39	44	50	55	61	66	72	77	83	88	94	100
16	42	48	54	60	65	71	77	83	89	95	101	107
17	45	51	57	64	70	77	83	89	96	102	109	115
18	48	55	61	68	75	82	88	95	102	109	116	123
19	51	58	65	72	80	87	94	101	109	116	123	130

Critical Values of U for Significance at α = .01 in a One-tail Test and α = .02 in a Two-tail Test.

N_S \ N_L	9	10	11	12	13	14	15	16	17	18	19	20
2					0	0	0	0	0	0	1	1
3	1	1	1	2	2	2	3	3	4	4	4	5
4	3	3	4	5	5	6	7	7	8	9	9	10
5	5	6	7	8	9	10	11	12	13	14	15	16
6	7	8	9	11	12	13	15	16	18	19	20	22
7	9	11	12	14	16	17	19	21	23	24	26	28
8	11	13	15	17	20	22	24	26	28	30	32	34
9	14	16	18	21	23	26	28	31	33	36	38	40
10	16	19	22	24	27	30	33	36	38	41	44	47
11	18	22	25	28	31	34	37	41	44	47	50	53
12	21	24	28	31	35	38	42	46	49	53	56	60
13	23	27	31	35	39	43	47	51	55	59	63	67
14	26	30	34	38	43	47	51	56	60	65	69	73
15	28	33	37	42	47	51	56	61	66	70	75	80
16	31	36	41	46	51	56	61	66	71	76	82	87
17	33	38	44	49	55	60	66	71	77	82	88	93
18	36	41	47	53	59	65	70	76	82	88	94	100
19	38	44	50	56	63	69	75	82	88	94	101	107

*Adapted and abridged from Tables 1, 3, 5 and 7 of Auble, D. Extended tables for the Mann-Whitney statistic. *Bulletin of the Institute of Educational Research at Indiana University*, 1, No. 2, 1953.

Table O_1 Table of Critical Values of r in the Runs Test*

(Given in the bodies of Table O_1 and Table O_2 are various critical values of r for various values of N_1 and N_2. For the one-sample runs test, any value of r which is equal to or smaller than that shown in Table O_1 or equal to or larger than that shown in Table O_2 is significant at the .05 level. For the Wald-Wolfowitz two-sample runs test, any value of r which is equal to or smaller than that shown in Table O_1 is significant at the .05 level.

N_1 \ N_2	2	3	4	5	6	7	8	9	10	11	12	13	14	15	16	17	18	19	20
2											2	2	2	2	2	2	2	2	2
3					2	2	2	2	2	2	2	2	2	3	3	3	3	3	3
4				2	2	2	3	3	3	3	3	3	3	3	4	4	4	4	4
5			2	2	3	3	3	3	3	4	4	4	4	4	4	4	5	5	5
6		2	2	3	3	3	3	4	4	4	4	5	5	5	5	5	5	6	6
7		2	2	3	3	3	4	4	5	5	5	5	5	6	6	6	6	6	6
8		2	3	3	3	4	4	5	5	5	6	6	6	6	6	7	7	7	7
9		2	3	3	4	4	5	5	5	6	6	6	7	7	7	7	8	8	8
10		2	3	3	4	5	5	5	6	6	7	7	7	7	8	8	8	8	9
11		2	3	4	4	5	5	6	6	7	7	7	8	8	8	9	9	9	9
12	2	2	3	4	4	5	6	6	7	7	7	8	8	8	9	9	9	10	10
13	2	2	3	4	5	5	6	6	7	7	8	8	9	9	9	10	10	10	10
14	2	2	3	4	5	5	6	7	7	8	8	9	9	9	10	10	10	11	11
15	2	3	3	4	5	6	6	7	7	8	8	9	9	10	10	11	11	11	12
16	2	3	4	4	5	6	6	7	8	8	9	9	10	10	11	11	11	12	12
17	2	3	4	4	5	6	7	7	8	9	9	10	10	11	11	11	12	12	13
18	2	3	4	5	5	6	7	8	8	9	9	10	10	11	11	12	12	13	13
19	2	3	4	5	6	6	7	8	8	9	10	10	11	11	12	12	13	13	13
20	2	3	4	5	6	6	7	8	9	9	10	10	11	12	12	13	13	13	14

Table O_2 Table of Critical Values of r in the Runs Test*

N_1 \ N_2	2	3	4	5	6	7	8	9	10	11	12	13	14	15	16	17	18	19	20
2																			
3																			
4				9	9														
5			9	10	10	11	11												
6			9	10	11	12	12	13	13	13	13								
7				11	12	13	13	14	14	14	14	15	15	15					
8				11	12	13	14	14	15	15	16	16	16	16	17	17	17	17	17
9					13	14	14	15	16	16	16	17	17	18	18	18	18	18	18
10					13	14	15	16	16	17	17	18	18	18	19	19	19	20	20
11					13	14	15	16	17	17	18	19	19	19	20	20	20	21	21
12					13	14	16	16	17	18	19	19	20	20	21	21	21	22	22
13						15	16	17	18	19	19	20	20	21	21	22	22	23	23
14						15	16	17	18	19	20	20	21	22	22	23	23	23	24
15						15	16	18	18	19	20	21	22	22	23	23	24	24	25
16							17	18	19	20	21	21	22	23	23	24	25	25	25
17							17	18	19	20	21	22	23	23	24	25	25	26	26
18							17	18	19	20	21	22	23	24	25	25	26	26	27
19							17	18	20	21	22	23	23	24	25	26	26	27	27
20							17	18	20	21	22	23	24	25	25	26	27	27	28

*Adapted from Swed, Frieda S., and Eisenhart, C. 1943. Tables for testing randomness of grouping in a sequence of alternatives. *Ann. Math. Statist.*, 14, 83–86

Table P Critical Values of D in the Kolmogorov-Smirnov One-sample Test*

Sample size (N)	*Level of significance for* $D = max. \|F_0(X) - S_N(X)\|$				
	.20	.15	.10	.05	.01
1	.900	.925	.950	.975	.995
2	.684	.726	.776	.842	.929
3	.565	.597	.642	.708	.828
4	.494	.525	.564	.624	.733
5	.446	.474	.510	.565	.669
6	.410	.436	.470	.521	.618
7	.381	.405	.438	.486	.577
8	.358	.381	.411	.457	.543
9	.339	.360	.388	.432	.514
10	.322	.342	.368	.410	.490
11	.307	.326	.352	.391	.468
12	.295	.313	.338	.375	.450
13	.284	.302	.325	.361	.433
14	.274	.292	.314	.349	.418
15	.266	.283	.304	.338	.404
16	.258	.274	.295	.328	.392
17	.250	.266	.286	.318	.381
18	.244	.259	.278	.309	.371
19	.237	.252	.272	.301	.363
20	.231	.246	.264	.294	.356
25	.21	.22	.24	.27	.32
30	.19	.20	.22	.24	.29
35	.18	.19	.21	.23	.27
Over 35	$\frac{1.07}{\sqrt{N}}$	$\frac{1.14}{\sqrt{N}}$	$\frac{1.22}{\sqrt{N}}$	$\frac{1.36}{\sqrt{N}}$	$\frac{1.63}{\sqrt{N}}$

*Adapted from Massey, F. J., Jr. 1951. The Kolmogorov-Smirnov test for goodness of fit. *J. Amer. Statist. Ass.*, 46,70.

Table Q Critical Values of K in the Kolmogorov-Smirnov Two-sample Test (Small samples)

N	One-tailed test		Two-tailed test	
	$\alpha = .05$	$\alpha = .01$	$\alpha = .05$	$\alpha = .01$
3	3	—	—	—
4	4	—	4	—
5	4	5	5	5
6	5	6	5	6
7	5	6	6	6
8	5	6	6	7
9	6	7	6	7
10	6	7	7	8
11	6	8	7	8
12	6	8	7	8
13	7	8	7	9
14	7	8	8	9
15	7	9	8	9
16	7	9	8	10
17	8	9	8	10
18	8	10	9	10
19	8	10	9	10
20	8	10	9	11
21	8	10	9	11
22	9	11	9	11
23	9	11	10	11
24	9	11	10	12
25	9	11	10	12
26	9	11	10	12
27	9	12	10	12
28	10	12	11	13
29	10	12	11	13
30	10	12	11	13
35	11	13	12	
40	11	14	13	

Abridged from Goodman, L.A. 1954. Kolmogorov-Smirnov tests for psychological reserach. *Psychol. Bull.*, 51, L67.

Table R Critical Values of F at 5% (Values Written above) and 1% (Lower Values) Levels of Significance

Degrees of freedom for smaller mean square	*Degrees of freedom for greater mean square*									
	1	2	*3*	*4*	*5*	*6* …	*8* …	*12* …	*24* …	∞
1	161.45	199.50	215.72	224.57	230.17	233.97	238.89	243.91	249.04	254.32
	4052.10	4999.03	5403.49	5625.14	5764.08	5859.39	5981.39	6105.83	6234.16	6366.48
2	18.51	19.00	19.16	19.25	19.30	19.33	19.37	19.41	19.45	19.50
	98.49	99.01	99.17	99.25	99.30	99.33	99.36	99.42	99.46	99.50
3	10.13	9.55	9.28	9.12	9.01	8.94	8.84	8.74	8.64	8.53
	34.12	30.81	29.46	28.71	28.24	27.91	27.49	27.05	26.60	26.12
4	7.71	6.94	6.59	6.39	6.26	6.16	6.04	5.91	5.77	5.63
	21.20	18.00	16.69	15.98	15.52	15.21	14.80	14.37	13.93	13.46
5	6.61	5.79	5.41	5.19	5.05	5.95	4.82	4.68	4.53	4.36
	16.26	13.27	12.06	11.39	10.97	10.67	10.27	9.89	9.47	9.02
6	5.99	5.14	4.76	4.53	4.39	4.28	4.15	4.00	3.84	3.67
	13.74	10.92	9.78	9.15	8.75	8.47	8.10	7.72	7.31	6.88
7	5.59	4.74	4.35	4.12	3.97	3.87	3.73	3.57	3.41	3.23
	12.25	9.55	8.45	7.85	7.46	7.19	6.84	6.47	6.07	5.65
8	5.32	4.46	4.07	3.84	3.69	3.58	3.44	3.28	3.12	2.93
	11.26	8.65	7.59	7.01	6.63	6.37	6.03	5.67	5.28	4.86
9	5.12	4.26	3.86	3.63	3.48	3.37	3.23	3.07	2.90	2.71
	10.56	8.02	6.99	6.42	6.06	5.80	5.47	5.11	4.73	4.31
10	4.96	4.10	3.71	3.48	3.33	3.22	3.07	2.91	2.74	2.54
	10.04	7.56	6.45	5.99	5.64	5.39	5.06	4.71	4.33	3.91
11	4.84	3.98	3.59	3.36	3.20	3.09	2.95	2.79	2.61	2.40
	9.65	7.20	6.22	5.67	5.32	5.07	4.74	4.40	4.02	3.60

(cont.)

Table R Critical Values of F at 5% (Values Written above) and 1% (Lower Values) Levels of Significance (*cont.*)

Degrees of freedom for smaller mean square	*Degrees of freedom for greater mean square*									
	1	2	*3*	*4*	*5*	*6* …	*8* …	*12* …	*24* …	∞
12	4.75	3.88	3.49	3.26	3.11	3.00	2.85	2.69	2.50	2.30
	9.33	6.93	5.95	5.41	5.06	4.82	4.50	4.16	3.78	3.36
13	4.67	3.80	3.41	3.18	3.02	2.92	2.77	2.60	2.42	2.21
	9.07	6.70	5.74	5.20	4.86	4.62	4.30	3.96	3.59	3.16
14	4.60	3.74	3.34	3.11	2.96	2.85	2.70	2.53	2.35	2.13
	8.86	6.51	5.56	5.03	4.69	4.46	4.14	3.80	3.43	3.00
15	4.54	3.68	3.29	3.06	2.90	2.79	2.64	2.48	2.29	2.07
	8.68	6.36	5.42	4.89	4.56	4.32	4.00	3.67	3.29	2.87
16	4.49	3.63	3.24	3.01	2.85	2.74	2.59	2.42	2.24	2.01
	8.53	6.23	5.29	4.77	4.44	4.20	3.89	3.55	3.18	2.75
17	4.45	3.59	3.20	2.96	2.81	2.70	2.55	2.38	2.19	1.96
	8.40	6.11	5.18	4.67	4.34	4.10	3.79	3.45	3.08	2.65
18	4.41	3.55	3.16	2.93	2.77	2.66	2.51	2.34	2.15	1.92
	8.28	6.01	5.09	4.58	4.25	4.01	3.71	3.37	3.01	2.57
19	4.38	3.52	3.13	2.90	2.74	2.63	2.48	2.31	2.11	1.88
	8.18	5.93	5.01	4.50	4.17	3.94	3.63	3.30	2.92	2.49
20	4.35	3.49	3.10	2.87	2.71	2.60	2.45	2.28	2.08	1.84
	8.10	5.85	4.94	4.43	4.10	3.87	3.56	3.23	2.86	2.42
21	4.32	3.47	3.07	2.84	2.68	2.57	2.42	2.25	2.05	1.81
	8.02	5.78	4.87	4.37	4.04	3.81	3.51	3.17	2.80	2.36
22	4.30	3.44	3.05	2.82	2.66	2.55	2.40	2.23	2.03	1.78
	7.94	5.72	4.82	4.31	3.99	3.75	3.45	3.12	2.75	2.30
23	4.28	3.42	3.03	2.80	2.64	2.53	2.38	2.20	2.00	1.76
	7.88	5.66	4.76	4.26	3.94	3.71	3.41	3.07	2.70	2.26

(*cont.*)

Table R Critical Values of F at 5% (Values Written above) and 1% (Lower Values) Levels of Significance (*cont.*)

Degrees of freedom for smaller mean square	*Degrees of freedom for greater mean square*												
	1	2	3	4	5	6	...	8	...	12	...	24	...	∞
24	4.26 7.82	3.40 5.61	3.01 4.72	2.78 4.22	2.62 3.90	2.51 3.67		2.36 3.36		2.18 3.03		1.98 2.66		1.73 2.21
25	4.24 7.77	3.38 5.57	2.99 4.68	2.76 4.18	2.60 3.86	2.49 3.63		2.34 3.32		2.16 2.99		1.96 2.62		1.71 2.17
26	4.22 7.72	3.37 5.53	2.98 4.64	2.74 4.14	2.59 3.82	2.47 3.59		2.32 3.29		2.15 2.96		1.95 2.58		1.69 2.13
27	4.21 7.68	3.35 5.49	2.96 4.60	2.73 4.11	2.57 3.78	2.46 3.56		2.30 3.26		2.13 2.93		1.93 2.55		1.67 2.10
28	4.20 7.64	3.34 5.45	2.95 4.57	2.71 4.07	2.56 3.75	2.44 3.53		2.29 3.23		2.12 2.90		1.91 2.52		1.65 2.06
29	4.18 7.60	3.33 5.42	2.93 4.54	2.70 4.04	2.54 3.73	2.43 3.50		2.28 3.20		2.10 2.87		1.90 2.49		1.64 2.03
30	4.17 7.56	3.32 5.39	2.92 4.51	2.69 4.02	2.53 3.70	2.42 3.47		2.27 3.17		2.09 2.84		1.89 2.47		1.62 2.01
35	4.12 7.42	3.26 5.27	2.87 4.40	2.64 3.91	2.48 3.59	2.37 3.37		2.22 3.07		2.04 2.74		1.83 2.37		1.57 1.90
40	4.08 7.31	3.23 5.18	2.84 4.31	2.61 3.83	2.45 3.51	2.34 3.29		2.18 2.99		2.00 2.66		1.79 2.29		1.52 1.82
45	4.06 7.23	3.21 5.11	2.81 4.25	2.58 3.77	2.42 3.45	2.31 3.23		2.15 2.94		1.97 2.61		1.76 2.23		1.48 1.75
50	4.03 7.17	3.18 5.06	2.79 4.20	2.56 3.72	2.40 3.41	2.29 3.19		2.13 2.89		1.95 2.56		1.74 2.18		1.44 1.68
60	4.00 7.08	3.15 4.98	2.76 4.13	2.52 3.65	2.37 3.34	2.25 3.12		2.10 2.82		1.92 2.50		1.70 2.12		1.39 1.60

(*cont.*)

Table R Critical Values of F at 5% (Values Written above) and 1% (Lower Values) Levels of Significance (*cont.*)

Degrees of freedom for smaller mean square	*Degrees of freedom for greater mean square*									
	1	*2*	*3*	*4*	*5*	*6* …	*8* …	*12* …	*24* …	∞
70	3.98	3.13	2.74	2.50	2.35	2.23	2.07	1.89	1.67	1.35
	7.01	4.92	4.07	3.60	3.29	3.07	2.78	2.45	2.07	1.53
80	3.96	3.11	2.72	2.49	2.33	2.21	2.06	1.88	1.65	1.31
	6.96	4.88	4.04	3.56	3.26	3.04	2.74	2.42	2.03	1.47
90	3.95	3.10	2.71	2.47	2.32	2.20	2.04	1.86	1.64	1.28
	6.92	4.85	4.01	3.53	3.23	3.01	2.72	2.39	2.00	1.43
100	3.94	3.09	2.70	2.46	2.30	2.19	2.03	1.85	1.63	1.26
	6.90	4.82	3.98	3.51	3.21	2.99	2.69	2.37	1.98	1.39
125	3.92	3.07	2.68	2.44	2.29	2.17	2.01	1.83	1.60	1.21
	6.84	4.78	3.94	3.47	3.17	2.95	2.66	2.33	1.94	1.32
150	3.90	3.06	2.66	2.43	2.27	2.16	2.00	1.82	1.59	1.18
	6.81	4.75	3.91	3.45	3.14	2.92	2.63	2.31	1.92	1.27
200	3.89	3.04	2.65	2.42	2.26	2.14	1.98	1.80	1.57	1.14
	6.76	4.71	3.88	3.41	3.11	2.89	2.60	2.28	1.88	1.21
300	3.87	3.03	2.64	2.41	2.25	2.13	1.97	1.79	1.55	1.10
	6.72	4.68	3.85	3.38	3.08	2.86	2.57	2.24	1.85	1.14
400	3.86	3.02	2.63	2.40	2.24	2.12	1.96	1.78	1.54	1.07
	6.70	4.66	3.83	3.37	3.06	2.85	2.56	2.23	1.84	1.11
500	3.86	3.01	2.62	2.39	2.23	2.11	1.96	1.77	1.54	1.06
	6.69	4.65	3.82	3.36	3.05	2.84	2.55	2.22	1.83	1.08
1000	3.85	3.00	2.61	2.38	2.22	2.10	1.95	1.76	1.53	1.03
	6.66	4.63	3.80	3.34	3.04	2.82	2.53	2.20	1.81	1.04
∞	3.84	2.99	2.60	2.37	2.21	2.09	1.94	1.75	1.52	
	6.64	4.60	3.78	3.32	3.02	2.80	2.51	2.18	1.79	

Bibliography

Chase, Clinton I., *Elementary Statistical Procedures*, International Student Edition, McGraw-Hill, Tokyo, 1976.

Cochran, W.G. and G.M. Cox, *Experimental Designs*, 2nd ed., Wiley, New York, 1957.

Edwards, A.L., *Experimental Design in Psychological Research*, rev. ed., Rinehart, New York, 1960.

_______, *Statistical Methods for the Behavioral Sciences*, 2nd ed., Holt, Rinehart and Winston, New York, 1967.

Ferguson, George A., *Statistical Analysis in Psychology and Education*, 3rd ed., McGraw-Hill, Kogakusha, Tokyo, 1971.

Garrett, H.E., *Statistics in Psychology and Education*, 6th Indian ed., Vakils, Feffer and Simon, Bombay, 1971.

Guilford, J.P., *Psychometric Methods*, 2nd ed., Tata McGraw-Hill, New Delhi, 1954.

_______, *Fundamental Statistics in Psychology and Education*, 5th International Student ed., McGraw-Hill, New York, 1973.

Heath, R.W. and N.M. Downie, *Basic Statistical Methods*, 3rd ed., Harper International, New York, 1970.

Hicks, C.R., *Fundamental Concepts in the Design of Experiments*, Holt, Rinehart and Winston, New York, 1964.

Lindquist, E.C., *Educational Measurement*, The American Council on Education, Washington DC., 1951.

Lindquist, E.F., *Statistical Analysis in Educational Research*, Indian ed., Oxford and IBH, New Delhi, 1970.

McNemar, Q., *Psychological Statistics*, 3rd ed., Wiley, New York, 1962.

Nunnally, J., *Psychometric Theory*, McGraw-Hill, New York, 1967.

Siegel, Sidney, *Non-Parametric Statistics for the Behavioural Sciences*, International student edition, McGraw-Hill, New York, 1956.

Tate, M.W., *Statistics in Education*, McGraw-Hill, New York, 1948.

Walker, H.M. and J. Lev, *Statistical Inference*, Henry Holt, New York, 1953.

Index